THE GOLDEN ECHO

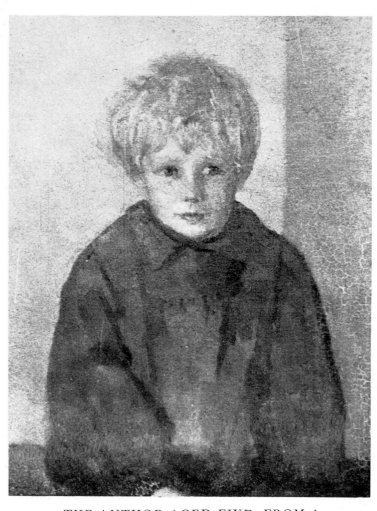

THE AUTHOR AGED FIVE, FROM A
PAINTING BY E. M. HEATH

DAVID GARNETT

THE GOLDEN ECHO

1953
CHATTO & WINDUS
LONDON

Published by
CHATTO AND WINDUS LTD.
LONDON
*
CLARKE, IRWIN AND CO. LTD.
TORONTO

Made and Printed in Great Britain by
WILLIAM CLOWES AND SONS, LTD.
LONDON AND BECCLES

Illustrations

vii

Intimations of Mortality
BY WAY OF PREFACE

MY title is taken from a poem by Gerard Manley Hopkins. The first half of it, *The Leaden Echo*, is a lament for perishable beauty.

Be beginning; since, no, nothing can be done
To keep at bay
Age and age's evils, hoar hair,
Ruck and wrinkle, drooping, dying, death's worst, winding sheets,
*   tombs and worms and tumbling to decay;*
So be beginning, be beginning to despair.

In the second half of his poem, *The Golden Echo*, the poet tells of a God who in Heaven preserves every hair and every eyelash so that

*   the wimpled-water-dimpled, not-by-morning-matched face,*
The flower of beauty, fleece of beauty, too too apt to, ah! to fleet,
Never fleets more, fastened with the tenderest truth
To its own best being and its loveliness of youth: it is an ever-
*   lastingness of O, it is an all youth!*

I do not share Hopkins' belief in God, or life beyond the grave. I know, as did Solomon, that every generation of men vanishes away like the leaves and flowers of forgotten summers. Yet, just as flowers may be pressed in books, a faint shadow of us may live on in works of art and written records, and thanks to them we may sometimes be right when we tell our friends that after our deaths

*   Yet meet we shall, and part, and meet again*
*   Where dead men meet, on lips of living men.*

ix

But another kind of life beyond the grave is also possible. We have reason to believe that every living creature is a fresh permutation of ancestral genes which determines its individuality. Half of the possible genes are passed on to the new individual from each parent, half are discarded. The hereditary constitution which results is infinitely more important than education or experience. But in a biography we can say little about it, for our lives are the stories, not of what we brought into the world with us, but what we have found in it after arrival. It is also very difficult to be certain of the inherited characteristics which play so large a part in determining our behaviour. I have sometimes found myself reacting in a familiar pattern to a quite novel situation and have recognised that, for an instant, I was my father Edward, or my mother, Constance. I was able to recognise this sudden identity because I knew both of them very well. I could not have recognised the momentary emergence of George Patten, one of my great-grandfathers, because neither I, nor any person living, can remember him, and the works of art he left, portraits and large allegorical paintings, are not obviously embued with the kind of emotion one suddenly identifies in oneself. Yet it is just possible that bits of George may live intermittently in me, just as I may be given a few moments of vicarious existence in my descendants.

For each kind of emergence after death—in the thoughts of many—or the natures of a few—a written record helps. Yet in neither case can there be any question of immortality. Even Shakespeare could not aspire to hold time's swift foot back for more than a few hundred or thousand years—and, long before the written word is cast on to the rubbish heap, the constant division and re-combination of hereditary genes will have broken up the patterns which determine the little traits of character which are passed on from ancestor to descendant.

This seems to me quite right and proper. In the ballad *The Twa Corbies* the horror of death is expressed in the remark of one carrion crow to his mate as they peck out the eyes of a dead knight:

His hound is to the hunting gane,
His hawk to fetch the wild-fowl hame,
His lady's ta'en anither mate,
So we may mak' our dinner swate.

In my opinion this is not tragic, or horrible, but a most satisfactory state of affairs. I hope my hound, hawk and lady do likewise when the crows get me.

The tragedy of death is the reverse of what the corbie, or the ballad-maker, thought. It is that the dead cannot so easily be forgotten. They reach out from the grave and haunt the living and drag them back into the past, poisoning its beauty with regrets.

Yet if one lives a good deal with them in the past, one is tempted to write about it and that is the third reason for the pages which follow.

D. G.

August 1953

I

ONE of the Garnetts of Otley in Wharfedale is supposed to have fought at Flodden Field, but the first ones living there to leave records were James and his wife Isabel. In their wills, dated 1536 and 1540, they left their souls to Almighty God, twenty pence to the parish for mending the ways about Oteley-Newall and land and cattle to their children. In the seventeenth century the Garnetts lived in a little stone farmhouse which is still standing and smelted ironstone on Baildon Moor. At the beginning of the eighteenth century they became possessed of the Otley watermill. In the middle of that century Jeremiah Garnett married into an Otley family called Flesher which had migrated to London where they became citizen stationers. One of them, Miles Flesher, was four times Master of the Stationers Company in the early seventeenth century but came back to be buried at Otley. One of his ventures was to buy up the stock of another stationer, after his death, from his widow. It included the unsold copies of three of the Shakespeare quartos, of *Venus and Adonis*, of both parts of Chapman's *Homer*, and Thomas Heywood's *The Heirarchie of Angels*.

As a result of the Flesher connection, Jeremiah gave up the trade of corn chandler and turned the mill into a paper mill. It still flourishes.

Jeremiah's grandsons were a remarkable set of men, and all of them were successful. Thomas took over a cotton mill founded by his uncle and made a huge fortune; he was also a keen naturalist, and some of his scientific papers were published. Jeremiah, the youngest, was a co-founder of the *Manchester Guardian*, the early numbers of which he set up in type himself. Later he became the second editor of the paper. Richard Garnett, the eldest of them, left a younger brother to carry on

the paper mill and became a clergyman who devoted himself to the study of philology. He was a great scholar and knew almost every European language, ancient and modern, as well as Sanscrit and Hebrew. His learning led to his being invited to become Assistant Librarian at the British Museum by Antonio Panizzi, who was transforming some miscellaneous collections into the greatest library in the world. The Reverend Richard Garnett died when he was sixty-one, and Panizzi very kindly offered his elder son Richard, aged sixteen, a job in the Museum Library.

Richard Garnett, my grandfather, spent almost his whole working life in the Reading Room. The books had not been catalogued. He organised the catalogue and carried it as far as the letter S. He also partly invented and introduced "the sliding press" or system of stacking bookcases side by side like books in a shelf. Each bookcase hangs from rails and runs on wheels and can be drawn out endways when a book is wanted. Richard was a minor poet, a translator from German, Italian and Portuguese and the author of innumerable articles and a number of biographies. His lasting claim to remembrance is *The Twilight of the Gods*, a collection of ironical stories which reveal his learning and his sly humour. He married Olivia Narney Singleton who came of an Anglo-Irish family of landowners in the County Clare. Their family of six children were brought up among books and treated the British Museum as their playground, for Richard had an official residence in the building after he became Keeper of Printed Books.

There was a row once when the young Garnetts were discovered to be climbing about on the Museum roof. The prospect of one of them falling through the glass dome into the Reading Room appalled the authorities, and roof-climbing was forbidden. But they were allowed to play ball on the lawn in front of the Museum entrance.

They were a very Victorian family, bound together by the love and devotion of Papa and all the children for Mamma— and by her warmly expressed love for each of them.

There was no coldness in Narney. She came of warm-

2

hearted, passionate, lavish, open-handed libertines and duellists. Her grandfather, Edward D'Alton Singleton, was a famous fox-hunter, notorious for calling off the hounds and letting the fox escape if Reynard had given them a long run. His sister Mary made a run-away match with a poor man and was the mother of John Singleton Copley, the painter. Edward, my father, inherited many of the Singleton characteristics.

The Garnett nursery was presided over by Chapple, a diminutive woman who had been Narney's maid before her marriage. She told me many stories of the Singletons and the Narneys and declared that I had the Brady nose, straight and rather thick.

A picture of the Garnett family on holiday at the seaside would be not wholly unlike Virginia Woolf's *To the Lighthouse* —and Leslie Stephen, the central figure in that book, was indeed a friend of Richard's. But the Stephens belonged to the world of Society. The Garnetts did not. Indeed a characteristic of the whole family was a dislike, which amounted in some of its members to a positive disapproval, of worldly or social success. Richard Garnett never used his position or made use of his friendships to push himself or to assist his children to make their way in the world. It would have offended his sense of the proprieties to ask a favour or to take for granted that it would be given. In my father the same unworldliness took another form. Edward's occupation was the discovery of talent in unknown writers. But when one of his discoveries achieved success Edward sometimes lost interest in his work. He definitely preferred the ugly duckling to the swan.

In some ways Edward absorbed and carried on the tradition of his father. But in certain respects he reacted against it. Richard Garnett knew all the scholars and critics of his generation—but Edward developed a contempt for what he called the academic critics, who he thought boiled the old bones of the great departed, but could not recognise a living genius. His own mission in life was to discover the genius and to fight for his recognition.

With this repudiation of the respectable academic approach,

Edward combined a distrust of all constituted authority. No man was ever more "agin the Government", not because of its specific shortcomings but because, being a Government, it was bound to be ruthless, ungenerous and usually in the wrong.

In all the Garnetts of that generation the critical instinct was stronger than the creative. This produced a partial paralysis in those of them who had ambition to write.

Yet they did not doubt their own capacities. Indeed it was inconceivable to Edward that he might be completely mistaken in a literary judgment. His taste might sometimes seem capricious, but he was obstinate in his caprices. Richard Garnett also delivered his judgments with an air of final authority, though he was always bland in their expression. Underlying Edward's occasional ferocity and Richard's ease and urbanity there was a hard-headed Yorkshire obstinacy. Neither son nor father would give an inch on the matters they cared about.

My mother, Constance Black, was the sixth of the eight children of David Black and his wife Clara Patten. He was a solicitor who settled in Brighton where his elder brother Peter was French Consul. David and Clara lived in a lovely old flint house, number 57 Ship Street, now occupied by a pawnbroker and gunsmith who has put in plate-glass shopwindows. David, who was the Brighton Coroner, had his offices on the front ground floor, and his family lived upstairs. He was a spare, black-haired, blue-eyed Scot with an aquiline nose, reserved in manner and dour in temper, intelligent but almost entirely lacking in social instinct. He was respected by all but had no intimate friends. His wife had married him greatly against the wishes of her father, George Patten, A.R.A., who was portrait-painter in ordinary to the Prince Consort. George Patten travelled extensively in France and Italy, taking his family with him. He knew everyone in the artistic world of Early Victorian London. Etty the painter, Macready the actor and the Landseer brothers were his close friends. Paganini was

4

a visitor to the house, and Patten painted his portrait. All the Pattens talked Italian fluently.

As a girl Clara Patten had been a friend of Geraldine Jewsbury and was thus brought into contact with Jane Welsh Carlyle. But by her marriage Clara cut herself off from all such intellectual circles, and the rest of her life was occupied in bearing children, bringing them up and managing a large household. David Black's four clerks had their midday meal in the house, and she brewed beer for their consumption. Constance was born in 1861. As an infant she was infected by tubercular cows' milk and was a cripple until she was six years old. She was a precociously intelligent child who learned to read very young, as a result of which her eyesight became weak and she became progressively short-sighted. One of her abiding memories of childhood was of the glare of the sunlight on Brighton front which produced vomitings and sick headaches. In consequence she hated Brighton all her life.

Once a year the Blacks went for a fortnight's holiday to some country village near Brighton. This was looked forward to with intense longing by all the children and, when the great day arrived, a farm wagon would draw up at 57 Ship Street to be loaded with beds and bedding, as well as all the usual luggage for a holiday, since the farmhouses at which they lodged were unable to provide beds for twelve extra persons—for the Blacks took two servants with them on their holiday.

Although so numerous they were isolated: no visitors stayed the night at 57 Ship Street and few except relatives were ever seen at its table. This loneliness was increased as they grew up, for when Constance was fourteen her mother died suddenly. After that the children lived alone with their father who scarcely ever spoke at meals or, indeed, at any other time. Isolation had its usual results. The young Blacks were all extremely shy of strangers, curiously innocent and alternately easily amused by the silliest little family jokes or intensely serious.

There was indeed a touch of the Brontë household about them: a resemblance heightened by family tragedies. The first

5

of these involved the eldest son who, after a disastrous marriage, committed suicide. He had been a brilliant mathematician whose work on the theory of probability was not worked out again, or published, until thirty years after his death.

When she was seventeen Constance won a scholarship for three years at Newnham College, Cambridge. She had come out top in the Senior Local examination among the schoolgirls of Southern England. When she heard the result she was consumed with dread that her father would not allow her to leave home. But his first words when she told him the news showed that she had misjudged him. "Of course you must go," he said. Thus, by her precocity and her brains, Constance made her escape from the suffocating prison of Victorian family life. Later, before her departure, David Black made her promise never to be seen in a hansom cab, which might be misinterpreted as a sign of her being "fast".

The girl who left Sussex for the first time at seventeen to go to Cambridge was an awkward, shy creature, with very fine fair hair, a lovely complexion and pale blue eyes behind steel-rimmed spectacles. She was naturally serious and never witty, but very easily amused. At Cambridge she conceived a secret passion for her tutor, Francis Jenkinson, and felt great pride because when a particularly beautiful passage was reached in the Greek he would usually invite her to translate it, knowing that she would do more justice to it than any of the other girl students.

Another passionate admiration was for Jane Harrison, then a young don at Newnham, whose short curls and freedom from the trammels of her sex aroused as much awe as envy. At the head of the College was the worldly-wise Miss Clough, a sister of the poet. Miss Clough's regard for the proprieties was exact, but she was a little cynical at heart about the conventions.

At Newnham, Constance enjoyed three years of rapturous bliss which at moments became so intense that she felt she could not bear it. She read classics; the beauty of Greek literature came to her as the revelation of a new world. Intimate

6

friendships were formed, and in early summer the song of the nightingales, the scent of flowering lime-trees and the beauty of the colleges made up a hitherto unimaginable earthly paradise. Before going to Cambridge she had never looked at a building as a possible object of beauty.

Among the friends she made there were William Bateson who later on founded the Cambridge school of Genetics, Florence Ada Brown who married John Neville Keynes while Constance was still at Newnham and so became the mother of my friends John Maynard Keynes and his brother Geoffrey. Other friends were Ernest Radford, the poet, his brother Charles and their sisters Florence, Ada and Audrey. During one vacation Constance visited the Radfords' home at Plymouth and was driven up and down the precipitous Devonshire hills in a dog-cart by Ernest. At Cambridge she also met J. K. Stephen and the Duke of Clarence.

Constance's years at Cambridge cannot have been wholly given up to friendships, emotions and an aesthetic awakening, for in her final examinations she came out bracketed top in the Classical Tripos. Women were not at that time given degrees, and when they were at last given retrospectively, Constance did not think it worth the payment necessary in order to add M.A. to her name. She was thus never entitled to the University vote.

Her success, equivalent to a first-class honours degree, was a good start in life and enabled her to earn her own living immediately. She first taught a modicum of the classics to the daughters of a cement manufacturer called White.

One evening, while dining with the family, she was placed next to a bishop who found her an intelligent listener. Talking to her about Greek Tragedy, he had occasion to use his handkerchief. She was listening politely when she was horrified to see him put his half-emptied glass of claret carefully into his coat-tail pocket with his left hand while he toyed with his handkerchief with his right, under the impression that it was a glass of wine. At that moment Mrs White looked round the table and rose. Constance followed instantly, and the gentlemen

7

were left to themselves. She never discovered the sequel, but the anecdote shows that Cambridge had left her still painfully shy and socially inexperienced.

A far more congenial job followed. Constance was employed to teach Greek and Latin to two of the almost grown-up daughters of Charles Booth, a philanthropic shipowner who was making one of the first social surveys, *The Life and Labour of the People of London*. Constance was very happy with them and became much attached to her pupil Antonia, and to Mrs Booth.

When the post of librarian to The People's Palace in the East End of London fell vacant, Charles Booth recommended Constance for the job, to which she was appointed, although she had no training in librarianship.

She then set up house with her two younger sisters in Fitzroy Street. It was at this time that she became a Socialist and joined the recently founded Fabian Society, to the Executive Committee of which she was soon afterwards elected. Indeed, for a time she became rather a rival of the famous Miss Beatrice Potter, afterwards Mrs Sidney Webb. Constance and her eldest sister Clementina cordially detested the Potter sisters and particularly hated the brand of State Socialism which owed so much to the efforts of Mr and Mrs Sidney Webb. This aversion led Constance readily to abandon her Socialist beliefs in later life.

It was through Clementina, rather than through her job as a librarian, that Constance met Richard Garnett and was invited to tea at the Garnett house in the British Museum where she met Edward who at once fell in love with her. He was a lanky, merry boy of eighteen who had done nothing since leaving school except hang about the bookstalls in Faringdon Road.

Constance was twenty-four and, though at first refusing to take him seriously, soon fell in love with him.

As a result he got himself a job in the office of T. Fisher Unwin, the publisher, where he almost at once became the reader. Constance used to take Edward to Socialist meetings,

8

but he listened with irreverence and frequently put her to shame by going off into fits of laughter. The Fabian Society was important in Constance's life as it led to various friendships. That with Bernard Shaw did not survive his telling her that he would like to marry her if he were able to afford to do so, but that an improvident marriage would injure his career. Constance was at this time engaged to Edward and intended to marry him, fully expecting to have to support him, and in consequence was not as much flattered as she doubtless should have been. This anecdote does not rest on her word alone—for, much to my surprise, Shaw did not forget the incident. In 1938 I had lunch with him and his wife. He came to the door of his flat alone to see me out and just before he said good-bye to me he remarked: "I would have married your mother if I could have afforded it, but I was very poor in those days." I laughed, but refrained from telling him that I should not have cared to have had him as a father.

A lasting friendship was with Sydney Olivier, an extremely handsome young man in the Colonial Office. Another enduring friendship was with Graham Wallas who married Ada Radford. Ramsay MacDonald, Edward Pease, the secretary of the Fabian Society, and his sister Dora (afterwards married to Charlie Sanger) were other friends made at this time. Edward put some of them into a very youthful novel called *The Paradox Club*, which was written when he was eighteen.

My father, on his side, was very sociable and had many friends. He did well at Fisher Unwin's and not only was lucky in the authors he recommended, but was full of suggestions for new series. I believe that he made Unwin's travellers push these on to the railway bookstalls and started two or three cheap series for this new market.

Before his marriage Edward walked down from London to Brighton. He was in no hurry and took thirteen hours to cover the fifty-six miles, but he finished so fresh that he at once went for a swim in the sea.

Old David Black, who for the last years of his life lay paralysed, dour and uncomplaining under his tartan plaid, liked

9

his son-in-law, and his children were astonished that their father talked eagerly when Edward was present.

Constance was always grateful for the way in which Edward amused her father and lightened the gloomy little house to which the Blacks had moved after David had been forced to retire by his illness.

Edward and Constance were a carefree couple. They enjoyed the East End and made friends with two families of neighbours in College Buildings. But their life there came to an end when, after three years, they decided to have a child. Constance resigned her job several months before my birth and they went to live at Henhurst Cross, Holmbush, Surrey, in a gatekeeper's lodge on the estate of some distant connections of the Garnetts, called Pennington.

The soil was heavy clay, and Constance, feeling better in health than ever before in her life, dug the garden assiduously. There had been a murder in the neighbourhood for the change of half a crown, and the murderer was still at large. As Edward had to be in London one or two nights a week, leaving Constance alone, he bought her a Derringer pistol.

One of the visitors who stayed with them was Ernest Radford who had married Dollie Maitland some years before. Ernest, who was in an odd frame of mind, picked up the pistol, told Constance it needed mending and that he would take it to a gunsmith, and put it in his pocket. On his return to London he called on an editor who had rejected some of his poems and fired a shot at him. Ernest then spent a year in an asylum, after which he recovered. Another visiting poet was W. B. Yeats, who was at that time a close friend of Edward's. Later Yeats quarrelled with him because Edward compared Lady Gregory's version of the Cuchullain saga unfavourably with a more scholarly book by Eleanor Hull.

During the months before my birth Edward got to know some Russian political exiles in London, through the Rossettis, and invited some of them to stay at Henhurst Cross. The first of these was Felix Volkhovsky, but friendships rapidly followed with Nicholas Tchaykovsky, Prince Peter Kropot-

kin, Prince Tcherkessov, a charming but very grubby little Georgian and, most important, Sergey Stepniak. Constance was interested in languages, and in the enforced idleness of pregnancy she began to learn Russian from Volkhovsky. She learned it very quickly and soon began to translate Turgenev, in which she was greatly encouraged by Stepniak. The first two volumes of her translation were published in 1894 when I was two years old.

Before then, however, Constance paid her first visit to Russia. For these new friends were not only Russians: they were revolutionists. Kropotkin was an anarchist, but all the others were members of the Social Revolutionary Party. All of them had endured imprisonment or exile for their opinions, though Stepniak had only been in prison in Italy, Bulgaria and Turkey and never in a Russian prison. In the year of my birth the harvest failed in Russia and famine followed. Money was collected in England for famine relief, but there was reason to doubt whether it would get into the right hands. Constance volunteered to take some of this money to Russia—she took it in ten-pound notes—and under cover of this humanitarian errand arranged to meet friends of Stepniak's and Tchaykovsky's, to carry letters and to arrange channels of communication between the exiles and the secret revolutionary organisations in Russia.

Thus, when I was only six months old, my mother left me to make what at that time was in any case an adventurous journey for a young woman, but which was rendered doubly so by the papers and the money she was carrying.

Why did she go? And why did Edward agree unquestioningly that it was right that she should? Why she went is obvious. It was a terrific adventure and she was more than a little in love with Stepniak. As for Edward: he had been brought up in a tradition of friendship with political refugees which had already existed for two generations.

Antonio Panizzi, one of the early nineteenth-century Italian patriots, had fled to England and though he had become a naturalised Englishman and ended up as Sir Anthony, a friend

of Brougham, Gladstone and Macaulay, he remained an ardent Italian patriot and devoted great energy to the support of Garibaldi during the years of the Risorgimento.

The close friendship between the Garnett and Rossetti families carried on the Panizzi tradition and led to Edward's meeting political exiles of all kinds. Until my grandfather moved into the official residence in the British Museum, he had lived next door to William Michael Rossetti in St Edmund's Terrace, Primrose Hill, and two doors away from Ford Madox Brown, who was William Michael's father-in-law. A number of letters from Christina Rossetti, living in Torrington Square, to my grandmother, living in the British Museum, remain to testify to their friendship and to their sedentary habits.

My father's younger sister, Olive, even contributed to *The Torch*, an anarchist broadsheet which was written, set up in type, and sold in Hyde Park by the children of William Michael Rossetti when none of them was over sixteen. Indeed, when Prince Peter Kropotkin first visited Rossetti, he was informed that his presence was requested in the nursery. He bustled off, full of benevolence, and was considerably surprised when a girl of fourteen handed him a printed sheet of paper and said drily :"Will you sign a statement to say that you agree with the political platform of *The Torch*?" The eminent anarchist was delighted to do so, but he never discovered that in England few people outside that little group of children took his political writings very seriously.

Political exiles and revolutionaries were thus nothing new to Edward, and it seemed right to him to help them. Moreover these Russians were very remarkable men who lived up to the standard of Panizzi and Garibaldi.

Sergey Stepniak (whose real name was Kravtchinsky) had been a young artillery officer who had become acquainted with a group of liberal-minded young people in Petersburg. They had been denounced as revolutionists, arrested and imprisoned, and two girls whom young Kravtchinsky had known personally were stripped half-naked and flogged by the orders of a

certain General Mezentzev. His brutality created one of the most dangerous enemies of the Tsar's regime. Without telling anyone of his intention, Sergey dressed himself in workman's clothes and hung about in one of the principal streets of Petersburg until he saw the General being driven towards him in his open troika drawn by three smartly trotting horses. Sergey ran out into the street, leapt on to the step of the carriage and stabbed Mezentzev to the heart with a dagger which he had concealed under his coat. He then leapt off the carriage and ran as fast as he could round a corner and down a side-street. The instant he was out of sight he turned in his tracks and began walking very slowly back to the scene of his crime. Dozens of pursuers and policemen dashed past him, but not one stopped to look at the stolid workman. It occurred to nobody to connect him with the murder. That evening, however, Sergey gave a second proof of his extraordinary coolness in danger. He went back to his flat, intending to leave it for ever. As he came down the staircase he heard the tramp of boots coming up. It was a policeman. "Why, have they sent you here too, mate?" said Sergey. "What fools they are at the office! I was sent to pick up this chap, but I can't get any reply and I'm pretty sure he's out." "Well, I suppose I had better go up and see for myself," said the policeman, and Sergey and he passed each other on the stairs.

Adopting the name of Stepniak, the young assassin went abroad and told no one his secret, which he did not reveal until a year or so before his death, when another revolutionist was arrested and accused of the murder of Mezentzev. Sergey's confession was a great shock to many of his English friends.

Stepniak was a short man with a broad Russian nose, a thick beard and a great domed forehead over heavy brows with a mass of dark brown hair which clustered over his ears and fell on his powerful neck. He had dark eyes with a slightly Tartar setting. He was a man of great strength and, like many physically strong men, very quiet in manner and slow of movement. But his warmth inspired all who met him with confidence.

My father told me, when I was three years old, that

13

Stepniak's mother was a princess but that his father was a bear she had met in the forest. I was somewhat awed by this story but after reflection said: "That bear that was Uncle Stepniak's dad was a *good* bear."

Stepniak was a clever craftsman who could work in metal and leather and carve wood, and I still possess a little pair of sandals which he made for me when I was two. He was the author of a number of books dealing with the Russian revolutionary movement. He was musical also, and was one of the first people to help Mark Hambourg to become known when he arrived in England as a child prodigy. Stepniak's wife, Fanny Markovna, was a birdlike, fuzzy-haired Russian Jewess, impulsive, passionate and apt to fly into sudden tantrums. She was, during Stepniak's life, violently jealous of every woman he met, including Constance. But I believe Stepniak kept her in order.

It was, then, largely on Stepniak's errands that my mother left her husband and her baby and went to Russia in the winter of 1892–93. Few railways had been built in Russia at that date, and Constance drove long distances in posting sledges in the depths of winter. She went as far East as Nijhni Novgorod (now called Gorki) in order to meet the Russian writer Korolenko who had returned from several years of exile in the Arctic Circle where he had married one of the aborigines, a Yakut woman. Korolenko told Constance that they had been devoted and as he had never learned any Yakut and she had never learned any Russian, they had never quarrelled.

In the neighbourhood of Nijhni Constance made friends with Vera Shteven, a young woman belonging to a landowning family, who was engaged in famine relief and who had opened a school for the peasants in her village on the model of Tolstoy's schools. With her my mother saw something of the famine-stricken peasants and the way in which they lived, and she spent some time in the school. A year or so later it was closed by order of the Government. When she was with her friend, Constance also visited a gipsy encampment where she saw a tame bear sitting outside one of the huts with one of the

14

gipsy babies in its arms. The baby was fast asleep and the bear swaying rhythmically.

On her return from Nijhni, my mother visited Tolstoy and stayed for some days at Yasnaya Polyana. While she was being driven alone, by a boy of fifteen, through the forest, he suddenly noticed that they were being followed by a pack of wolves. He at once pulled up and, jumping out of the sleigh, cracked his long whip with the sound of pistol shots. The wolves faded away into the forest and did not follow them again. He told her that wolves must be driven away immediately they are seen—the longer they follow a sledge the more dangerous they become.

These stories of my mother's visit to Russia were among the earliest of my childhood's memories and were powerfully reinforced by her musquash shuba which would not have been enough to save her from being frozen to death. Fortunately a kindly merchant had insisted on giving her a great wadded outer shuba to wear over it.

I have, however, left out my birth, which took place on the ninth of March 1892 at 40 Buckingham Place, Brighton. I wish I had been born in the lovely old flint house in Ship Street where my mother was born and where my grandmother once sheltered a smuggler who was being pursued by Revenue officers. Before he left he rewarded her with many yards of lace which he was carrying round his waist.

Constance's confinement was long and dangerous and she never had another child. I was injured by the surgeon's forceps which damaged a muscle in one of my eyes.

My earliest memory is of when I was two years old. It is a vivid picture of watching a small white dog running across the road outside Henhurst Cross Lodge. I have several other memories of the place. One was of touching the noses of cart-horses which were being fed with lumps of sugar over a five-barred gate at the end of a path through a wood.

In the winter of 1894, my parents left Henhurst Cross and went to live in Richmond, sharing a house with a Swedish family.

While we were there, David Black died, which was, as they say, a blessed release.

The Blacks had been connected with Russia in an earlier generation. For David's father, Captain Peter Black, who had been press-ganged in the Napoleonic wars and risen to be master of a sloop in the Navy, had later studied engineering and shipbuilding and become Naval Architect to the Tsar Nicholas I. Peter Black's daughter had been married in Petersburg and the Tsar had given her a wedding present and danced with her at a ball, and Peter Black himself had died and been buried in the Russian naval fortress of Kronstadt near the mouth of the Neva.

David Black had lived in Russia and Germany and, as a young man, had once skated over the frozen Baltic from Finland to Sweden.

On his death, Constance inherited about a thousand pounds and resolved to buy a piece of ground and build a small house which would be near enough to London for Edward to go up and down once or twice a week. Both my parents began to look for sites, and Edward went down to visit Sydney Olivier and his wife, who had just converted two cottages into a house for themselves at Limpsfield Chart in Surrey. The Oliviers had four daughters, and one of the reasons why my father decided to look for a site near Limpsfield Chart was that I should grow up knowing the Olivier children.

Limpsfield Chart in those days was a scattered hamlet with cottages clustering behind a big wooden windmill on the edge of a strip of common. There was a smithy opposite a large pond, now dried up, and there was no church. The common was bounded on the south by fields falling steeply away and giving a splendid view which extended from Crowborough Beacon in the east to Hindhead in the west. Clayton Mills on the Sussex Downs and Blackdown near Haslemere were visible to the long-sighted. Half a mile from the Chart hamlet, the common was bordered by the High Chart—open woodlands in which the villagers had wooding rights (estover), tall woods of beech and pine with undergrowth amongst which the

16

whortleberries and bracken grew thickly. A mile further on, the High Chart was bounded on its eastern side by the county border with Kent, at Kent Hatch, and there were miles more common and woodland in that direction. Edward, with the Oliviers, went in search of a site for his house on the southern edge of the High Chart. The Greensand escarpment was wooded and formed a slightly curved line facing south, with a wood plunging down the hillside to meet a line of pasture fields known as Scearn Bank. These fields were sheltered by the wall of forest. The branches of great beeches and tufted larches hid the roots of those rising behind them, and, along the edges of the meadows, banks of primroses reflected the pale sunlight of the spring. Edward chose half the topmost field as the site for our house. But before he had seen Constance, she also visited the district independently and came back having fixed upon a site. There was consternation, even anger, on both sides until they discovered that they had fixed upon the same spot.

It was indeed a beautiful and lovely pasture encircled by beechwoods. But why did they choose it? There were I think psychological reasons for the choice, valid or compelling for many of my parents' generation, which would not have existed earlier. Nobody would have thought of building a house half a mile away from any highroad, approachable only by a rough cart-track through a lonely waste of woodland, in the time of Jane Austen or even of George Eliot. It was remote from a village and was not part of any existing community. There was no church within two miles, no rookery, no immemorial elms, no ancient red brick or mellowed ashlar walls, no water, no fertile soil.

Instead there was a great horizon, solitude, and the encompassing forest which may have given these fields their name —for they are encerned or encircled by the woods. My parents might have been the pilgrim fathers building a blockhouse in New England. They were indeed pioneers, who would not have been happy in a community, or on the outskirts of one. Their choice of a site was due to an awareness that they did not

belong, that they rejected and did not wish to fit into the Victorian social hierarchy.

This had, as I grew up, some advantages and some disadvantages—but on the whole I think the good effects cancelled out the bad. Some of our friends called us "the wood people", which was a pleasant name, but none of the village people felt that we in any way belonged. And growing up in that spot I was shy, wild, afraid of people and came to believe that there was virtue in such anti-social qualities, particularly as my mother was shy owing to her upbringing.

On the other hand I did acquire independence of character and thought, a readiness to do things for myself and a love of nature, an ability to handle an axe, light a fire of wet sticks, sleep out of doors in comfort, even in wet weather, and so on.

Thirty years later, when I settled in a Huntingdonshire village, it was an unconscious rejection of a part of my upbringing. It was because I wished to accept village life and its traditions and to become part of a community.

I do not want to exaggerate. My parents, though among pioneers, were not alone. All along the sandy pine-clad wastes of Surrey, villas were soon to spring up among the gorse and bracken, until today every patch of useless ground from Limpsfield to Haslemere and Hindhead has its jolly, healthy inhabitants, and the heretics who first colonised the wastes are forgotten.

The field was bought from the Leveson Gower Estate and Edward's brother-in-law, a young architect called Harrison Cowlishaw, was asked to prepare plans. He had never built a house before and was a disciple of William Morris with a love of the medieval. The first plan was for a great hall open to the roof, in which the family should eat and sleep, with a solar chamber on one side. There was to be a central open fire, with louvres in the roof instead of a chimney.

Fortunately my parents rejected this plan and a second was produced. It was to be a small house on an L-shaped plan, the rooms of which were made smaller still by the enormous thickness of the outside walls and by the gigantic stone fireplaces

partially screened by low oak beams and inglenooks from the rooms they were to warm.

The building of the house presented many problems. As there was no water, a well had to be sunk in what is now the scullery before building could be begun. The well-sinker went down sixty feet in all. The water was good but with an iron sediment. Since there was only a rough woodland track leading to the site, all the building materials had to be carted on tumbrils, which were tipped back with their weight resting on skid-beams as they came down the steep hillside. The wheel of one went over the edge of the track, and the whole thing crashed down the hillside, killing the shaft-horse. All the stone for the house was hewn out of the quarry on the Chart common, and the larger pieces for the fireplaces were carved in the quarry by the master mason.

While the house was being built, my parents went to live in a cottage at Froghole near Crockham Hill about two miles off. That summer Stepniak and his wife took a cottage on Limpsfield Chart to be near my parents, and one of my memories is of being carried on Sergey's shoulders over Crockham Hill Common when we were all going to see how the building of the Cearne was progressing. Constance was walking beside Sergey and they were talking quietly while Fanny and Edward, ahead of us, were rushing to and fro among the pine trees, collecting edible toadstools.

I remember two visits to the Cearne itself while it was being built—once seeing the rafters against the sky and once watching the carpenters working in the "big room".

As the house approached completion, a great housewarming was planned and Sergey promised to get a bear's ham from Russia for the occasion. But when the time came, there was no housewarming: for Sergey, who had gone back with Fanny to live near Shepherd's Bush, was walking over the level-crossing which still existed there, when he was run over by a train. Some supposed that the act was suicide, for the driver blew the whistle continuously, but Sergey took no notice. His friends knew the explanation: the noise in the Turkish prisons had

been appalling and he had developed the power of being able to shut out exterior sounds when he was thinking. In a state of concentrated thought he could, at will, make himself actually deaf. Stepniak's death was a blow from which it took my mother long to recover. But it only cemented more deeply friendship with his widow, Fanny, who came to live at Crockham Hill so as to be near us, and with other Russians, particularly those who had been close friends of Sergey's. The chief of these were Prince Peter Kropotkin and Felix Volkhovsky and his daughter Vera.

Kropotkin was of medium height, with a magnificent fan-shaped beard spreading over his chest. His eyes sparkled with excitement and benevolence behind silver-rimmed spectacles. There was nothing to indicate that he was a prince belonging to one of the oldest and most aristocratic families in Russia except his absolute lack of self-consciousness and his air of culture.

It is difficult to describe his immense charm—it was due largely to his intellectual vitality, his unawareness of his own charm, and his infectious excitement about whatever subject cropped up. He listened to whatever anyone present might say and paid equal attention to all views—which was extremely flattering. The sweep of his mind, his capacity for seeing contemporary events in their relation to the general movements of history, was greater than that of anyone I have known except H. G. Wells.

Volkhovsky had no such intellectual eminence, but a most lovable sweetness of character, and Edward was very fond of him. He did not often visit us in the country, but his daughter, a dark upright girl, was a frequent visitor.

Froghole, where we lived until the Cearne was finished, was an old cottage overrun by rats.

A year or two after we left it, it was bought by E. V. Lucas, the essayist and editor of Charles Lamb's works, who was at that time an intimate friend of Edward's. Lucas was a keen cricketer, and Edward occasionally joined in the matches

organised by him between Crockham Hill and neighbouring villages.

After we settled at the Cearne, Edward spent two days in London every week but did his principal work of reading manuscripts in the country, preferably out of doors. While he was at Froghole one of these manuscripts was missed in the autumn. The following summer an ancient rustic came over to the Cearne with a roll of manuscript which he had discovered with the point of his scythe when mowing the Froghole orchard. My father promptly rejected it for publication, and it was returned to its author, very little damaged by a winter in the open.

We moved into the Cearne in February 1896, and a full realisation of our new grandeur came to me on my fourth birthday. I remember strutting up to the stable in a new long coachman's coat, talking to our new man, Bert Hedgecock, while Nettle, a pretty red bitch, played about us—my dog. Bert was grooming Shagpat—my pony. The sense of property was intensely developed, and I was conscious of being monarch of all I surveyed.

I think Constance awoke the sense of property in me. She was no doubt feeling the same about her new house. Certainly no-one could have had less sense of property than Edward. He was always generous and as a young man would press books and anything else that was handy upon the parting guests. Nor was this generosity confined to what was strictly his own. Almost to the end of her life Constance remembered that he had given away a wedding present which was hers. So many wounds are given in married life; so many injuries are received and smilingly forgiven and forgotten. But this wound remained for ever open. What was the object, or objects, which Edward had so wantonly bestowed on some casual—and I think— female acquaintance? Green china. Yes, it was green china vegetable dishes, part of a dinner service. They lived on, unforgotten in my mother's heart, for forty years after the rest of the service had been shivered into fragments.

My parents never shared a bedroom in my memory. Edward

slept in the west bedroom at the opposite end of the house from my mother and myself. He always sat up late reading or writing. This was almost always in the long stone porch of the Cearne, where he had a long wicker chair in which he lay working. On the low stone wall beside him he had a wooden packing case with the side towards him removed and a hole burned in the top. In this stood the little copper lamp for which Stepniak had forged him a tripod of iron.

Edward worked at night partly because he suffered from sleeplessness, and it was to overcome this that he later on took to drinking claret or burgundy after supper, acting in this on Conrad's advice. Later on wine became necessary to him, but he was not a wine drinker when we first lived at the Cearne.

He made up for not sleeping at night by going on sleeping in the mornings, long after the rest of the household was astir. Frequently he did not come down to breakfast till eleven, and in the morning hours it was of the first importance that no noise should be made which might awaken him. In this matter I was trained carefully by Constance, and I learned early to be a silent child.

When my father did wake up, his heavy lunging tread could be heard going to and fro upstairs from his bedroom to the bathroom. Whatever the time of year, he always took a cold bath, and this included pouring a bucket of cold water over himself. Much of this fell outside the bath and trickles of water commonly descended through the ceiling into the kitchen below. Edward often went about naked upstairs and persons entering the house by the front door and going into the study would have been able to catch a glimpse of him at the head of the stairs as he went to and from his bath. Such possibilities distressed Constance, as did his lifelong carelessness about doing up his fly-buttons.

Rising late, Edward ate little breakfast: a cup or two of coffee or of China tea, a crust of bread and an apple or an orange was usually enough for him. He often ate a meal in the middle of the night, being particularly fond at that hour of cold baked apples.

He was not particular about food but felt the evening meal incomplete without a hot soup. His love for the exotic showed itself in food: he was sure to like any new foreign dish. At one time my parents brewed themselves fermented milk or kéfir from the yellow fungus which ferments and acidifies milk. This was bottled in screw-stoppered flagons and poured out foaming, like white champagne. My parents were greedy about it; each had a bottle which the other might not touch. Edward also loved such adjuncts to a meal as celery with the cheese, nuts, raisins, dates and tangerines. He liked the burnt outside skin of a milk pudding better than the pudding itself, and the jacket of a baked potato was a delicacy.

He was an extremely easy person to feed, as his natural contrariness led him to partake of whatever dish was unpopular. I think he also had a feeling of chivalry over dishes which were failures. He was a far better cook than Constance, though he did not develop this talent until fairly late in life.

Among his favourite experiments was the cooking of edible fungi, in which he was encouraged and abetted by various foreign ladies—Fanny Stepniak, Natasha Ertel and, later, Anjuta Cyriax. I was conservative and cautious about food and seldom partook of these dishes, which I have no doubt were much the best which appeared at the table. Edward, by his own account, only once made himself seriously unwell by eating a poisonous toadstool, and he cooked and ate fungi for forty years.

We had not been long at the Cearne when I had my first attack of acute tonsilitis. Dr Maude of Westerham said that my tonsils ought to be cut out, but Edward unfortunately had a prejudice against their removal, and I remained a victim to recurrent attacks of acute tonsilitis until I was seventeen. I learned to read at the age of four, after great struggles with Constance. Finally, realising that resistance was useless, I said: "All right, I will learn to read. But when I have learned, I never, never shall." I was not stupid and soon was reading incessantly.

Septic tonsils made me stupider than I should otherwise have been. If they had been taken out when I was four, my

intelligence might have continued to develop when I was at school. I might have learned much there instead of nothing, and if I had won a scholarship to Cambridge my life would have been very different. As it was, my intelligence was arrested at about the age of ten or twelve. My tonsils made me for a time an obstinate rebel against society and a complacent failure.

While my attack of tonsilitis still kept me in bed, Edward suddenly fell ill with typhoid fever. He was put to bed in the sitting-room at the Cearne, the room which was always called "The Study".

As soon as I was well enough I was sent to Brighton to stay with my mother's brother Ernest.

Edward's illness was long and nearly fatal, as he developed clots in the blood. When he seemed to be at the point of death, the country people were much impressed by two omens: a black dog haunted the garden, and a carrion crow came to perch outside his window. The dog can be readily explained by the fact that Nettle was a bitch. The crow is harder to account for. The bird may have scented a man very near his death.

However, Edward recovered and became extremely temperamental during convalescence, on one occasion throwing a helping of tapioca pudding into the face of Mary Belcher, a friend who had come to help my mother nurse him.

At Brighton the atmosphere was very different from that of the Cearne. My uncle Ernest was a short, bald, pale man who wore spectacles. No man was better named: he was earnest, deeply serious, devoid of passion and, though not by any means devoid of humour, had no disposition to extravagant mirth or extravagance of any kind: the soberest man alive. The Black shyness manifested itself in him by a preference for the little things in life, about which he felt knowledgeable. The great ones he avoided and left to his sisters.

He was married to Minnie, a tall, shrewd woman, one of three sisters of a family of Bermondsey leather-merchants called Eastty. She was humorous, in the true English way, a twinkle always in her eye.

Both were intelligent and capable people, but they were

entirely unintellectual, accepting the world as they found it, taking practically no interest in any of the abstractions of the mind. In this Ernest and his younger sister Katie were unlike Constance, Clementina and the rest of the Blacks, and Minnie was unlike her sister Annie Eastty.

Several years after this visit to Brighton, my cousin Kenneth Black asked his mother what was meant by a spirit. Minnie boggled brightly at the question. I do not think she had much more idea of an answer than bright-eyed Mistress Mouse—and Ernest was a serious slow-moving dormouse and could not have helped his son as regards spirits. Kenneth, like many children, supplied his own answer which, to do her justice, Minnie realised was completely satisfying. "My idea of a spirit is Aunt Annie without a body." Annie took after her mother who was a half-sister of Richard Heath. He was also an embodied spirit, if ever there was one. I shall have more to say about him and his children very soon.

Of course, at the age of four, I did not formulate what made my Uncle Ernest unlike my own parents, but I did observe the difference, and one little incident has remained in my mind as symbolic of this difference.

One morning my uncle came into my bedroom and found me sitting on the chamber pot. He told me that I must not sit on it because it was unmanly and I was a little boy. Girls and women sat on chamber pots. If I could not stand up and hold the pot in front of me for fear of spilling its contents, I had better kneel down in front of it to use it. I did what he asked while he was there but secretly thought him a fool. For, like both my parents, I was born with an innate contempt for ritual, and have only come to value it as I have grown older, as I now recognise that it is ritual alone which preserves, or tries to preserve, the world from continual change in an age in which there is too much change.

Two volumes of Caldecott were much loved before I could read. To one of them I am indebted for the nickname which has now clung to me for fifty-seven years. For the picture of

Baby Bunting crawling on the floor in his rabbit skin provoked such adoration—as though it were a holy picture—and my rapture was so lasting, that a rabbit skin was eventually cured with alum and saltpetre and made into a little cap for me to wear, as a result of which I was promptly called Bunny by the village boys, and Bunny I have remained. And to Caldecott's illustrations of "When I was a Farmer, a Farmer's boy", I owe the memory of my first adventure in search of employment.

One morning after my return to the Cearne I slipped away, crawled through the post-and-rail fence at the bottom of our garden and set off across the long meadow to the barn. Mr Bassett must have seen me coming, for he came out of his yard, and I remember him standing watching me, with his ash-stick in his hand.

He was a stout old man in breeches and gaiters and wore a low-crowned old pot-hat. He had white whiskers and a beard under his shaven chin, so that white curls encircled a face as red, and eyes as blue, as those of the little boy walking steadily towards him.

I know quite well what I wanted to say to him but I cannot tell quite how I said it. We must have been at cross purposes for a little while and I must have had to repeat what I had come to say several times. "I've come to be a farmer's boy. I'm going to be your cow-boy." When Mr Bassett understood, he seemed pleased. Instead of talking at me and pointing across the meadow with his stick, he took hold of my hand and led me back to the barn and agreed with me. "Yes, yes, yes," he may have said, "You'll be my little cow-boy. And what do you want me to pay you?" I do not know what wages I asked, probably a penny, since I had not heard of shillings or half-crowns. But I know it was settled that I was to drive his cows in, every morning, to be milked, and that I was to be paid, and that I was to work for Mr Bassett. I had no doubt I should do all the things in the Caldecott illustrations of the Farmer's Boy on the banks of the Aire-Oh.

Mr Bassett took me to the far side of his barn, where he unlocked a door, and, looking in, I saw a shadowy unlighted

26

room lined with shelves covered with apples, and there were bushel baskets of apples piled up on the floor.

Mr Bassett told me to wait outside while he went in to the apple-store alone. His back was turned to me, and I stood on the threshold, peering past him into the dark room with white-washed walls and shelves of fruit and baskets.

Then Mr Bassett came out carrying two enormous apples, with red cheeks. "They is for dumplings," he said. "You tell 'em I give you 'em for you to have dumplings on 'em. Mind you don't eat 'em raw. You tell your girl to bake you some dumplings. Tell 'er Mr Bassett said you are to have dumplings."

I was made to repeat his words, and he nodded approval. The apples were so big that I could not hold them in my hands; I had to carry them in my blue smock. Then he led me back into the meadow and told me to hurry back home. We parted well satisfied with each other.

When I got home, still with my apples, I found that a fuss was going on. I had been missed and was being searched for in all directions but the right one. However, I remained serene until the commotion had died down, for I had got my first job and was going to have two great apple dumplings all to myself.

I got the dumplings all right, and though I never became Mr Bassett's cow-boy we were friends, and whenever I saw him, he acknowledged his promise and told me I was to come along one day soon to look after his cows.

Bert Hedgecock was surprised at Mr Bassett's liking me and told me that he used his stick on boys who went near his orchard. But I was privileged and went often to the barn. Once I heard a sound of knocking inside. When I looked through the door I saw a man threshing corn with a flail. He was old Collins who lived in Scearn Bank cottage and worked for Mr Bassett, who himself lived at the millhouse and owned the windmill.

Mr Bassett drove everywhere in a tall two-wheeled cart with a big grey mare, and, on at least one occasion, I remember

sitting up beside him and driving along the road to Westerham. How did I get there? I cannot tell. But memory opens with my being high up above the dusty white road on the movable cross-seat of the big cart, looking down at the old mare's haunch and the wrinkle on it that came and went, came and went, with every one of her jogging strides. There I was, all alone with Mr Bassett. His whip, covered with plaited thread and bound with brass rings, swung from a leather socket. There were sacks in the back of the cart, behind our seat, and his dog running along the road in front. How did I come, a little boy of four or five, to be going somewhere all alone with Mr Bassett? I was very happy and felt quite grown up, and with the memory of that happiness, darkness descends.

I visited him also at the mill, but Constance went with me, and I cannot actually remember Mr Bassett himself being there at all. But the mill was awe-inspiring. It was built in two parts, a lower circular chamber of brick, and an upper structure rather like a great wooden ship stuck on end, which turned round to meet the changing winds and carried the sails. Thus the whole aspect of the village changed when the wind changed, because the mill had been swung round into a new position. One day the sails would be facing you as you came up over the edge of the hill and whirling round in a clockwise direction, another day they would be edge on, and when the north wind blew the mill had turned its back and the sails whirled round anti-clockwise. The four sails were fastened high up, and on the other side, at the back, a great black beam, which was there to balance the sails and to turn the mill around, projected downwards with broad wooden steps fastened beside it.

Constance and I looked into the lower circular storey filled with sacks of flour and bran, and I went with a man up the broad wooden steps and looked into the upper part at the great millstones, the grain trickling and the ladders leading upwards. There was the creak of the wooden cogwheels, and the sound of the great sails sweeping past, and their shadows coming and going. If Mr Bassett had showed me the mill, he would have given me something, if only a pocketful of bran for the white

28

rabbit at home or a handful of the wheat I had seen old Collins threshing with the flail.

The rabbit came from old Collins. Mrs Collins was a familiar figure, since she came once a week to do the washing. On Mondays the copper fire in the scullery was lit and Mrs Collins presided in clouds of steam, through which her coarse red face and huge arms could just be seen. She was a fearsome woman; she was said to beat old Collins with her copperstick. One day she came with a black eye, owing, she said, to a clothes-prop falling on her from behind a sheet. But the truth was that:

> Mrs Collins and Mrs Cork
> Had a quarrel about some pork

Old Collins kept a pig in the stye just on the right-hand side as you go down the steps to the cottage—it has been turned into a greenhouse now. Mrs Cork was a gigantic virago who wore a man's cap and, with several perambulators and a tribe of weaker vessels and children, spent her days "wooding", since she lived in one of the cottages which enjoyed rights of estover.

She had bought a joint of pork which came from the Collins's pig, but she refused to pay for it, alleging that the meat was tainted and that "the pig had been killed to save its life".

A hand-to-hand battle had resulted and it must be supposed that for once Mrs Collins met her match. Mrs Cork never did pay for the pork.

It was from old Collins, who was gentle and charming, that we had the first of all our dogs—the red terrier bitch called Nettle. She gave birth to a puppy who was called Nietsche and lived with us for ten years, but she herself died early.

Edward recovered from typhoid fever and went to Italy to stay with the forgiving Mary Belcher who had got married to a man called Houghton, a dilettante who lived in Florence and collected *objets d'art*.

For about a year we lived in some style, with Bert and Alice and the pony. Shagpat was a clever little beast and learned to draw back the bolt of the stable door with his teeth, after which a great chase ensued over the grass plot before he could be captured. He was friends with a tortoiseshell cat which used to sleep on his back.

One afternoon Bert took me to a wild beast show in Westerham. But on the way he so terrified me with stories of little boys being eaten by lions that I refused to go in when we got there and remained so obstinate that he had, much to his annoyance, to return home with me without seeing it himself.

On another occasion Sydney Olivier was driving Constance and, on his standing up, the bottom of the governess cart fell out into the road. Olivier was not hurt and leapt nimbly on to the cushioned seat that surrounded the gaping hole.

My first acquaintance with the Oliviers must have been at that time: Noel, the youngest of their four daughters, was a little girl nearly a year younger than myself, with a disproportionately large head and steady grey eyes. She showed me the grey parrot which slowly climbed about its large cage in the conservatory. And as important as the parrot itself was Noel's white fur monkey which danced from a piece of elastic sewn onto the crown of its head. Her sister Daphne also had a similar fur monkey. Both Noel and Daphne loved these monkeys, but Daphne made cruel fun of hers. I thought she was unkind to bait it.

I put Noel first and apart, because for me, and many others, she became more important than any of her family. But I did not realise that for a few years. She was quiet and the least conspicuous of the four sisters. Margery, the eldest, was tall, brown-eyed and brown-haired, handsome with the impulsive warmth and sudden chilliness of her father, an Olivier in temperament and character. Brynhild was the outstanding beauty of the four and grew into the most beautiful young woman I have ever known. She was rather fairer than Margery; with the most lovely bone structure, a perfect complexion with red

cheeks, and starry eyes that flashed and sparkled as no other woman's have ever done.

Daphne was darker, more dreamy, and, in her childhood, wrapped in the skin of some beast, or crowned with flowers, was exactly as I have always imagined several of Shakespeare's heroines—she was Ophelia, Perdita, Juliet and the Gaoler's Daughter in *The Two Noble Kinsmen*.

Their mother, Margaret, was a beautiful woman, with clearly cut features, blue eyes, and a characteristic manner of exhibiting detached amusement. She was cold rather than passionate, and inwardly, I believe, unsure of herself. Although her beauty and her nimbleness in conversation greatly attracted men (among whom was Edward) she was less graceful than her daughters. She had perhaps unconsciously modelled herself on a Meredith heroine. Everyone was reading Meredith at that time; he was for most of my parents' friends the greatest living writer.

What an observant little boy I must have been to be sure! Yet oddly enough my earliest memory of the name of Meredith, long before he conveyed anything to me, is linked with Margaret Olivier and not with our pony who was called after Meredith's *The Shaving of Shagpat*. Olivier himself was tall, warm and dark in colouring, with bold dark eyes, an aquiline nose, a well-kept beard and an air of benevolence and nobility. In the country he wore pale clothes, silk or flannel shirts, with a pink tie of shantung silk worn through a gold and turquoise ring. For the Colonial Office he wore a morning coat— sometimes a brown or light fawn one, and one of those hard pot hats—a cross between a bowler and a topper— which became extinct long ago except on the head of Sir Winston Churchill.

He was, as I have said before, a very handsome man, handsome in a way which revealed his French ancestry. In manner he was aloof, with a certain native *hauteur* which at times was broken through by warm affection: at other times he retreated into a sudden chilliness, and in the middle of general conversation would pick up and study a timetable as if to show that

31

he was more interested in looking up the times of trains than in any of the assembled company.

The early summer of 1897 was hot and dry. It was Queen Victoria's Diamond Jubilee. During the day I had been taken by Bert to see the Jubilee celebrations at Crockham Hill and had watched the young men trying to climb the greasy pole and the matrons of the village competing to hold an active young pig by its well-greased tail.

In the evening there were glow-worms everywhere, and after dark Edward collected them and decorated our hats with them: ugly beasts when you see them in daylight but giving a bewitching green light in the dark.

The whole rim of the weald was aflame with bonfires: on Hindhead, Leith Hill, the Sussex Downs, Ashdown Forest, Crowborough Beacon—and along our own Greensand ridge and on the summits of the North Downs behind us. There can never have been so many bonfires since the Armada, and no country, at the close of a day of patriotic rejoicing, can have retired to sleep so certain of the peacefulness and security of the world.

Who were we watching the twinkling lights of the beacons upon the Sussex Downs, and who were the ladies whose hats my father decorated with

> those country comets which portend
> Nothing but the grasses fall

as Marvell called them? The party which strolled from Kent Hatch to the top of Crockham Hill consisted of Fanny Stepniak, who had come to live permanently at Crockham Hill, Prince Peter Kropotkin and his wife, my Aunt Lucy and her husband Harry Cowlishaw, my Uncle Arthur Garnett and a young man from Tasmania, Lyndhurst Giblin, who was named after the Lord Chancellor, a cousin of my father's mother. Giblin was related to Felix Wanostrocht, the great cricketer who was connected by marriage with my father's Horsfall cousins.

It was owing to these distant connections that we first met Giblin. When my mother announced to her brother-in-law that a young man from Cambridge called Giblin was coming to see us, Arthur, then a lanky schoolboy, looked at her with astonishment and awe and stammered out: "You don't mmmmmm, me . . . mean, Gib . . . Gib . . . Giblin the int . . . int . . . int . . . international?"

"No, he's certainly not a Marxian Social Democrat and I don't think he's even a Socialist," replied my mother, to whom the only members of the International were the disciples of Marx and Engels. Giblin was, however, an International of another sort—he played rugger and had been capped for England. The story is told that on one occasion, when a man tried to collar him and Giblin could not shake him off, he picked him up under his arm and ran on to score a try.

Giblin had the physique you would expect from that exploit. He had just come down from King's College, Cambridge, after taking his degree in mathematics. He was senior Optime and would have done better if he had not regarded rugger, cricket and beer as subjects to be studied as seriously as mathematics. His first action on coming to stay at the Cearne was to drive Shagpat into Westerham and return with a pint of Bushell & Watkins' strong Westerham ale. He sat listening silently to my mother's expositions of Russian politics and revolutionary aims, with a mug of this in his hand, sipping it at longish intervals and afterwards pronouncing it one of the best beers he had tasted from the south of England. Of course some of the Cambridge beers and some North Country beers were a different matter.

There was a strength and a repose about Giblin, even as a young man, which set one immediately at rest. Hurry of any sort and the urgent petty occupations of daily life were, in his presence, revealed as unnecessary and futile. There was any amount of time for things that mattered. . . . He was reading Richard Jefferies' *Bevis* with profound attention for the fourth time and was going off, after that visit to the Cearne and to E. V. Lucas at Froghole, to try his luck in the Klondike gold

fields. Before leaving he made me what I took to be a solemn promise. He would bring me back four golden chairs.

Soon after he left the pleasant and spacious life of the first year at the Cearne proved to be beyond my parents' means. There was a sudden reform, and like many of our reforms it was due to a letter from the bank manager. Alice left us to get married, Bert Hedgecock was dismissed and Shagpat sold.

II

MY mother's sister Grace had been a beautiful girl. She had married an engineer called Hugh Human who was employed in experimental work on torpedoes. But before she would marry him, Gracie insisted, on pacifist and idealistic grounds, that he should give up this work in which he was brilliant. He did so and got a job which he never cared about in Ceylon, teaching engineering to the Sinhalese. Before they went out to Colombo, Gracie bought the furthest of the Scearn Bank meadows, about half a mile away from the Cearne. Harry Cowlishaw was commissioned to build a cottage for her. I can remember looking at a model which he made to send out to the Humans after their departure. It was made of wax, and it melted in the Red Sea.

The first tenants of Gracie's Cottage were Ford and Elsie Hueffer. Ford's father, Dr Hueffer, was a German who had settled down in London and had become musical critic of *The Times*. He married a daughter of the painter Ford Madox Brown whose sister had married William Michael Rossetti. All these were old family friends of the Garnetts; my father had known the three Hueffer children, Ford, Oliver and Juliet, from their childhood, when they frequented the houses of their grandfather, Ford Madox Brown, and their aunt and uncle, Mrs and Mr William Michael Rossetti.

There was a deep temperamental difference, however, between the young Garnetts, who were sceptical, unworldly and over-critical, and the Hueffer boys, who were credulous, worldly (without being worldly-wise) and over-confident. The young Garnetts were inclined to regard the Hueffer boys as half egregious asses and half charlatans. The Hueffers, who originally respected the Garnetts, became more and more exasperated by their sceptical attitude and their strait-laced

almost puritanical contempt for success and notoriety, which constituted the breath of romance for Ford and Oliver.

I never knew Oliver, who was enormously fat and became a successful journalist. He soon deserted the aesthetic world of artists and bookworms into which he had been born. Ford, however, remained in it all his life. He later adopted the name of Ford Madox Ford, and some people regard him as a great novelist. At the time I first remember him, Ford was a very young man, tall and Germanic in appearance, with a pink and white complexion, pale, rather prominent, blue eyes and a beard which I referred to when we first met as "hay on his face", in spite of the fact that I had been well broken in to beards by those of Sergey Stepniak and Peter Kropotkin.

Ford married Elsie Martindale, whom he first met at school when they were both small children. Elsie was tall, high-breasted and dark, with a bold eye and a rich, high colour, like a ripe nectarine. She dressed in richly coloured garments of the William Morris style and wore earrings and a great amber necklace, and I, at the age of five, was at once greatly attracted by her. Without undue hesitation I proposed marriage, and when Elsie pointed out that Ford was an obstacle, I said cheerfully that it would be a good thing if he died soon. Although Ford was at once informed of my intention of superseding him, he bore no rancour and was a most charming entertainer of my youth. He would suddenly squat and then bound after me like a gigantic frog. He could twitch one ear without moving the other—a dreadful but fascinating accomplishment. He would also tell me stories, just as he told everyone else stories —but I do not think I ever believed that anything he said was true.

Ford was at this period playing at being a farmer and an expert on agriculture, so he wore a smock frock and gaiters. The only sign of the farm was that he kept ducks. There was no pond for them, so Ford sank a hipbath in the ground and the ducks stood in a queue, waiting their turn to swim in it. These birds were named after my mother and my aunts. When Ford dug in the garden at Gracie's Cottage, the ducks stood

36

round him in a semi-circle, waiting to gobble up earthworms. "Lucy is so very greedy," Ford would pronounce in a sorrowful drawl, "she always manages to eat some of Connie's share." "Katie was such a clumsy thing, she broke one of my tomato frames. Really I could *not* feel fond of her, so we had her roast on Sunday. Rather tough." It was a simple way of teasing, but effective. My aunts would repeat such remarks to each other, but their laughter was not without a trace of indignation.

One day a family of Russian Jewish political exiles descended upon us—the man was David Soskice and with him came a French-speaking wife and a litttle boy called Victor, of about my age. An empty cottage was found for them at Kent Hatch, but Madame Soskice did not care for English cottages and, having decided to part from her husband, returned to Paris, taking Victor with her.

David Soskice was a squarely built man, with a curly black beard, a square forehead and the simplest ideas of right and wrong which he put into practice with little regard for consequences. For instance, he believed that Dreyfus was innocent and he believed one should tell the truth in all circumstances —a much more doubtful proposition. So finding himself in the middle of a vast crowd in Paris which was howling for Dreyfus's death, Soskice shouted "Vive Dreyfus" and only the solidity of his construction saved him from being torn in pieces. He had a literal mind and no imagination. What he liked were facts, and for some time after his arrival he was always asking questions about England and jotting down the answers in a notebook. It must have contained some very peculiar information, for one of his chief sources was Ford who loved walking to and fro in front of the cottage telling Soskice about England while Soskice sat on the doorstep scribbling busily with the notebook on his knee.

I can only remember two examples of the information Ford imparted to him. The first was that the largest grain crop in Britain was rye, all of which we exported to the Continent; the second that the most profitable crop in England was a very

37

tall cabbage, the stalks of which supplied the walking-out canes for soldiers in the British Army.

Ford was not necessarily lying, but his statistical principles were peculiar. On one occasion my father and he were having lunch in London when a successful journalist came up to them and Ford began to talk about the wonderful success of his last novel. The journalist inquired about its sales. "It has sold twelve thousand copies in three weeks," drawled Ford, "and it is still heading the list of best-sellers." After the journalist had gone away, Edward asked Ford: "How can you tell him such awful lies? You know we have only sold just over a thousand copies." "My dear Edward," said Ford, in his very slow drawl and in his most *dégagé* manner, "Truth is relative. You and I know that my book has done extraordinarily well to have sold twelve hundred copies, but that fellow would never have understood that. When I told him it had sold twelve thousand copies it astonished him just to the same degree that you and I are astonished by its having sold twelve hundred. Truth is relative."

It was no doubt in the intervals of taking down the relative truths of Ford's statistics that Soskice first met Juliet Hueffer.

She was a ravishingly beautiful blonde, a good deal like an idealised child's doll. That is to say, she had the complexion of a wild rose, masses of golden hair and enormous innocent blue eyes. She was always plump and grew steadily stouter as the years went by, but her beauty never faded. When I last saw her she had the loveliness of an immense armful of Gloire de Dijon roses, dropping their petals. David Soskice fell in love with this glorious creature, and, much more extraordinary, Juliet fell in love with him. He was certainly the antithesis of her brother in being a man of the strictest integrity whose every word could be relied upon. Soskice was able and industrious and was a qualified Russian lawyer. Juliet had a great capacity for enjoying life, and a rich sense of humour, which her husband was unable to share. She was, moreover, much more intelligent and gifted than he was. Her translations of Nekrassov in two volumes in the World's Classics are the

best translations of Russian poetry in English, with the possible exception of Frances Cornford and Mrs Salaman's little volume *Poems from the Russian*.

The marriage of this curiously assorted pair was a very happy one. They had two sons, one of whom became Attorney-General in Mr Attlee's Government.

A more romantic influx of political exiles were Avetis and Murro Nazarbek, with their two children and a large body of retainers which in my memory consists of about a score of stalwart men, but in reality cannot I think have numbered more than nine or ten. They were Armenians who had escaped from Turkey during the Turkish massacres of 1895.

Avetis Nazarbek was dark, slender, very handsome in an oriental style, and played the violin. Murro, his wife, was a dark moody woman with a sallow skin, so devoured by jealousy that she could scarcely endure watching Avetis speak to another woman and was convinced he was being unfaithful if he was out of her sight for more than five minutes.

The advent of the Armenians excited great interest and compassion among various humanitarian ladies of Limpsfield, for Avetis could relate appalling stories of the "unspeakable Turk", and of the Kurds who had butchered whole villages of his people. There was tremendous indignation in England at the time against the Turks, from whom these poor Armenians had escaped to become homeless wanderers in the world. The good ladies were eager to hear these terrible tales at first hand, told by Avetis over their tea-tables, and to assist by raising a subscription for him and his. But these benevolent emotions received a rude shock and were transformed into surprise, indignation and outrage when the jealous figure of Murro appeared and suggested they were offering her husband money in order to enjoy carnal intercourse with him.

The Nazarbeks stayed for a little while at the Cearne but proved difficult guests, and in such cramped quarters we could not accommodate the bodyguard. Edward therefore persuaded a Scottish farmer called Stevens to let them an empty old farmhouse, the Old Dairy Farm near Crockham Hill. They moved

in and summoned the bodyguard from London. These men were all skilled at different trades: they cooked, made bread in the brick ovens, constructed furniture, did the housework, acted as nursemaids to the two Nazarbek children, Vatya, a noble looking little boy, and Byelka, a horrid little girl. I remember several visits to the Old Dairy Farm during which I watched one or two of the bodyguards making tables and chairs, while another was cooking shashliks of mutton wrapped up in vine-leaves—for by lucky chance there was an old vine growing on the south wall.

One of the Armenian bodyguards was a man with an extraordinary-shaped head, like an oval cake with straight sides. He knew no languages but Armenian and Turkish and assailed the virtue of any young woman with whom he was left alone and thus caused scandals and commotion. The Nazarbek bodyguard had little notion of how strictly the laws of property were interpreted in England. If they wanted straw they helped themselves from the nearest stack, if they needed firewood they pulled down and broke up fences. It was not long before the whole neighbourhood was humming like an angry hive of bees, and if Mr Stevens had not turned them out of the farmhouse, there might have been a massacre of Armenians in the weald of Kent, at a time when Mr Gladstone was still thundering against the unspeakable Turk.

One relic of the Armenian invasion has remained with me to this day, a copy of *Turkey and the Armenian Atrocities*, by Frances M. Willard. It contains eye-witness accounts of the massacres. I read as much of it as I could when I was six or seven, and the illustrations showing babies being tossed on bayonets made a profound impression on my mind.

My early memories of London are almost entirely of hansom cabs and the galleries of the British Museum. Whenever I was taken to London—to visit Mr Underwood the dentist, or Mr Brayley the oculist—Constance and I stayed the night at the British Museum, and I was plunged into an unforgettable family environment. The chief figures were my grandfather,

my grandmother and Chapple. Somehow, though their characters were very different, they were complementary, and the atmosphere of the house was extraordinarily harmonious.

My grandfather was tall, round-shouldered, stooping. He had a grey, rather closely clipped beard, silvery grey hair, steel-rimmed spectacles, a broad and big forehead. In London he would wear a black open frock-coat with silk revers, and a broad flat silk cravat. Yet he was by no means a well-dressed man, for he would sometimes wear an old coat with a torn lining, and when he went out he would absent-mindedly brush the nap of his top-hat the wrong way. The umbrella, from which he was seldom parted, was, like the seraglio of the Emperor, for use rather than for ostentation. On one occasion, when he was in his sixties, he was assailed by three young ruffians in Endell Street and wielded it so vigorously that he put them to flight. Under his gentle scholarly appearance there was a reserve of strength, the heritage of a long line of Yorkshire dalesmen. Even at the time I knew him he would undertake a walk of fifteen miles or so without preparation and arrive with no signs of fatigue.

Gentleness, perfect courtesy and slyly hidden humour were characteristic of Richard Garnett, and I well remember his gentle rebuke to Majestic, his favourite cat, when she was found on the dining-room table, attacking the sirloin when we assembled for lunch. He did not show annoyance or surprise, nor did he remove her forcibly, but after remarking gently: "Manners, Majestic, manners!" he cut off a bit of outside into which she had bitten and helped her first, depositing her and her helping upon the floor beside his chair before he began carving for his guests and family.

All the Garnetts had great love and understanding of cats. Edward, as a boy, edited a family periodical called *The Cats' Newspaper* in which the social intelligence, births and deaths, if not the marriages or *liaisons* of all the St Edmund's Terrace cats were chronicled. This love and understanding of cats was deeply implanted in all my Garnett uncles and aunts

and contrasted strongly with Constance's later relationship with her cat—a "doctored" female. Constance felt friendliness and even some respect for her cat, and Topsy loved her company. But Constance never stroked Topsy, never took her on her knee or had her in the house by the fireside. There was no physical intimacy between them.

Conversation at my grandparents' table was usually rather good, and my grandfather's memory was so perfect and his reading so wide that he could quote from authors whom few of the company had ever read. He did not parade learning, and he was never a bore. Nor did he monopolise the conversation, and unlike my father he never grew heated or forced his opinions down people's throats. He was a more civilised being than Edward.

Narney had humour also, and gentleness, but my impression is that she was more downright in the expression of her opinions than Richard, whose approach was usually oblique and whose own opinions had to be inferred from his jests and his ironic grave questions.

He treated me always with great consideration, choosing subjects to talk about which would interest me. One day when I spoke to him of bows and arrows he went at once to a shelf in his library and took down Eckermann's *Conversations with Goethe*, opened it almost at the page he wanted and read the description of Eckermann's showing off his oriental bow to Goethe. Richard always knew where his books were and went straight to the book and he usually knew in what chapter to find the passage he wanted. His memory was prodigious.

One morning he took me with him, and we walked together into the forecourt of the Museum. I was thrilled by the salutes which were given by the porter in his gold-laced top-hat and the policeman standing beside him.

What was still grander was that Grandpapa led me into the Reading Room into which, I knew, it was forbidden to go until one was twenty-one. I kept close to him, and we passed the policeman, but he made no move to stop me. Following Grandpapa I traversed one of the curved passage-ways under

the dome, and then we found ourselves in the King's Library, beyond which was a room in which Richard worked and had his papers. I was given an armful of Japanese illustrated books with pictures of fishing-boats, mountains and tigers and remained happily there for an hour or two while he wrote.

On other mornings the door leading from my grandfather's house directly into the Manuscript Department was opened and I was led into the main galleries of the Museum and turned loose into one of the anthropological galleries.

An early visit to London to the dentist was followed by a visit to my aunt and uncle, Katie and Charles Clayton, who then lived in a cottage with a pleasant garden in the heart of Croydon. In the evening I was taken to a pantomime. The comic man had a bald head, with a central tuft of hair rising up like a cock's comb, and his loud voice, vulgarity and easy familiar manner terrified and disgusted me. "I've been to the dentist, must I see the pantomime as well?" I asked plaintively. But I was persuaded to stay and I cheered up later when I saw Cinderella put on the glass slipper and drive off in a coach drawn by six tiny Shetland ponies.

Next morning there was an unfortunate misunderstanding. Charles Clayton asked me at breakfast if I liked kidneys. I turned very red indeed and then said, "I hope you do not eat kittens here."

For some time after Bert and Alice went we were "done for" by Mrs Ingram and her daughter Nelly. Mrs Ingram was upright, hardworking and virtuous. Her husband drank and was a poacher. He was proud of having a French grandmother and every spring he picked himself wild salads in the hedgerows and fields, blanching dandelions and gathering wild corn salad, or *mâche*. He taught me at a very early age how to set snares for rabbits and rats.

Nelly Ingram was a very pretty girl of about fourteen who came every morning to do the housework. She had very red, almost scarlet, cheeks, black ringlets, a saucy eye and a well-developed figure. She loved chattering about her amours with

the village boys, and I loved listening to such initiations while she washed up or made the beds. From her I learned the difference between "walking out", "keeping company" and "courting", and she told me the end of the true story which I later wrote as "Colonel Beech's Bear".

It was when I was five years old that I was first rudely made aware that my parents were atheists. We had at that time a boy aged twelve, called George Cowlard, working for us. One day while he was cleaning the knives he told me with relish that my father and mother would burn in hell for ever, because they did not go to church. I was a good deal horrified at this prospect, but native scepticism returned, and I replied. "You only say that because you're the boy that cleans the knives." My rejoinder had the merit of truth and I think I was well justified in using this class weapon, considering the difference in our ages.

My parents were indeed atheists, and we never went to church. This was the first fact that made me realise the difference between us and most of our neighbours. I myself grew up to be a Rationalist with a dislike of religious observances and an antipathy to priests and clergymen of all descriptions. I have never been able to sympathise with people who feel the need of supernatural consolations. I do, however, understand the religious emotion and have experienced it. I think my mother was unduly afraid of my shocking other people's religious susceptibilities. I was not only brought up to behave in a properly reverent manner in church (if I ever went into one) but to assume a somewhat hypocritical air of pious decorum when religious matters were referred to. This may have made for social easiness, but as I was naturally rather a hypocrite, I think it was bad for me. It would have been better, perhaps, to have taught me to testify in and out of season to my lack of faith.

The summer of 1898 was exceptionally hot: it was marked by a grilling sun, long grass burned brown and the advent of Sybil Rudall. Her father had been the assistant musical correspondent on *The Times*.

Sybil was dark, with very black eyes and a gipsy look. She was an inspired cook, and when Conrad came to stay she surpassed herself, knowing that she was cooking for a connoisseur. In those days our food was usually rather plain and British and my father did not often drink wine, but there was always a decanter of whisky on the sideboard for men visitors.

The Hueffers departed, and one result of their going was that my mother and Sybil laboured during that hot summer in the field in front of Gracie's Cottage, part of which was planted with potatoes. First they earthed them up, then they dug them, and I played about. The sun beat down upon us, and we drank jugs of blackcurrant tea. And then they struggled to and fro through the woods carrying a clothes-basket filled with potatoes from Gracie's Cottage up the steep woodland path to the Cearne.

That summer my education began in earnest, at a little school in Limpsfield where I was broken of writing with my left hand. And once a week the children of many of the new residents of Limpsfield were taken for a nature ramble through the woods, first by Princess Kropotkin and later by a daughter of Alfred Russell Wallace who was a good deal better qualified to teach us. There were the four Olivier girls, myself, the two Pease boys and two or three others. On one of these walks I first made friends with a very handsome little dare-devil, Harold Hobson.

One day Miss Wallace pointed out a squirrel's drey and told us that in it the mother squirrel brought up her family of dear little squirrels. Harold rushed at the tree, swung himself up by the first branch and proceeded to climb it rapidly. Having arrived at the nest he disregarded all warnings and orders from Miss Wallace and to our horror pulled out the baby squirrels and waved them in the air. "Here are the dear little squirrels," he shouted and threw them down to us one after another. Our horror at this awful act was heightened when we discovered that they were long dead and indeed putrid. Hastily we were led away to admire more pleasant aspects of mother nature. Harold had to climb down after his audience had departed.

In the winter, when I was six years old, Constance had the first of a series of attacks of sciatica, which were to last intermittently all her life. Doctors advised a warm dry climate. Montpellier was fixed upon, a *pension* was found, and in mid-December 1898 Constance and I set off across the channel. In Paris we stayed some days with the widow of the Russian revolutionary Lavrov, whose daughter, aged about ten, found me very deficient in worldly knowledge. She knew that old gentlemen were actuated by most sinister motives if they smiled or made faces at her, and she pointed out one who was sitting on a bench in the Luxembourg Gardens muttering to himself as one who would not hesitate to attack her. I was sceptical and still am.

In Paris I bought my mother a diary as a birthday present. I had a word or two of French, and I actually went into the shop alone and bought it by myself.

The journey in the P.L.M. railway where the line runs beside the Rhône is a vivid memory. We travelled third class and often sat on wooden seats opposite peasants with bundles of rags, and like them we carried our food and ate it at intervals when we were hungry.

At Avignon we changed trains: the mistral was blowing and my new French beret blew off and was caught somewhere under the wheels of the train. Nothing daunted, Constance went down on hands and knees and retrieved it. I was expecting the train to move and behead her at any minute and was very angry with her for her folly. It was her birthday, the nineteenth of December, and in the train I gave her the diary; the paper had red edges, and it had an elastic band to keep the brown linen covers closed. The present was such a success that I asked for the diary back and presented it again and again. Those who give presents often feel like this about them but usually have to employ more indirect methods in order to spin out the delights of generosity.

Montpellier proved to be a lovely town though full of electric trams. There was an open space called Le Perron, full of fountains with black swans floating upon ornamental water, and

46

near by the Roman Aqueduct still supplied the city with water which rushed through a conduit borne upon tall arches across an intervening valley from the neighbouring hills.

We stayed in a *pension* kept by a couple called Cornelier. Most of the *pensionaires* had come to Montpellier because of the university. There was a Russian girl studying law and a Swedish botanist and his wife, who took us to the Botanical Gardens in which Constance discovered a patch of rhubarb neatly labelled. Its interest was purely scientific, the comestible qualities being wisely unrecognised by the French.

I was sent every morning to a French school. There was a door in a side-street which led into a walled garden partly fruit and flowers, which were forbidden to us, partly a paved or asphalt playground. At the far end of this playground was a low building with french windows opening into the two class-rooms presided over by two sisters who were fierce and voluble but rather remote. I was put back to pothooks and hangers for a time, but a *dictée* proved difficult.

I learned most from my companions, who ranged in age from six to ten—long-legged little French boys with shaven heads, bare calves and striped socks. They collected in professional groups to play marbles. I also, as a humble foreigner, played marbles with them. But the chief attraction was not my male companions but Madeleine who (omitting Elsie Hueffer) qualifies as my first love. She was perhaps a few months older than I, plump, with liquid black eyes, abundant black corkscrew curls that fascinated me, a dark flush upon her cheek, fat little legs and fat little fingers. I fell in love with her and tried to spend as much of our morning break as possible by her side. But she disapproved of such a public relationship, and though she would throw me a melting glance or two now and then— to keep my feverish excitement at the right pitch—she ostentatiously preferred an older boy called Raoul and referred to me as *"le petit nigaud"*.

Finally my passion became public property, and she avoided me. The hopeless failure of my love for Madeleine made me a

47

bit of a cynic by the time I was seven years old, and helped, I think, to awaken my intelligence. I was told recently that my reputation at the school was "*très sauvage*". We stayed in Paris for several days on the way home and returned to England just before my birthday. I was for a few months almost bilingual and read *Sans Famille*, *Les Petites Filles Modèles*, and *Les Malheurs de Sophie* for pleasure with no difficulty. Some little while later my mother asked me what I thought of *Les Petites Filles Modèles*. I gave a Gallic shrug, a cynical smile and remarked: "*Il ne faut pas faire pleurer la petite Elise.*" I have no idea whom I was referring to, and a cursory re-reading of this delightful book does not help.

One result of my early acquaintance with the French language has been to make me believe all my life that I know it better than I do. In spite of frequent evidence to the contrary, I have always believed I know French almost as well as English.

Soon after our return the Heaths, whom we had met in Paris, came to live at Gracie's Cottage.

Richard Heath was a small man, with silver hair and beard, blue eyes in which one was surprised to detect a twinkle of humour. My friendship with him was rapid, for he occupied himself in the garden in building gutters with little bridges over them so that when it rained water should flow down the appointed gutters and not encroach upon the paths. These little bridges where paths crossed waterways were most ingenious and made of the largest flat pieces of sandstone that he could find. I cannot believe they served much useful purpose, but they satisfied his inherited Dutch instinct for irrigation, and they enchanted me.

He was a revolutionary in his way, but with a difference which marked him off from the terrorists to whom I had become accustomed. For, like his fellow-engraver, William Blake, Richard Heath was greatly concerned with God. He was the author of a number of books. *The Via Dolorosa of the English Labourer* was the best known of them, and in *The Lamb Slain from the Foundation of the World* he identified the

NELLIE HEATH

poor, the agricultural labourer, and the dwellers in the slums of the great cities with Christ.

"The agricultural labourer is but the type of suffering humanity everywhere, and in all time, from the victims of the Cains and the Nimrods, to those of the world's plutocracy and Russia's autocracy, Christ, as the Universal Man, has been, and is identified with all those sufferers."

The setting free of these age-long sufferers by Socialism was Richard Heath's religion and politics.

It was a very different view of Socialism from the apotheosis of the Civil Service imagined by Sidney and Beatrice Webb— very different from the smug parasitism of the Trade Union bosses on Capitalist enterprise which in alliance with that of the Webb bureaucracy was to impose the Welfare State upon this country. But the religious force of ideas like those of Richard Heath played a large part in bringing such Socialism about.

Mr Heath was a widower, and his surviving family consisted of one son and two daughters. His eldest daughter, Grace, had died of tuberculosis, and his second daughter, Margaret, who married Arthington Pease, became infected with the disease. Carl and Margaret were teachers in board-schools, but for a year or two Carl came to live in Limpsfield and gave lessons to the Olivier girls, to me, to Harold Hobson and to various other children in the neighbourhood. In some ways Carl was remarkably like his father, but his pale complexion and colourless hair seemed to indicate a lack of that exuberant vitality which one associated with the glow of his father's cheek. Moreover, the twinkle that lit up his father's sea-blue eyes was more subdued. But like his father he was a revolutionary greatly concerned with God, a true descendant of the Puritan Levellers.

How shall I describe Richard Heath's youngest daughter, Nellie, who later became practically one of our family? The first impression was of extraordinary softness, a softness physically expressed at that time in velvet blouses and velveteen skirts; a softness of speech and a gentleness of manner and

disposition which made it difficult and painful for her to dis-
agree with, and impossible flatly to contradict, any statement
made to her. And after more than fifty years this lovable
gentleness and sympathy for everyone is still her most outstanding characteristic.

But under this softness was an iron will-power which has
sometimes reminded me of Emily Brontë. She would not be
driven; she refused, in spite of her extreme gentleness, to
be coerced. If I stress this quality it is because for many years
I was the frequent witness of Edward's exasperated and well-
meant efforts to coerce her. To force her, for instance, to take
nourishing food when she infinitely preferred foods lacking in
nourishment.

Nellie was a painter and had studied in Paris where her father
had lived for some years. She had also worked under Sickert
when he was in his greyest period. Sickert influenced Nellie's
painting more than anyone. She was a most sensitive and
charming painter, at her best, I think, in small landscapes of
haymaking and harvest time or of an old oak in winter. Unfortunately she gave up painting in middle life to do welfare
work in prisons.

Edward could not resist teasing and he particularly delighted
in teasing the women he liked. Nellie at first was rather apt to
take teasing seriously, whereas Constance either giggled with
enjoyment, or brushed it on one side, according to her mood.

One evening, when Edward took me with him to the
Heaths' cottage, he told me we were cavaliers in the time of the
Civil War going to the house of a puritan maiden, and this
game was carried on when we arrived. Nellie may have appreciated the game, but was distressed because she took the issue of
the Civil War seriously. She *was* on the side of the Roundheads,
and she found it painful that my father should declare himself a
cavalier and encourage me to value lace ruffles and aristocratic
manners more than the liberties of the people.

The seriousness of Nellie about subjects which she felt really
important was one of the things which helped me to grow up
into a hypocrite. She detested blood sports; I was by nature a

hunter and a poacher and spent a lot of my spare time catching rabbits with Nietsche. In Nellie's presence these occupations were minimised and lip service given to a hatred of hunting and shooting. This hatred was generally felt by most of our friends and neighbours. Henry Salt, the leading humanitarian and vegetarian in England, lived with his wife at Crockham Hill and was a great friend of both the Heaths and the Oliviers, and he certainly influenced them. Edward greatly enjoyed Henry Salt's savage and ironical wit, and his own pessimistic defeatism inclined him to sympathy with Salt's humanitarianism. The wanton destruction of innocent and beautiful animals and birds, and their extermination, fitted in with his philosophy of the triumphant survival of the most brutal and the most vulgar.

But what held true on land and in the air did not extend below the surface of the water. Edward had a passion for fishing. He was never a good fisherman, but the prospect of a holiday beside sea or lake or river always led to his getting out a mass of tangled lines, insecure gut, split shot, fearsome hooks and even a moth-eaten fly or two. These he would furbish up, sprinkling them with the shreds of tobacco which fell from his hand-made cigarettes as he did so. He took these preparations, and indeed the whole subject of fishing, with perfect seriousness. And he had no humanitarian qualms about catching them, thank goodness. But he was not very good at it.

The leafage of summer enabled visitors to approach our house along the woodland track behind and above it without being seen—but also without their being able to see us. This was particularly blessed if they came in parties, for then their voices could generally be heard, and we would stand listening intently, like deer startled when grazing, and we would take the appropriate action. Sometimes an almost incredibly loud high-pitched voice was heard rasping out a Scottish jargon. At these sounds Edward would start to his feet from his wicker couch, and grasping an armful of manuscripts would fly across the grass, scramble over the opposite fence and vanish. A startled and stoical look would come over Connie's face as she retired indoors to prepare a welcome, and a moment or

two later the skirl and shriek of Scottish accents would reach a crescendo as a very tall lady with a scarlet face framed in sandy hair issued from the woods in strange attire and came down the path preceded by two little boys in kilts of the "hunting Stuart" tartan. K and L, for so I will call them, were a year or so older and a year or so younger than myself, and their technique for subduing me was different.

K was large and ugly with big square teeth, and he made a lot of spluttering and hissing noises, displaying his teeth and gums, all of which could be interpreted as benevolent superiority. He had learned various social forms of indicating condescension which he enjoyed practising upon me. Saying: "How-dy doo?" and extending two fingers for me to shake, or repeating "dontcherknow?" at the end of every sentence. I have never enjoyed being patronised, even by my intellectual equals or superiors, and in consequence I found K quite insufferable.

L, his younger brother, had wits as sharp as a needle and a changeling's wizened charm. This was put down, by my parents, to his having been brought up on goat's milk as a baby. But he was for me an insidious charmer, as he had a genius for swapping things, and after one of these visits, when the kilts had fluttered bravely away into the woodlands, I usually found myself bereft of my greatest treasures, grasping a few handfuls of fools' gold that turned to dust as I inspected them. It was my first friendship with "a Friend", for they were of Quaker stock. These visits, when they came to tea with us, had the advantage of being expected. There were also many unexpected descents and raiding parties in the summer when picnics in the woods were very frequent. Their mother then sometimes dressed in "rational costume" which took the form of large pale blue Turkish trousers made of Harris tweed, sandals, a green jacket, one or two tartan scarves and a necklace of hammered silver. Seldom could this Meg Merrilees give anyone her undivided attention, for she was either dragging a reluctant Shetland pony to and fro or making a fire or brandishing a boiling kettle.

During picnics we would play games. But it was a relief when picnics were over and we could go back quietly through the woods which had fallen silent again. Sometimes I was invited to their house and spent hours with K and L in their stern—though not very wild—Caledonian surroundings.

K would grin and splutter and work off strange and novel methods of indicating superiority. L would initiate me into a new currency of harrow-teeth to supersede the existing one of disused ploughshares he had successfully floated two months before.

I was embarrassed at tea by the jokes inscribed upon the pottery. Indeed I refused to help myself to butter because the legend "Be canny wi' the butter, it's no sae cheap" offended my sense of decency. If people used butter-dishes like that I decided that they must endure the shame of seeing their guests eat dry bread.

Nevertheless, such childish rufflings of the spirit quickly disappeared, and I often greatly enjoyed myself with K and L.

*　　　*　　　*　　　*

Constance used to get up by half-past six or seven in the spring and summer, and we soon sat down to our breakfast of porridge, with milk for me and coffee for her. Her day contained so much that I cannot easily fit it all in. First thing in the morning she used to go round the garden, while the dew was still on the plants, and collect those miscreants, the slugs. This was a moment of self-indulgence, for the serious day's work was before her. Some of the housework had to be done, then I was called in and my lessons started and, leaving me to work out a sum or to learn a proposition of Euclid, Constance would open the Russian volume which she was translating and begin work. Sometimes, but not always, I would work in the same room with her and, letting my pencil lie idle on the paper, I would watch the changing expressions on her face, eager, frowning, puzzled or amused. The Russian words were translated not only on the foolscap sheet of paper in front of her, but into English features and flesh and blood. Her face

53

was so expressive that I could guess at the emotional tension of what she was reading. Even if I did not interrupt, there would soon be a knocking at the back door, or Edward would come in with a letter in his hand, worried until he could read it to her and work off his irritation by a discussion. It was a blessing for her when Carl Heath started giving lessons and I went to little classes, sometimes with the Olivier girls, sometimes alone.

III

ONE afternoon in the summer of 1899, Sydney Olivier arrived in a state of tremendous excitement. He was a senior Civil Servant in the Colonial Office, and he had just seen the draft of the ultimatum which Joseph Chamberlain, the Colonial Secretary, had persuaded the Government to send to the Transvaal Republic. War would certainly result. Indeed, war in which the independent Boer republics were to be annexed was Chamberlain's object. Such a war was to the advantage of the shareholders of the Johannesburg gold mines and Kimberley diamond mines but were our soldiers' lives and the Boers' liberties to be sacrificed for them? Sydney Olivier, accompanied by Edward and Constance, set off at once through the wood to Gracie's Cottage to tell Richard Heath the news. I went with them, picking up scraps of information as I went. I remember Richard Heath standing short and resolute with blue eyes flashing as he heard the news and the sense of seething indignation in all the members of the little group. A new era had begun. The last gift of the Victorian age to the new century was war.

Its other gift was the death of the Queen, a year later. Three hundred years before, the death of Elizabeth and the accession of James may have promised much. If Richard Garnett's theory that *The Tempest* was written as a tribute to James I—pictured as Prospero—is correct, Shakespeare may have hoped that a Scholar King would inaugurate a new era of intelligence and wisdom.

But Victoria's death, in the middle of the South African war, dismayed all classes equally. Whatever the heretics had felt about the Victorian reign, they realised that it was great. The Eminent Victorians had lived and died in such profusion that it was possible to pick and choose amongst them. If Tennyson

55

had disappointed, Browning and Swinburne had spoken for the intellectuals and the aesthetes. But what promise did Edward VII offer? To most he seemed to be a reversion to the dismal reigns of the Hanoverians who had preceded Victoria. And Kipling and Alfred Austin were the poets of the age. Richard Heath, who was given to dreaming, summed up the change while asleep. He dreamed that he was riding on the top of a horse bus with his partner in his engraving business. Suddenly a portly goggle-eyed figure approached them and tapped him on the shoulder.

"I beg your pardon," said the Prince of Wales, "but I've come out without any money. Can you lend me half a crown?" Richard Heath immediately produced the coin. The Prince of Wales—King Edward—received it with guttural thanks and hurriedly got off the bus without paying his fare.

Richard Heath's partner, who had remained silent, then spoke up.

"You'll never see that half-crown again," he said.

That dream symbolised the attitude of part of the public to our new monarch and contrasted ill with Shakespeare's hopes of Prospero. This hostility turned out to be mistaken. Edward VII was a most admirable monarch and his work in promoting the *Entente Cordiale* with France laid the foundation of a sane foreign policy.

Soon after the beginning of the South African war, Giblin was rumoured to be returning from Klondike, and when he actually arrived I was still young enough to be acutely aware that he had promised me four golden chairs on his return. I was old enough to know that such a gift was not altogether likely. But I did expect something by way of a token payment—something in gold—a bag of dust or nuggets at least. The shock I received when he appeared at breakfast to be totally unaware of his obligations towards me was most disillusioning. But if I got no gold, I did get a mine of stories.

One day, after Mr Bassett had been to market, his mare turned in to the yard between the mill and the millhouse with

the reins lying loose on her back, and Mr Bassett was found lying in the bottom of the cart. My old friend had died upon the road, and the mare had brought him home for the last time.

For some time Scearn Bank Farm and the mill on The Chart were tenantless. Then they were taken by a man of a very different stamp from old Bassett. "Grab-all" was his nickname in the village—I shall not give his real one as he has left descendants whom I respect. Grab-all kept the public-house and when no farmer or miller came forward as a tenant, he took over the farm and the mill. The mill he utterly neglected and destroyed because it was out-of-date and did not pay. No longer did the sails turn endlessly, for up there the wind was always blowing. No longer did they sweep down faster, it seemed, as they reached the ground, and slower as they mounted, receding into the air. No longer did teams of three great carthorses, gleaming with shining brass, stand patiently while men hoisted sacks of wheat from the tailboard of the wagon with a pulley, into the upper part of the mill, and then loaded the wagon with sacks of flour and sharps and middlings and bran in their stead. After Grab-all had it, the mill stood idle and stationary. It was never turned to meet the changing winds, and one after another the sails were blown down in big gales, until it stood black and bleak, like the hulk of a wooden barge set up on end with its bows pointing to heaven. And then, a few years later, it was pulled down altogether. The millhouse was let to a woman who took in lodgers. Mrs Conrad and her baby stayed there for a fortnight while Conrad stayed with us at the Cearne, and later on the new curate had lodgings there.

Scearn Bank Farm went to rack and ruin like the mill and for the same reason—because Grab-all cared only for money. His first action was to nail up a notice *Trespassers will be Prosecuted* on the barn, which is there yet. Then he turned the Collinses out so as to let the cottage at a higher rent. Collins had been a good gardener. There were little dwarf box edgings to all the paths, one or two larger box bushes and a damask and

a moss rose; there was never a weed to be seen in his beds of onions.

One day my father, going by the cottage, saw Grab-all hacking up the box edgings with a pick-axe. My father asked him what he was doing, and he replied that he had sold them to a nurseryman. The big box trees and the roses were hacked up also, because they were useless, and in a few years the beautiful garden was a waste of docks, nettles and couchgrass. A little triangular piece of ground stood at the junction of my aunt Gracie's land and the cottage garden. It was common land like the great wood which bordered the farm meadows. One day Grab-all suggested to my father that they should fence this little piece of land in and divide it between them. This would have been stealing simply for the sake of stealing. Grab-all did not own the land he had and scarcely cultivated it, and the little patch, hardly ten yards by ten, could have been no good to him. But Grab-all disliked it, perhaps because it had no owner who could put up a board about trespassers; perhaps only because of the ragged robins and bluebells which grew in its sandy soil. If Farmer Bassett typified Old England, Grab-all typified the new century.

The tenant who came after old Collins had departed was even more representative of the change which was to come in old-world cottages. She was a lady who had done welfare work among the girls in the East End of London. She had gathered round her four or five of the gentlest of them and brought them down to live with her at Scearn Bank Farm.

The girls, who had been rather knocked about by life, were supposed to form the workers of an ideal community. They were told to address their benefactress as "Little Mother". Two of them went out to work by the day and brought home their wages; two of them worked as Little Mother's unpaid servants. In the evenings they would sew and Little Mother would read aloud *Towards Democracy* by Edward Carpenter, *Leaves of Grass* by Walt Whitman or Ruskin's *Sesame and Lillies*.

Little Mother was *petite*, with long fair hair, which she wore in her more childish moments in two long plaits. When she

was more oppressed by the world, the plaits encircled her head and framed her brow. She had very blue eyes and a small straight mouth with narrow lips. She wore apple-green frocks, low-waisted, with a pocket hanging low down from her girdle, and in the summer went sandalled or even barefoot.

Constance engaged one of the girls, and I at once attached myself to the new-comer, out of curiosity. Little Mother returned my interest and asked me to show her the secrets of the woods. I did so and soon was made to lose my heart to her, and, sitting on the moss under a great beech-tree, she held me very close and asked me if I loved her more than anyone else in the world. When I swore I did love her, she told me that the world was very full of wickedness and that evil people were all around us, whispering cruel and evil things.

To my astonishment, Edward and Constance, who let me spend hours talking to Crazy Mary, who came to beg bread and tea at the back door and spent her life laying fronds of bracken over the woodland pathways to propitiate the fairies, flatly forbade my further association with Little Mother, and my chances of fighting for her against the wicked whisperers were nipped in the bud.

A few years later this happy community at Scearn Bank Farm broke up. Li Whale, the most intelligent and strong-minded of the flock, rebelled and came to live with us.

Later still, Little Mother, having rather exhausted the soil in Limpsfield, withdrew with the girls who remained faithful to another district and set them weaving homespuns. Li Whale then took on Scearn Bank Farm as a home for her sisters and her old father.

The Boer War lasted nearly three years, and its effect on my upbringing was profound and unfortunate. My parents were violently opposed to the war and detested the flood of imperialistic jingoism and hypocrisy which swept over the country. They were, in common parlance, pro-Boers, and they were not alone in their opinions. Sydney Olivier was not able to express his publicly, but his daughters burned Joe Chamberlain, a guy easily identifiable by his eyeglass, on the fifth of

November 1899, on Limpsfield Chart Common, in public. That was in time of war!

But if Olivier's lips were sealed, J. A. Hobson took an extremely active part in writing against the war. Moreover, he had Cronwright-Schreiner, the husband of Olive Schreiner the novelist, to stay with him at Elmstead, and great was my excitement when he brought him over to see us.

When Harold or I appeared on Limpsfield Common, we were pursued by angry cries of "Krujer!" and sometimes by volleys of stones. The Olivier girls may have suffered cat-calls, but they were not stoned. It was unlucky for me that Carl Heath should be living within a short distance of Limpsfield Common schools and that my arrival at his house should coincide with the mustering of some hundred or two young patriots arriving from all points of the compass. To be booed and stoned with some regularity at the ages of seven and eight is a good foundation for persecution mania in after life. But the injury was not really that. The effect of belonging to a minority is to give one an overwhelming contempt for the judgment of one's fellow-men. And as, in the case of the Boer War, I saw the minority justified in its opinions a few years later, I was confirmed in my contempt.

The minority of pro-Boers were indeed the guardians of England's honour, much in the same way as the Free French under De Gaulle were the guardians of that of France in the dark days of 1940. That remark may be obscure to some, but I refer to the concentration camps into which the Boer women and children were swept up, so that they could not keep the farms going while their men were away fighting. In these concentration camps they died in hundreds and but for Miss Emily Hobhouse they would have died in thousands.

It is the duty of an honest patriot to see his country as it is seen by other peoples. When Sir Nevile Henderson protested to Goebbels about the iniquities of the Nazi concentration camps, Goebbels took down the dictionary, opened it at *Konzentrationslager* and read out: "invented and first used by the British in the South African war". The evil that men do lives after them.

At the age of seven or eight I could not distinguish between the duty of opposing a political error by one's country and the crime of aiding the enemy. The label pro-Boer, if unjust to most, fitted me. I gloried in Boer victories and, as I naturally wanted to play at soldiers, I spent my time galloping an imaginary pony up the sides of kopjes and ambushing and shooting down British soldiers. I think this was a very bad and wicked thing and regret that my parents should have allowed it. For it was all very well Edward pretending to be Irish and a rebel, when he was in fact of mixed Yorkshire and Anglo-Irish blood, but I was English, and I was to live among and love my compatriots. If I was not English I was nothing, and I should have been encouraged to love and honour England. Instead of which Constance entered into my games, and when we walked together through the woods she invented a game in which she was a Boer mother and I her son, escaping after our farm had been burned by General Roberts.

Edward joined a body of militant pro-Boers who volunteered to attend meetings against the war armed with ash sticks and defend the speakers. Luckily this organisation fizzled out without his being seriously hurt.

One fortunate result of the Boer War was that it cemented my friendship with Harold Hobson. We were stoned together by the village boys and shared many other important experiences. When about my eighth birthday I discovered "the facts of life" by inductive reasoning, it was to Harold that I immediately imparted my theory. He listened with interest.

"Let's go and watch those two horses in the next field and see if you are right," he suggested. But he was sufficiently clear-headed to see that my theory had not been disproved because it had received no supporting evidence after two hours watching a pair of geldings.

Shortly before the end of the War we had a visit from Kropotkin who prophesied that bubonic plague would infallibly sweep the country on the return of the British Army. My parents scouted the idea, and Kropotkin poured out torrents of voluble explanations and reasons. But he did not shake their

scepticism. It is perhaps worth recording that the great scientist's prophecy was not *absolutely* wrong. Britain was not, it is true, swept by a new Black Death, but two or three cases of bubonic plague occurred in Liverpool and were immediately isolated. If England had been Russia, perhaps there would have been an epidemic.

My grandfather, Richard Garnett, was fervently patriotic during the Boer War and wrote a sonnet on President Kruger, which appeared in *The Times*, to the effect that he could not be pitied in defeat owing to "his greed and guile and penury of worth". I think there was some open disagreement or expression of disapproval on his part of my father's political opinions, and my father always spoke with regret of his father's volume of poems, *The Queen*, which contained four sonnets on the death of Queen Victoria.

Joseph Conrad paid many visits to the Cearne. On one of the first occasions, when I was five years old, I asked him why the first mate of a ship was always a bad man and the second mate good. I don't know what stories I had been reading which had put this into my head, but I remember Conrad's laughing and confusing me by saying: "For many years I was a first mate myself."

It was next morning that we made friends. There was a jolly wind, and it was washing-day. I was alone with Conrad, and suddenly he was making me a sailing boat. The sail was a clean sheet tied at the top corners to a clothes-prop and hoisted with some spare clothes-line over one of the clothes-posts. The sail was lashed at the foot, and I held the sheet fastened to the other corner in one hand while it bellied and pulled. The green grass heaved in waves, the sail filled and tugged, our speed was terrific. Alterations were made and the rig perfected and when, an hour later, Edward came out looking for his guest, he found him sitting in our big clothes basket steering the boat and giving me orders to take in or let out the sail.

Once I saw Stephen Crane, who came to live at Oxted so as to be near Edward, talking to Edward and Joseph Conrad at

the bottom of our garden. But I cannot remember his voice or that he spoke to me.

My next meeting with Conrad was when my mother and I were staying with Ford and Elise Hueffer at Aldington Knoll, a little Kentish farmhouse looking out over Romney Marsh. Ford was at his most lovable and genial. There was a stream running through the garden, and Ford had installed a little wooden water-wheel with two brightly painted wooden puppets who seemed to be working very hard as they bent down and straightened up incessantly. Really the water turned the wheel and the wheel made them move up and down, bending their backs.

One day, while we were there, Elsie drove us over to visit the Conrads, who were living a few miles away at Pent Farm.

Jessie Conrad told Elsie and Constance that a labourer called Hunt had gone mad and had besieged Pent Farm for two days trying to get hold of the Conrads' maidservant. It happened that Conrad was finishing a story, and Jessie knew it would be fatal to disturb him. She therefore told him nothing about the madman, and during the siege Conrad went on writing, unaware that neither the butcher, grocer nor postman dared to come near the house.

This story made a great impression on Constance, as well it might, and she often said that Jessie was a woman of amazing physical courage and devotion and, in spite of what one might think, just the wife for Conrad. Anyone, however, who reads Mrs Conrad's *Joseph Conrad and his Circle* will find a completely different version there. Both versions were invented by her and, like so many others, redound to her credit and to the discredit of her husband.

There was a half-witted labourer called Hunt, because Elsie and Ford, who had lived at Pent Farm, had known him. There is something particularly funny in Jessie's having taken in Ford and Elsie with the romantic story of the siege. For Ford was an arch-liar himself and Elsie ought to have been experienced in detecting tall stories.

While we were at Aldington Knoll we were driven over to

Brede Place in a hired wagonette to see Stephen Crane and his wife and were accompanied by Henry James riding a bicycle.

It must have been about the time of this visit that my Aunt Olivia Garnett and Elsie Hueffer went to tea with Henry James at Lamb House and Elsie announced that Ford and Conrad had just finished writing a novel in collaboration to be called *The Inheritors*. Henry James listened and then said: "To me this is like a bad dream which one relates at breakfast! Their traditions and their gifts are so dissimilar. Collaboration between them is to me inconceivable."

The two ladies sipped their tea and ate their bread and butter, and no more was said upon the subject.

James was perfectly right as regards *The Inheritors*, which was unworthy of Conrad. His part in it was very small. But I value the book for the portrait of Edward, as Lea the publisher's reader, which shows the regard in which he was held by the collaborators. Their second collaboration *Romance* is, I think, a rattling good story.

The next time we saw the Hueffers they had moved from Aldington Knoll to Winchilsea, and we stayed in lodgings next door to them. The South African War was drawing to a close: it was perhaps the late summer of 1901. There was a flower show in Winchilsea the day after we arrived, and troops paraded in dark green uniforms with felt hats turned up on one side, and a military band played *The Last Rose of Summer* and other airs through a long, hot and dusty afternoon. I had been given a Brownie Kodak. A few days later we went over in a hired wagonette to Rye and called upon Henry James, whom we found dressed in an extremely tight-fitting pair of knickerbockers and an equally exiguous jacket of black-and-white checks. When he came out with us and showed us Rye he wore on his vast head a very tight-fitting cap. In this costume he was kind enough to pose for me, and the photograph I took came out perfectly. Lamb House astonished me by its tidiness, the beautiful furniture in the drawing-room, the perfection of a passage and the beautiful garden. Ford, tall and fresh-coloured, smiling and showing his rabbit teeth, enjoyed himself,

patronising my parents on one side and James on the other. Perhaps my parents were aware of the possibility that they were being thrust upon the Master by Ford. If they were right in that suspicion, I am duly grateful to Ford, for I should not otherwise have had tea with Henry James in Lamb House. He walked back a little way with us, and we said good-bye to him on the edge of Rye and walked down from the high ground to where our conveyance was waiting.

The Boer War was in its closing stages when a new visitor came to the Cearne to win my heart. He was W. H. Hudson, a very tall lean man with red-brown eyes which could flare up with anger or amusement and then die down again. He had a short beard, a twisted aquiline nose that had been broken in some fight in South America, a wide forehead and a curiously flat top to his head, and big bony hands. His voice, gentle and deep in tone, became suddenly rasping and fierce when Edward teased him—which he was always doing. Hudson wore an old-fashioned tail-coat made of some pepper-and-salt or brown tweed with pockets in the tails and a stand-up, stiff white collar to his shirt. On his first visit he announced that he was going to have tea with Miss Hall, an old lady who lived in Westerham, and that he would take me with him to show him the way. Miss Hall lived in a house called Little Squerries at the bottom of Hosey Hill, not far from Quebec House, General Wolfe's birthplace. The principal feature of the establishment, in my eyes at all events, was a monkey which had come into the lady's possession in an odd way.

Several years before she had been driving in her pony carriage up Westerham Hill when, looking over the hedge, she saw a new packing-case standing just inside a field. She stopped and told her coachman to see what it was. It contained a monkey, which she took home and fed and called Jacko. He proved to be gentle and well-behaved, and I was allowed to feed him with a piece of banana in the conservatory and to talk to him while Hudson and our hostess talked and walked about the

garden. It was winter and it was quite dark when we came back along the footpath through Westerham Park and down from Kent Hatch through the Chart wood. I knew the way perfectly and was able to tell Hudson whenever a big root or stone stuck up in our path. For I was accustomed to help my mother in this way and thought all grown-up people needed such guidance. Hudson let me guide him, and that walk was the foundation of our friendship.

It was in the years from seven onwards that I became familiar with the Chart woods—familiar is too feeble a word: I learnt them by heart. My visual memory for places is phenomenal, and I learnt to remember every tree and stone and turn in the paths. These memories are still with me, and I can remember exactly where scores of trees stood that have since been felled, and the stones and roots which stuck up in paths that have been abolished or transformed.

Not only is my memory loaded with the physical details of these woods, but it is also packed with the associations each spot had for me. Some of these were due to actual events, but an immense range of associations arises from my habit of visualising the stories which I read as taking place in some locality intimately known to me.

Nor was this phenomenal memory of places and of associations with them limited to my boyhood. I still possess both to a considerable degree. My memory of places seems to be much greater than that of any of my acquaintances. I can visualise very large parts of the Yorkshire Dales where I have walked, and associations rise up connected with hundreds of these scenes. Unfortunately my verbal memory is bad.

Hudson's first visit was in winter, but he came again in the spring and summer following. One spring morning I went out with him into the woods; the majority of the trees were still bare; only the hawthorn and a few forward sprays of beech were in leaf. I was astonished because he continually identified birds by their song, and the song of a misselthrush led us to a misselthrush's nest in the fork of a young oak. Standing silently in the warm spring sunshine, listening to the

66

wild and rapturous song of the storm-cock, I felt very close to my tall companion.

I told him that I had seen a frog unlike other frogs. Together we went down across the fields below the Cearne to Trevereux pond where there was a nightingale singing, and there Hudson found my "other frog" which was in reality a kind of toad—a natterjack.

Hudson introduced us to pimentos, which my parents had not tasted before, and to Valdepeñas wine. My father and Hudson sat beside the blazing fire in the big room with glasses of Valdepeñas and Hudson told stories. One story, about Valdepeñas, cannot have been true. He said Valdepeñas was a deep and narrow valley, hemmed in by mountains with no way out except up and over the mountainside, and that out of every load of barrels that came safely out of the rich and magic valley, several were dropped and the staves knocked in and the wine drunk by the thirsty men who drove the loaded ox-wagons.

Hudson's next visit was in the summer. It was a warm balmy night. I had been allowed to stay up and we were all sitting in the front porch, when the sound of a nightjar calling, not far off, aroused Hudson.

We followed him silently to the top of the garden, and there in the next field, we hid under some bushes. I was under a gorse bush and had to keep motionless and silent in spite of its prickles.

Then Hudson began calling to the birds, imitating their whirring rattle perfectly. Soon a nightjar answered him, then after a pause Hudson called again, and so it went on, bird and man calling to each other until in the end, the birds—for there were more than one—came to investigate. There was a sudden clap of wings over our heads and a dark shadowy bird whirled away, then another warning clap of wings as another swept over and discovered the imposter. After that it was no good, and we got up, brushed the leaves and prickles off our clothes and walked back, delighted by our sudden contact with the nightjars.

There were glow-worms that night in the grass, and it was then that I told Hudson that I had seen a phosphorescent light like a chain of green beads and, on lighting a match, had found a centipede. Once again my observation was confirmed and I won praise.

Hudson gave me three books. The first was Barrie's *The Little White Bird*—and the book nauseated me. I have never been able to stomach anything by Barrie except his short plays, *The Twelve Pound Look* and *The Will*, for he is an author who is only endurable when he is cynical. I disliked *The Little White Bird* so much that I wrote and told Hudson and sent it back. The next book he gave me was his own *British Birds* which was a treasured possession, continually referred to until it was replaced as a work of reference by the new edition of *The Handbook of British Birds* in five volumes. The third book he gave me was his own: *A Little Boy Lost*. I did not care for it, but I concealed my indifference and am glad to have it with its inscription, on the shelf between *British Birds* and Hudson's own signed copy of *Green Mansions*. I always wrote to Hudson when I was in any difficulty about identifying birds.

A visitor who impressed my imagination rather than won my heart was Robert Bontine Cunninghame Graham. He was tall and extremely aristocratic in appearance. For many years he was a very close friend of my father's.

Graham had the affectations and *panache* of the most noble of Dumas's Three Musketeers, Athos. Yet in spite of these airs, Graham was genuine enough; that is to say he was a Scottish laird of ancient family; he rode a horse well, and had lived with the Gauchos in South America and the Moors in Morocco. But when he made a speech or wrote a book he adopted a pose, and his vanity overcame him.

During his visits he taught me half a dozen words of Arabic. At intervals he used to send useless and tawdry presents to Edward: a Moroccan dagger, a brass lamp designed for the wick to float in a pool of oil, which could naturally not be used, another set of three brass lamps equally useless and ugly. My father, however, completely accepted Graham, liking the man

and believing him to be a good, if not a great, writer. For Edward was absolutely tolerant of vanity and enjoyed in his friends every characteristic which assisted in the expression of personality.

Another visitor who came about that time was a short, thickset man of great energy and determined character—Hilaire Belloc. During his visits he seldom listened to anything my parents said and never stopped talking; he sat up late drinking wine and talking to my father and then got up much too early next morning. But he not only had energy himself: he imparted it to all of us, and for a short time after his visit the defeatist atmosphere that my father's philosophy imparted to me was blown away.

Nothing in the world could be more poisonous to a boy than that philosophy. For Edward usually spoke as though he believed that the finest talents were never recognised; the most sensitive and charming people were ruined and oppressed by the coarse and brutal; that the survival of the fittest meant that ruthlessness, brutality, ugliness and stupidity triumphed and exterminated the beautiful, the sensitive and the gifted. And I was, of course, axiomatically to regard myself as one of the doomed minority. This philosophy, which might have had some truth in it had it been propounded by the Last of the Mohicans, was grotesque nonsense. But I did not realise what nonsense it was until I was nearly twenty, when one day I said to myself:

"For hundreds of thousands of years the weakly and the stupid have died; the ugly girls have gone unwed and the beautiful ones been chosen for the mothers of the race by the strongest and most intelligent men. I and everyone else in the world are the inheritors of the successful: why should I fail now when the blood of the winners in life's race runs through my veins? I will not identify myself with a dinosaur."

The memory of Hilaire Belloc's self-confidence faded away; a more lasting memorial of one of his visits was a huge red-and-yellow casserole which he sent to my mother for making *bœuf en daube*.

A far more frequent visitor, and one more congenial to Constance, was a bald serious man of about Edward's age who was to become for many years a close friend of both my parents. He wrote to Constance, in the first instance, because he admired the works of Turgenev, which he had read in her translations, and had himself literary ambitions. Indeed, he had already published a novel and a volume of verses under the *nom de plume* of John Sinjohn. He was John Galsworthy, and my parents invited him down to the Cearne and at once adopted the position of his literary mentors.

On his first visit he arrived at the same time as a cat with a kitten. Before departing on holiday with their family, some neighbours, knowing us as cat-lovers, brought us their half-wild cat which had newly kittened. Two days later I found our palsied dog Puppsie bouncing in on cat and kitten in the big room. I rushed forward and grabbed Puppsie by the collar and was dragging him away when the cat sprang at me and, missing my eye, tore my eyebrow asunder. In spite of the pain and one eye being full of blood, I remember looking with awe at the mother cat, which had sprung on to the mantelpiece where she remained with arched back and rigid tail, a spitting fury.

The incident had unhinged her, and she subsequently attacked everyone who entered the room. Jack Galsworthy was scratched, though not so severely as I. At last she was trapped in a basket, and Jack and Constance carried the yowling animal and its kitten back to their home, where they liberated them in a woodshed, leaving enough provisions for a few days.

Most of the people I had hitherto known would have been flustered or would have reacted in some way to the savage fury of the maddened animal yowling horribly and tearing at the wicker basket. Galsworthy did not so react; he remained calmly detached. The cat might have been gently purring for all the emotional response it evoked from him. On one of his early visits the miscreant Puppsie dug up, and was dragging into the house, a bullock's head which had been bought many weeks before with some intention of making soup, or feeding the dogs, but which had been buried because bluebottles had

laid their eggs on it. These had now reached their greatest development, and maggots were falling from it in legions when my mother and Galsworthy intercepted Puppsie with it in the hall. The literary aspirant did not turn a hair, though the stench would have overpowered most people. He calmly fetched a shovel and a wheelbarrow, conveyed the horrible object to the bottom of the garden, dug a large hole, buried it and then returned to wash his hands carefully and dust his knees with a handkerchief scented with a few drops of eau de Cologne.

My chief interest in Galsworthy was that he had stalked deer with a Red Indian guide. He was kind and generous to me, and I rewarded him with the honourable title of Running Elk.

At this stage of his life he was in violent revolt against the Forsyte traditions, and my parents influenced him considerably and not only with literary advice. It was from Edward that Galsworthy drew Bosinney in *The Man of Property*—which gives a certain piquancy to the violent discussion, published in their correspondence, in which Edward assailed Jack for not understanding Bosinney's character, and Bosinney's creator defended himself as best he might. The reason for Galsworthy's revolt against the Forsyte traditions of his family was that he was in love with Irene (Ada) who was married to his cousin.

For several years he was deeply unhappy, and all his best work was written at this time. Finally, after his father's death, Jack and Ada resolved to take the decisive step: she left her husband and went to the man she loved. From that moment Galsworthy was finished as a serious writer. He was happy; he soon became successful and influential, and his natural goodness, his serious desire to assist all the deserving causes near to his heart, ruined his talent. Ada was a sensitive and beautiful woman, with dark hair turning grey and brown eyes, and there was about her something that made me recall bumble bees seen among the velvety petals of dark wallflowers.

She was musical and sang songs of which the words were by Jack. One was called "Straw in the Street". It is odd to reflect that the phrase "Straw in the Street" has no association with illness and death to anyone under forty-five to-day. Often,

in the West End, one saw straw laid thickly for twenty or thirty yards outside the house where someone was desperately ill to deaden the sound of the trotting horses.

Later on, when I was about fifteen, I remember going with Constance and the Galsworthys to a concert. On taking our seats, Ada unpinned her tocque and skewered it on to the back of the stall in front with a steel hatpin. Shortly afterwards a gentleman was shown to the seat in front of her. He sat down and leant heavily back in it. There was a violent exclamation and he jumped up. Ada was overwhelmed with concern, which was not dispelled by the gentleman exclaiming: "Madam, you might have caused my instant death!" and his departing in search of a doctor. During the interval he returned and took his seat in a gingerly manner and, when the concert was over, informed Jack that the doctor thought no vital organ had been touched. I thought the whole incident was extremely comic, and the deep and anxious concern of Jack and Ada added to my amusement, so that I found a good deal of difficulty in suppressing my merriment. My mother also grew very flushed in the face for the same reason. I don't think any of us was able to devote full attention to the music.

When I was about nine, Edward wrote the first of two plays for us to act. The Oliviers were at home that winter and they, with an aunt of theirs, made up the principal characters of the cast, the other members being Harold Hobson and his elder sister Mabel, my cousin Speedwell Black and myself. The subject was Robin Hood. I was a comic Friar Tuck; my cousin Speedwell was Robin Hood; Margery, the hero, a young outlawed nobleman, Mabel the wicked Baron, and Harold his headsman. Noel was the Baron's jester. My impression of the play is that it was fairly close to *As You Like It* in its setting. The comic business was left to Noel and me. I had a bald head and a big belly. Daphne was a romantic heroine wandering in the woods in the skin of a snow leopard.

The play took place at the Cearne, and in the woodland scenes we had bracken and dead leaves littering the stage and a

DAPHNE OLIVIER, DAVID GARNETT, MARGERY
AND BRYNHILD OLIVIER (Behind)

real fire with a pot swinging over it, which had to be whisked away when the curtain went down. The play was a great success, though Harold and I had a fight in the green room between the acts because we were both in love with Daphne. The audience knew nothing of that, however. It was sufficiently distinguished, for it included Bernard Shaw who was brought by Henry Salt and his wife. The Oliviers and the Hobsons and E. V. Lucas also brought many guests.

Edward turned out to be a most excellent producer. He knew exactly what he wanted and could storm at us in pretended rage, or tease, or coax, or flatter until he got it. I was at first puzzled and then suddenly got the idea and developed into a wonderfully ribald ham actor. The result was my first personal triumph: Bernard Shaw told my mother that I was a born actor and that it would be a crime if I were not trained for the theatre, an opinion which he repeated on the two subsequent occasions when he saw me on the stage. The Limpsfield intelligentsia may have been a trifle condescending in their appreciation of the play, but the second performance, which was attended chiefly by village people, was wholeheartedly enthusiastic. On this occasion, however, the comic passages did not get nearly so much applause as the pathetic, and Daphne, wandering in the forest, and then captured and maltreated by the ruffianly minions of the wicked Baron, stole the show. However, I did not mind that, since I shared the feelings of the villagers. It was my first and most acute passion for one of the Oliviers.

A week or two after the performances of Robin Hood, my father took on Bill Hedgecock (the brother of Bert whom we employed when we first came to the Cearne) as an odd-job man, and a few weeks later he had an attack of homicidal mania. The whole of that story I have told in detail in *Beanyeye*. I shall not describe it again, except to say that every word in the book is as true as I could make it, and that Edward's courage, patience and humanity in dealing with Bill are not in the slightest degree exaggerated. Edward was not the bravest man I have known, but his behaviour on the morning when Bill went mad was the bravest I have witnessed.

IV

EARLY in 1904 my mother began to teach me Russian in preparation for a visit which she was hoping to make in the summer, taking me with her. I learned it extremely rapidly, but with little idea of grammar. On hearing of her prospective visit, the Russian novelist Alexandr Ivanitch Ertel invited her to stay for some weeks in the Tambov province. Ertel was a friend of Tchehov's who had given up writing and become an estate manager. Altogether he managed three separate estates for absentee landowners. He lived with his wife and family upon the smallest of these—a mere seven thousand acres—at Alexandrovka, a village ten miles from a railway station and a day's journey by road from the town of Morshansk.

We travelled by sea from Hull to Helsingfors, stopping at Copenhagen and calling at various Swedish ports. We had a rough passage across the North Sea, but I revived in time to look out as we passed Elsinore and was filled with excitement when we reached the lovely harbour of Copenhagen and wandered through the ancient cobbled streets of the town. Three or four days later we reached Helsingfors. My mother had some acquaintance with a Finnish lady, and we had tea with her and were given an illegal picture-postcard of the Russian double-headed eagle tearing out pages of a volume entitled Lex which a distressed female, symbolising Finland, was clasping in her arms. More exciting, my mother bought me a lovely little Finnish sheathknife, like the knives which all Finnish men and boys carried, black-hilted and in a black leather sheath.

Then we got into the train and arrived next morning at St Petersburg. We stayed, as we had done in Paris six years before, with Madame Lavrof, who had since returned with her daughter to Russia. Madame Lavrof had stayed with us at the Cearne a year or so before, so that we were quite old friends.

We found her living in a flat with large rooms with polished wood floors, a grand piano in one and the skin of a Russian bear on the floor of another. I went out with her one morning to buy fish. We went down to the river Neva in which a barge had been sunk and surrounded with wire netting and converted into a fishpond. We went aboard, walking along planks, and Madame Lavrof selected her fish, a fine sterlet, pointing it out with her parasol, and the fishmonger dextrously netted it and killed it, and an hour later we ate it for lunch.

We stayed in St Petersburg for a fortnight, visiting friends at Tsarskoe Selo, going to the Hermitage and to a concert conducted by Arthur Nikisch. Of the many things which impressed me, the most exciting was seeing a fashionable lady driving down the Nevsky Prospekt, in an open troika with an enormous bearded coachman on the box, while beside her on the seat of the carriage was a large bear cub, about half-grown.

The chief impression of Petersburg was of soldiers and uniforms. The streets were thick with officers in white blouses, peaked caps and epaulettes, high boots of Russian leather, jingling spurs, sabres worn in the Russian manner, back to front, and rolled grey overcoats worn slung round the body like bandoliers. There were Cossacks, Circassians, Generals of enormous size, military of all arms and all ranks, and the saluting was incessant. We visited Russia in the middle of the Russo-Japanese War.

My mother and I watched a review of cavalry in front of the Winter Palace, seeing galloping aides, horses pulled up onto their haunches, flashing sabres and fanfares of trumpets. These foreign uniforms and strange weapons were secretly fascinating to me. I longed to handle the sabres and the revolvers, and the old triangular bayonets, but I knew better than to express such emotions, as Constance would have disapproved.

We went away as soon as we could from the review and returned to Madame Lavrof's flat. The bearskin on the floor was irresistibly fascinating and, before we left, I cut off the smallest of its claws with my Finnish knife and stole it. I did

not let Constance see it until we had returned to England, when I got a well-merited scolding. But I still possess the claw.

From St Petersburg, we proceeded to Moscow, where we were met by Madame Pagosky and her son Leo who were just going to start a shop for the sale of Russian Peasant Industries in London. They had taken a lodging for us near Madame Pagosky's brother and sister-in-law. Madame Lenev was engaged in collecting phonograph records of Russian peasant music and transcribing them. My mother afterwards collaborated with Fanny Stepniak in translating the words of these songs which were published with Madame Lenev's settings.

Leo Pagosky had lived in America and had acquired an American accent and the habit of emphasising his remarks with the words: "Yes, Sir!" and spitting. He was an active, medium-sized man, with black hair, yellow eyes and a small Stevensonian tuft-beard under his lower lip. He was a typical Russian merchant in his habits, though not in his beliefs. He was enterprising, an all-round craftsman and largely wrapped up in his business. But his opinions were cranky, for he believed in living *according to nature*—which was, by definition, living as he felt inclined, and he disapproved violently of people who lived differently, that is, not according to the laws of nature.

Thus he went without washing for several weeks and then had a steambath; he despised and disapproved of people who washed more frequently, but perhaps less thoroughly, with soap and water. His beliefs varied, and the natural way of life varied accordingly. Thus at one time he ate meat, at another became a vegetarian, then would only eat uncooked food, and for a time was converted to going without food for several weeks at a stretch. Salt was at one time an unnatural poison, at another the essential constituent of life.

I became a friend of Leo's, and he taught me to plait birch-bark and to begin to play the balalaika, in return for which I provided a respectful audience for his theories of life.

Our friendship was resumed later in England, first in the basement of Hengler's circus where I met a tiger being led

along a passage with only a string round its neck, and later when he lived in Hampstead and had a smart little shop in Bond Street for the sale of Russian Peasant Industries. In Moscow we went together to the Sunday Market of Sakhuriya Bashnia, which was one of Leo's hunting grounds for antique peasant work, and we stayed also with the Lenevs at their country datcha, at Sheremetovka outside Moscow.

After about a week, however, we set off on the long railway journey to the Tambov province. The distance does not look very great on the map, but the Russian trains were neither fast nor punctual. Also, owing to the war, the lines were crowded with trains of wagons filled with men and horses and hay— trains which bumped along at ten miles an hour interminably while we waited for an hour in one siding, and an hour in another, watching them go past. I stared at the thousands of faces; gay: bored, friendly, sullen, every expression was there except, perhaps, that of masterful intelligence—rarely notice-able in any crowd.

Those endless troop-trains made an ineffaceable impression. In one part of my mind I still thought of war as a romantic affair of flashing sabres; but in another I lucidly perceived that it meant shifting men for thousands of miles in cattle-trucks on a slow journey to the slaughter-house. And when war came again into my own life, I vividly recalled the troops being taken to Manchuria.

Finally we reached our station, and there were friendly gay faces with cries of welcome to meet us, and willing hands and flashing smiles with white teeth, and soon we were trotting in a troika along a road of beaten black earth through fields of corn bordered with wildflowers.

The Ertel household consisted of Alexandr Ivanitch himself, a big man, rather aloof and Olympian in manner, his excitable, kind and slightly fussy wife and his two daughters, Natasha, who was about nineteen, and Lola, about fourteen, with their adopted sister, Lenotchka Grigorevna Gontcharov, who was a year younger than Natasha. There was also Babushka— who was Alexandr Ivanitch's aunt, an absolutely delightful

old woman who supervised the dairy and almost always wore a kerchief like a peasant woman. There was also Miss Haslam, an English Governess who talked English with Lola and Natasha.

Of the three girls Natasha was the most intelligent. She had a keen, indeed brilliant, intellect, rather sphinx-like features and a considerable sense of humour—a very remarkable young woman. Lenotchka was the most conventionally beautiful of the three, taller, with a willowy figure, and beautiful large grey eyes with dark eyebrows and lashes and dark hair. She was always using her big eyes and pouting lips to mock at any male creature that was around and was not above flirting with a boy of twelve. There was a careless good nature about her which particularly attracted me. Lola was a warmhearted, impulsive and eager girl, but she was of softer material than Natasha.

My mother and I were put to live in a log house in the garden where we could be more independent. The big house itself was a new white building of wood and brick, with a metal roof painted green, and stood on the edge of an old park not far from the stables, farm buildings and the houses in which many of the farm workers and grooms lived.

The estate was in the black-earth district of Central Russia and grew huge crops of rye and wheat, buckwheat and potatoes. There was a small vodka distillery by a lake. It was also a stud farm for breeding some of the most famous Orloff trotters, which in winter won races on the ice at St Petersburg.

Alexandr Ivanitch was a big man with humorous eyes and a sparse beard, wearing a blue flannel suit with a chalk stripe, polished top boots and a broad brimmed hat. He used to walk up and down in the flower garden in the evening with his arm linked in that of Natasha, whom he rightly adored. He gave orders that I was to be provided with a pony, but otherwise took little notice of me.

The pony was a bay with a wall eye and was reserved for my use. Unfortunately, after one attempt to ride on the English saddle which Alexandr Ivanitch had provided, I persuaded him to allow me to learn on a Russian saddle, a heavy affair

with a wooden frame and a leather cushion behind and in front between wooden pommels. It is far easier to stick on a horse on a Russian saddle, because little balance is required.

I very quickly learnt to ride, and after a few days was allowed to venture out alone. I soon found that there were large herds of horses a mile or two away, in charge of boys of my own age whose duties were to prevent their straying from the pastures into the fields or getting mixed up. The herd-boys rode ponies and wielded long stock-whips or knouts. There were three herds: one of mares and foals, and two of young unbroken or half-broken horses. For most of the day the herd-boys rode slowly round the grazing herds, but at midday one of them made a fire and cooked a meal. There were two iron pots. In one of them millet was boiled in salted water. When it was cooked the water was poured into the other pot and a few potatoes were boiled in it, and, perhaps, a bone or little fish which were caught by dipping a basket into the lake and pulling it up suddenly. This made a weak potato soup which was eaten first. Meanwhile the cooked millet was put on the fire until it was dry and began to brown on the sides, when a little fat or oil was added to it.

When the meal was ready, the boy who had cooked it waved his arms and shouted, and the others rode up and slid off their bare-backed ponies. For only one or two had saddles; the others had long loops of cloth made like a roller towel, flung over the back of the horse, in the ends of which they thrust their bare feet. Thus they had stirrups without a saddle. The ponies were tied to willow trees near the fire, and then all the boys stood in a circle and crossed themselves and bowed their heads in prayer before they unfastened the wooden spoons hanging from the string tied round the waist, and sat down to eat their meal. I immediately made friends with them, helped the cook to make the fire, stirred the pot, and then crossed myself before I sat down with them.

At first I was required to go back to the house for a late luncheon, but soon I obtained permission to join the peasant boys, and sometimes was able to take them some butter or oil

to put in their kasha. But there was no begging on their part and no calculation that I should bring my share. Before the cruel mockery of Marxian Communism, there was religious communism among the peasants of Great Russia. Several times while we were eating, some passer-by came along and one of the boys would always get up and call out an invitation. Sometimes it was a peasant they knew, sometimes an old beggar or pilgrim who seated himself beside us and dipped his spoon in the common pot. Chrestyanin or Christians these peasants of Great Russia called themselves, and they had little idea of other races except those traditional enemies of their religion, the Tartars and Turks, and the Jews who had betrayed Christ.

These herd-boys ranged in age from eight or nine to fifteen or sixteen, and there were ten of them at most. They all wore a string with a cross hanging down round their necks under their Russian shirts which were red, or yellow, with spots; and trousers or jeans of blue- and-white homespun linen. The older ones wore lapti, shoes woven of willow bark, and fastened with cross-garterings of string or linen; the younger ones were barefoot. Most of them were bare-headed and had thick mops of hair, trimmed occasionally with a pudding basin. I picked up lice in my hair from them but learned something of primitive Christianity, a most moving and beautiful religion to see practised. I have never come across it since.

The casual stranger who repaid his hosts for their hospitality with a rambling, and to me, unintelligible discourse, was not the only excitement of these simple meals, for on two or three occasions a spirit of mischief entered into the herds of horses, which became mixed up or stampeded towards the cornfields which were protected only by low ditches.

Instantly the boys leaped to their feet and flung themselves upon their ponies. I followed last of all and we were soon engulfed in a whirling mass of galloping horses. Ahead of me, my friends were chasing the leading mischief-makers, and the cracks of their knouts rang out among the drum music of hundreds of unshod hoofs.

80

I shall never forget the wild excitement of one of these rides. My pony was for a time completely out of my control, and horses were on all sides of me, their manes tossing, their eyes rolling in mischief, the earth trembling under us, Kolya, ahead of me, cutting out and heading off a chestnut two-year-old, and Vanya, who was only about ten and riding bareback with rope reins on his old bridle, passing me on the right, going like the wind and performing prodigies with the twelve-foot lash of his stock-whip. Ten minutes later we were dismounting by the lines of willows and dipping our lacquered wooden spoons into the pot of cooling kasha.

My closest friendship, however, was with a groom in the stables called Nikita. He was a tall dark young man with black eyes and a merry expression. I liked him immediately and spent a good deal of the afternoon and evening after my ride in the company of him and the other grooms, in the stables where the finest of the stallions and mares were kept in large and extremely solid loose boxes. Once I saw a groom rattle the handle of his broom on the bars at the top of the loose box door. A stallion reared up and catching one of the iron bars between its teeth tore it out of its setting. Gavril Semyonitch, the foreman of the stud was almost as furious in his rage with the unfortunate groom as the stallion had been. Luckily the offender was not Nikita.

I witnessed two other dramas in the stables. One was the thrashing of a stallion which had savaged one of the grooms. It was a terrible sight—the stallion, held by two men with long ropes on each side and the foreman, who was a coarse powerful fat fellow, lashing it with all his might, absolutely regardless of danger, for the splendid beast would have killed him if it could have got at him. In the end its spirit was broken and it was led away dripping with bloody foam.

The other occasion was almost as public as the first, and on this occasion the foreman of the stables was the victim and Alexandr Ivanitch himself inflicted verbal punishment. Ertel had been away when the news came that the Tsar was visiting Morshansk, and an order, or request, came for landowners to

send their carriages to carry the Imperial retinue. Gavril Semyonitch at once despatched the two best carriages on the estate, each with four horses harnessed abreast and two coachmen dressed up in their very best, wearing sleeveless black velvet coats, with the big white sleeves of their embroidered Russian shirts puffing out, and their beards newly washed and combed. The coachmen had got drunk and had returned with two of the best horses lame and one of the carriages slightly damaged.

Alexandr Ivanitch had Gavril Semyonitch out in the yard and told him exactly what he thought of him in front of all the stable boys. In fact there was a most frightful row and it went on for some days.

Nikita took me back to his home, and I had a meal there. The family consisted of his father and mother, his elder brother and the brother's wife and two children, Nikita and the girl he had recently married and an unmarried sister. Their log hut was large and well built and consisted of an outer shed or vestibule in which all sorts of gear was kept, and the living room which was pretty spacious, as it needed to be for a family of nine, though the stove took up a large part of it. There was also a loft which could be reached with a ladder.

Nikita's wife agreed to make me a red Russian shirt and to embroider it. I still have this embroidery, put into a new red shirt big enough for me to wear. Nikita's family had forty-five acres of land, a horse and a cow or two. They grew just enough to live on and were fairly well-to-do. But like all Russian peasants they had not enough land and hated the central Government, for it took their young men for four years' military service and exacted taxes in grain, for which they got nothing in return. Had there been no central Government, they would have been better off. For the Tsarist Government provided nothing that the peasants wanted or needed—indeed, it is difficult to think of anything it did provide of a useful kind except postal and railway communications. And the Russian peasants would scarcely have noticed the disappearance of either.

Schools were provided by the zemstvos or Local Councils.

Justice was chiefly carried out by the village Mir, or Communal Council of village elders. Constance and I went to a meeting of the Mir. The cases were chiefly family quarrels. A widow brought an action against her brother-in-law, who had taken her field, and the aggressor raised a laugh by exclaiming: "Why does she want a field? She's got no cattle but a cat." The village elders decided that the brother-in-law should continue in possession of the field, but must pay her a fixed sum in rent, or half the crop.

A more serious charge of malicious wounding was reported to the District Commissioner, with a request for the exile of the offender.

Another scene that made an impression on me was a service when the peasants took their horses to the church to be blessed by the priest and he moved round the ranks of quiet, patient animals with a censer, sprinkling them with holy water.

One day I went with the post-boy to the railway station. There was a blue, cloudless sky; it was very hot; we rode down past the lake and the vodka factory and over the rolling slope beyond, through interminable fields of rye and wheat and flax. There were strings of women working in the fields in gay kerchiefs and bright bodices of red and white and yellow and black. We descended a slope into a long straggling village and climbed a hill beyond which there was a great windmill. I don't know how far it was—ten miles or so, I should guess. When we got to the station we tied our ponies to a railing in the shade and waited for hours, and a crippled tramp, crusted with running sores, came and drank from the water-bowl. I was parched and dried up with thirst, but I would not drink the unboiled water, and I would not drink after that dreadful creature. At last the post-boy got his sack of letters and we set off home. The sun was very hot; my pony and I were very tired, and we lagged behind. I was alone when I urged my jaded pony to a trot through the strange village, where the little boys ran out and watched and the dogs barked as I passed. My head throbbed and ached, and when at last we came over the slope and I saw the familiar lake and vodka factory, I felt

extraordinary relief. It was late afternoon when I got back to the house. They all declared that it was wrong to have let me go and too much for a boy of my age. But I should have been all right if I had taken a water-bottle. I was sore next day.

The food was always abundant and delicious at the Ertels', and at a dinner-party when friends and neighbours had driven over it was marvellous. I attracted attention to myself by pouring out a glass of what I thought was water and taking a mouthful of neat vodka. The soup was accompanied by little pies, always filled with delicious and unexpected delicacies—minced cockscombs, sweetbreads, mushrooms and sour cream. Then there was caviare in large dishes and hot toast; an enormous fish with wood mushrooms; a couple of roast sucking pigs, stuffed with buckwheat kasha, which drank up the fat; new peas, thin pancakes with sharp cranberry sauce and thick layers of sour cream, and lastly a vast ice pudding, stuffed with grated pistachio nuts and fragments of candied peel and angelica; what the Italians call *cassata*.

Kirik Levin may have been present at this meal. He was a young protégé of Alexandr Ivanitch, who had come across him in a strange way.

About twenty years previously Ertel had been driving with a friend away from a big fair or market held in a provincial town in winter. It was already dark; it was snowing and the roads were covered with freshly fallen snow, through which their sledge ran softly. Suddenly they felt a bump and Alexandr Ivanitch called to his driver to stop. They got out and found the runner of the sledge had touched a bundle of clothes. He picked it up and found inside a baby boy, who turned out to be none the worse for the adventure. From his clothes he might have belonged to a well-to-do peasant or small merchant family. Inquiries were made, but the parents of the child were not discovered. Ertel called the baby Levin, after the hero of *Anna Karenina*, and paid a village woman to look after him. Levin went to the village school, where he showed exceptional intelligence and precocity. Ertel continued to take an interest in him and, after employing him in the estate office, finally sent

84

him to Moscow University. Six years later, when I met him again, he was a Lecturer in Ancient History.

At one of the dinner parties was a Russian boy of about my age whose manners provided a striking contrast to my uncouth simplicity. He was dressed in uniform with a great many buttons, and when dinner was over he walked round the table to Maria Vassilievna, his hostess, drew himself to attention, clicked his heels smartly and bent over and kissed her hand. Provoked by Lola or Lenotchka, I attempted to follow suit, but my efforts were a failure, as Maria Vassilievna rumpled my tousled hair and did not play her part seriously.

One day when we were returning from a walk in the park with Alexandr Ivanitch, Maria Vassilievna, Natasha and Lenotchka, we were met by Lola, her face lit up with joyous excitement. Clapping her hands, she cried out: "What do you think has happened! Plehve has been assassinated!" Wild excitement followed among all those present, who would have greeted the news of an overwhelming victory over the Japanese enemy with comparative indifference. But, though steeped in revolutionary ideas, Constance was somewhat taken aback by the unquestioning delight with which a young girl announced the murder of the Prime Minister of her country.

Miss Haslam was, I suppose, deeply shocked; but my memories of that perfect representative of Britain are not so full as they should be. She bored me, and I scarcely noticed her. She was undoubtedly disappointed in Constance and thought I was lamentably brought up—a very unfortunate example of a British little boy. My hair was long and unbrushed, and I combined social awkwardness with an imperturbable belief in the value of my opinions. In fact, she privately pronounced me ill-conditioned and conceited, and she was quite right. She was always urging Lola and Lenotchka to take exercise instead of lolling all day in deck-chairs, eating sweets and reading novels.

Miss Haslam was accordingly very pleased when I idly suggested our having a paper-chase. Lola and Lenotchka took up the notion; so did one or two spotty-faced young men who frequented the house. Without waiting to take counsel further,

we tore up newspapers; Lola and I were sent off as hares, and ten minutes later one of the most miscellaneous packs which can have ever taken the field set off in pursuit of us under the guidance of Miss Haslam as whipper-in. Lola was caught in the orchards, but I broke cover from the old Park and ran down a hill towards the village. The Russians were a good deal astonished at the idea of people running on a hot summer's day of their own free will and without an object.

A few days later there was a jingle of bells while we were at tea, and the Zemsky Natchalnik, or District Commissioner, was shown up. A pleasant and intelligent young man, he was welcomed, and while he was drinking his second or third cup of tea, Lola told him about the paper-chase. He laughed more then seemed reasonable and asked a few questions. Afterwards he was closeted for a few minutes with Alexandr Ivanitch and departed.

When he had driven away, Ertel came in and explained the reason for the visit. Reports had been sent in that we had been scattering revolutionary leaflets all over the countryside, and that the peasants had been picking them up and reading them. The Natchalnik had thought it best to come over and see for himself. He had told Alexandr Ivanitch that of course he was satisfied with the explanation and would see the reports did not go to higher authority, but he ended with a warning that there had better be no more paper-chases, since they could easily be misunderstood. Ertel was lucky that the District Commissioner was not an enemy or evilly disposed, and that he was intelligent and imaginative enough to take in the idea of paper-chases and believe in ours.

The time for us to leave the Ertels arrived, and we set off to visit Vera Yershov, my mother's old friend, with whom she had stayed during her first visit to Russia when, as Vera Shteven, she was organising schools for the peasants near Nijhni. Tolstoy had originally started such schools to educate the peasant children in his district and had written a whole series of admirable and amusing little stories for their reading primers. His example was widely followed by others besides

Miss Shteven, but the Central Government took alarm. Tolstoy's own schools were first closed and later the others as well.

Since my mother had first met her, Miss Shteven had married a landowner called Yershov, who lived on his estate in the Tula Province only a few miles from Yasnaya Polyana, Tolstoy's home. The journey was a long one, though the distance was relatively short, since Tambov and Tula provinces are adjacent.

But, as before, our train was held up continually by interminable goods trains full of troops, hay and horses bound for Manchuria, so that we spent two days on the journey. We had to change at Ryashk and at Ryazan, and at the former place night overtook us in an extremely crowded station. The floor of the main hall was covered with sleeping soldiers and peasants—men and women—and, completely exhausted, I pushed my way between two of them, lay down and fell asleep on the filthy floor, while Constance sat patiently near me on our trunk. A sleepless night for her was almost always followed by a migraine, and she was feeling rather shaky next day, while our train spent the morning dawdling across the province of Tula.

At last we descended at the little wayside station, and when the train had departed we discovered to our dismay that, apart from the stationmaster and the telegraphist, we were alone. No carriage had come to meet us. But as the Yershovs' village was nearly fifteen miles away, we thought that perhaps a horse had cast a shoe and that the carriage would turn up later. We waited for two hours, and then a carriage with three horses was driven up at full gallop. The driver told us he had been ordered to gallop all the way and had reached us in little over the hour. Afterwards we found out that Yershov had, the evening before, told his wife that he forbade her to receive her English visitors, but that at the last moment he had suddenly changed his mind, for he was a man of moods. We were greeted by our flustered hostess, who explained that she had arranged for us to live in the house of the village schoolmistress, who

87

was away, but that we were to have meals in the big house. Yershov was a small fat man of yellow complexion, somewhat like a Mongol Napoleon in appearance. He never smiled, and his conversation consisted of statements which it was unwise to challenge. There were two small children of the marriage, both sickly. The cook had left, the servants were terrified of their master, and it was almost impossible to obtain anything to eat. Breakfast in the nursery was supposed to be at nine o'clock, but it was past noon before I and the children got a miserably small bowl of curds, filled with dead flies, and a roll of bread. Constance had to wait till three o'clock in the afternoon for her first meal, and then the food was so covered with flies that we could scarcely tell whether the bread was white or black. The soup was full of flies; there were live flies struggling on one's plate and dead flies stewed in the food.

When we retired to the schoolmistress's wooden house in the village, we were bitten severely, for there were bugs. Next day breakfast was as far away as ever and it became clear that we were in for a famine. Finally we got tired of waiting and Constance managed to buy some stale kringles (biscuits made in rings) in the village and made tea on her methylated-spirit stove. This, as always in Russia, we drank without milk, after which we went down to the river in the park, and I started fishing with the schoolmistress's fishing-rod. But my hopes of getting a meal in that way were disappointed.

The country was lovely and the soil more fertile than in Tambov. Wildflowers grew everywhere and they seemed all to be larger than elsewhere. The trees were stately and overhung the slow-running river. The crops in the fields were magnificent. But when we passed peasants in the village they looked scared, then gave us a hard, long look. They hated Yershov and were frightened of him, but I don't think the hatred extended to his wife. She took us one afternoon to the house of some well-to-do peasants, and a young woman of great beauty showed us her dresses and embroideries, and finally Constance bought a dress from her. Every thread in it had been grown as hemp or flax, retted, spun, dyed and woven

by the woman from whom she bought it. The only parts not home-grown were the buttons and the gold and silver thread used in embroidery. I still have it, a beautiful relic of a happier age.

The peasants in Tula were exceptionally attractive, but there was no doubt they were hostile or frightened, whereas the Tambov peasants felt complete trust in the Ertels and loved and respected them.

We were frightened of Yershov too, and his expressionless, yellow, Mongolian face. He scarcely spoke at meals—when the meal did arrive—and did not encourage others to speak either. I remember his once unbending sufficiently to ask Constance whether we did not have as many flies in England. She tactfully replied: "No, but we have plagues of wasps." "I wish they were all wasps," he replied and the conversation lapsed.

One evening when we were sitting with Madame Yershov on the verandah, we noticed a glow that grew steadily larger on the horizon. It was a village on fire about fifteen miles away, and the sight seemed a dreadful one to the two women who had been such friends twelve years before. Presently Yershov joined us in a high state of delight. Fire, he said, was the only way in which Russian villages ever got cleaned up. They would have to rebuild it, and timber was dear and they would have to borrow a lot from the moneylenders. He gloated over the destruction, because he disliked the peasants and their prosperity angered him.

Next morning the news was confirmed that a whole village had been burned down. A year later, during the abortive revolution of 1905, we heard that the Yershovs' house had been burned by the local peasants in his absence, and that Yershov had decided to live in St Petersburg and not go back to his property in Tula. The memory of his gloating over the destruction of that village made it seem poetic justice.

It was impossible for us to stay where we were, starved by day and tormented with bugs by night. We could not, as Constance had greatly hoped, visit the Tolstoys at Yasnaya Polyana, less than twenty miles away, for Yershov could not

endure Tolstoy's name to be mentioned and would not have allowed us to have a carriage to go there. And Constance did not feel that she could send a message appealing to Countess Tolstoy (who was in charge of all the practical management of the estate) to fetch us. It was even uncertain that Yershov would allow us to have a carriage to go to the station when we wished to leave. Constance accordingly wrote to the Ertels and told them of our position and two days later a telegram arrived inviting us to return to them. This was delightful, and the prospect gave me, at any rate, courage to endure the hunger which gnawed at my stomach. Luckily the day before our departure an incident occurred which put Yershov into a good temper. He had bought a reaper-and-binder made by the American firm of McCormick. Some part or other had been smashed owing to the clumsiness or malevolence of the peasants employed to use it. Yershov had informed the McCormick agency in St Petersburg and, three days later, an American mechanic arrived with the spare part in question. He knew scarcely one word of Russian; he wasted no time, fitted the spare part, gave the reaper-and-binder a trial, adjusted it and oiled it, and within three hours of his arrival had got into the droshky which had brought him and had disappeared.

Yershov was, for the first time since we had seen him, in a good temper. A little of his good opinion of the American came the way of other English-speaking people, and he almost jovially agreed that we could have the carriage to take us to the railway station. This was clearly a great favour in his eyes, though he was obviously anxious to be rid of us. We reached Alexandrovka safely and fell, almost fainting, into the arms of the Ertels. I had been weighed the day before my departure. I was weighed immediately on my return and found to have lost twelve pounds in eight days. And almost at once Constance fell seriously ill with some kind of enteric.

She lay in a darkened room in the little log house in the Ertels' garden, and I hung about in a state of uneasiness, looking in at her and going away, only to return again. The gentleness of the peasant girl Doonya, who walked in and out on her

bare feet noiselessly attending to my mother's wants, was a great comfort, for she was so strong and healthy. One morning when my mother was very ill, the old doctor who happened to be staying with the Ertels, prescribed cream of almonds, and Babushka prepared the dish and Natasha brought it to the little garden house, but then I took it from her and carried it in. It was the turning-point. Constance was able to digest cream of almonds and in a few days was on the road to recovery.

Meanwhile a telegram had been sent to Edward to announce a delay in our return owing to Constance's illness. There was, however, a delay of a particularly Russian sort in its transmission. For the post-boy who took it to the railway station brought it back saying that the telegraphist had refused to send it off. He had, it appeared, a book containing a list of the telegraph stations in the world and was not allowed to accept telegrams addressed to places not in the official volume. Unfortunately, the pages containing names beginning with L had been torn out. In this dilemma he would only take the risk of sending off the telegram if Alexandr Ivanitch would assure him from personal knowledge that there was a telegraph office called London.

One afternoon when I was riding back from the village, the sky grew black. As I came to the garden gate I was overtaken by a spotty-faced student named Kolya riding Nyenahodetz, a pacer. The young man told me to run indoors before the storm broke and offered to take my horse to the stables. I jumped off, gave him the reins and ran for the house. The rain came down as I got to the wooden stairs leading up to the raised verandah. I dashed up them, and as I reached the french window of the drawing-room there was a blinding flash of lightning and deafening clap of thunder.

I opened the french window and ran into the drawing-room. Tea was in progress, but none of the assembled company turned their heads or answered me when I spoke.

Maria Vassilievna was in the act of pouring out a cup of tea: I saw the tea running over the top of the cup into the

saucer. For a second or two, I stood dumbfounded, gazing at a group of what seemed to be waxwork figures. Then, suddenly, they all simultaneously came to life and exclamations burst from their lips. "Boje Moy! What was struck? Was it the church?" And Lola ran to the window to look at the church. They were all quite unaware of their strange paralysis, which had lasted long enough for me to enter the room and speak to them and stare for a few bewildered instants.

Nor was I able to explain. All were still eagerly talking about what could have been struck, when someone rushed into the room, unannounced, and asked if we were all right and none the worse. The house had been struck, and a piece of the chimney-stack had fallen into the yard. They had been momentarily stunned by the shock, while I, being outside the house on the wooden verandah, had escaped it. But they remained unaware of what had happened and I did not persist in trying to enlighten them about one of the strangest scenes I have ever witnessed.

A few days later we set off for home. All the good, kind, generous Ertels came to the station with us to say good-bye. The train was fourteen hours late in arriving. But luckily we had had notice of this from the stationmaster. We stayed some days in Moscow on our way back, spending most of the time with the Lenevs at their summer cottage.

On the day we were leaving Moscow, we discovered that the concierge, or dvornik, whose job it was to get our passports stamped with exit permits, had got drunk instead. Constance and I rushed round to the police station, where we were kept waiting for some hours before the police captain could be approached on the subject by one of his subordinates.

We waited in a large ante-room with cells leading off it, which had bars in the upper halves of the doors. In several of these cells were women who I did not then realise were prostitutes, with whom one or two policemen in uniform were carrying on desultory conversations, and I saw two of the women being given cigarettes.

To my eyes, the most attractive person present was an old man with dirty, unkempt hair and beard, with a quill pen behind

one of his ears and a large tortoiseshell cat fast asleep on his bent and stooping shoulders. He it was who eventually took pity on us and deigned to listen to Constance's explanations. He it was who ushered us into the presence of an immensely beefy and somnolent police captain; he it was who showed that august figure where to sign his name. A few questions were asked; we were admonished for coming in person at the wrong hour instead of sending the dvornik—we should have waited until he was sober. However, to oblige a lady he was willing to make an exception. The old man showed us out with the cat still fast asleep upon his shoulder, and Constance gave him a couple of roubles.

We returned overland, and when we reached Warsaw and had to drive from one railway station across the city to another, we found the whole town brilliantly illuminated and a prodigious firework display in progress along the banks of the Vistula. Our questions brought no answer we could understand from the Polish cabman, but Constance learned from a Russian guard at the railway station that a Tsarevitch had just been born, the heir to the Empire of all the Russias.

V

BEFORE the events described in the last chapter, I had been sent as a day boy to a preparatory school about five miles away from the Cearne, on Westerham Hill. I bicycled there and back every day. It was typical of my family that I was taught to ride a Bantam, a diminutive variety of the old ordinary or "penny-farthing" high bicycle. It had a front-wheel drive geared with a series of cog-wheels, a large front wheel and smaller back wheel, though the difference was less than in the "ordinary." There was a plunger-brake on the front wheel and, though the tyres were pneumatic, there was no inner tube and outer cover, they were of one thick tube, unmendable if punctured and irreplaceable when worn out. It had been ridden by my uncle Arthur as a boy and it lasted me about six months. Mounted on this museum specimen and wearing a French beret over my untidy mop of hair, I presented myself to the critical inspection of the other little boys and was at once christened "Onions". But they were not unkind to me, and I was not bullied by the boys. Unfortunately it was otherwise with the masters. The headmaster was a pleasant man, but if he was likeable, his partner was in my opinion detestable: a cheery, jovial sportsman, ignorant and contemptuous of culture. I particularly loathed the tufts of coarse yellow hair that grew on the backs of his freckled fingers. Once I remember I used the words *sarcasm* and *irony* in an English essay. Mr H. read them out and asked me what I meant by them and told the class he bet I didn't know. I replied that sarcasm was making fun of people, as he was making fun of me, but that irony was when the truth was funny, because it was quite different from what people pretended. It would be irony if he punished me. I was a horrid little prig. But it is a bad school-

94

master who tells small boys to stick to words they understand and holds precocity up to ridicule.

It was spring. I bicycled down a long private road through Squerries Park—a road which was kept spick and span, gravelled and without a weed, so that the Warde family could drive to the distant corners of their property without going on the public roads up the long steep hills of Goodleystock and Hosey. The private road ran beside the infant stream of Darenth, which was expanded into a chain of little lakes by dams and ruined watermills and overhung on the far side by giant beech-trees. Along the sides of these stretches of water, moorhens and one or two wild ducks nested, and it was impossible for me to pass them without stopping to see what progress had taken place since the day before.

So I was continually late at school. Once I played truant for the whole day, hiding by a flat-topped yew in the Chart woods and eating nothing except two wholemeal biscuits, which I mixed with bark from the trees before I ate them. My mother easily detected my transgression when I returned home, but she did not give me away to my schoolmasters.

Three scenes made a strong impression on me while I was at this school. The first was one morning when, after prayers, the headmaster told us that his son (aged twelve) had been discovered committing the most filthy and unmentionable wickedness by getting into another little boy's bed, and that he was going to punish him. There followed a public thrashing in which two canes were broken, and the son bit his father in the leg. I had not the remotest idea what it was all about, but this scene made me decide that I would kill any master who beat me. It was not long before I had an opportunity to test my determination.

In the absence of the headmaster in London, Mr H. lost his temper with me during a lesson and told me to see him after school. I went to his room and, to my surprise, he made me bend over and caned me. It did not hurt much, but I was furious at what I felt was an outrage and an insult.

As I was leaving the school buildings, I noticed a crow

sitting on a fence about a hundred yards away. Mr H. had a ·22 rifle and was in the habit of shooting at crows. I went back to his study, much to his surprise, and told him about the crow. He came out with his little rifle and looked, but said the crow was too far off. He often let favoured boys carry his rifle and sometimes allowed them to have a shot. If I could have got the rifle into my hands, I would have shot him. Disappointed at not being able to commit a murder to vindicate what I felt to be my honour, I got on my bicycle and rode home. Was I abnormal, or was there something wrong with my bringing up?

I was never revenged on Mr H., but I begged so hard that my parents did not send me back to school after the end of the summer term. I was learning very little at school, but it was a mistake to remove me. For I was being brought up to believe that I was different in kind from other people and that the rules governing them did not apply to me.

When we came back from Russia, Constance decided to teach me herself, but thought it would be easier if I had a companion, and so it was arranged that my cousin, Patrick Clayton, should come and live with us. He was a dark-eyed little boy, a year or so younger than I was, and he became another Indian who could roam with me through the Chart woods with feathers in his hair.

In our activities we were a good deal encouraged by a much older tribesman called Sitting Bull, who had earned this soubriquet because he always carried in a side-pocket a little folding indiarubber mat to preserve himself from the ill effects of sitting on the damp ground.

Seated on this, he would fill his pipe and puff away vigorously beside our camp fire and impart all sorts of exciting information. I can see him now: red-cheeked, with a little carefully trimmed grey beard, his short fat legs always in stockings and knickerbockers and with a Norfolk jacket. How his grey eyes twinkled with enthusiasm as he talked about the Blackfeet and the Sioux!

He was always making us weapons in his spare time and

96

bringing them out on Saturday afternoons when the bank closed at Westerham, for he was a bank clerk by profession. When I visited the bank to cash a cheque for my mother, there he was, wearing unfamiliar pince-nez pushed far down his nose and over the tops of which his eyes twinkled merrily, though he gave no other sign of recognition but came forward and inquired gravely how I wanted it—gold or silver?

When he visited us there was a strap in his hand holding three or four novels, which he was returning. He then borrowed some more books from Edward and came out to join us in the woods.

Sometimes he brought a book for us to read: he owned a copy of Catlin's *Life among the Indians* and *Great Battles of the British Empire*, in which I first read about the slaughter at Badajoz and Inkerman.

But more often he brought weapons: assegais made with hardened oak heads secured to long bamboo shafts; a noble sword with a flat, broad blade of ash, which lasted me many a year. And when my father's romantic play *Dermot and Grania* was produced, with the Oliviers and myself and Harold in the cast, it was Sitting Bull who arranged for a supply of suitable spears and shields and swords made by the Westerham blacksmith.

It was Sitting Bull, or Mr Dumauresq, to give him his real name, who introduced me to the woods on the other side of the High Chart, where there was a huge hollow beech in which a hermit might have lived, and which he called the Bedonian Tree, after the hero of some book he had read, who lived owlishly in a hollow tree.

Looking back, I can see that my father and mother thought Mr Dumauresq a most prodigious bore, and he recognised that they did so. For when he had no books to return, I once or twice, in later years, came upon him standing by our gate, saw him hesitate and then think better of it, and, taking out his famous indiarubber mat, squat down on the bank under the larch-trees. So have I seen a downcast little dog hesitate before scratching at the door, whimper and sit down again.

And when he saw me Mr Dumauresq's grave red face suddenly brightened with pleasure, and his eyes twinkled, and soon he would be telling me of how he, as a boy, the son of an Army Captain, had travelled to South Africa in a troopship and seen Kaffirs and Boers and zebras and antelopes.

He knew that by us children he was accepted and beloved, a sturdy enthusiast on subjects which were always delightful. He loved to talk of swords and rapiers and the differences between the Italian and French methods of fighting duels.

A bore! I can recall my father's restiveness as Mr Dumauresq talked about the books he had borrowed and compared W. W. Jacobs to Joseph Conrad, or my mother's efforts to be friendly when he stayed to tea. Yet to me Sitting Bull's conversation was always fascinating. He could talk for hours about the old Brown Bess and the Snyder rifle and the modern Lee-Metford —and all the different kinds of pistols and revolvers and highwaymen and flint-lock pistols . . . and grown-ups thought him a bore!

Hut-building of one sort and another in the woods was a feature of all my childhood, and there were huts of all kinds. The Peases dug out holes in a bank of their garden, burrowed deep to make a cave and then drove a chimney-shaft down through the earth to meet it, and, having made the fireplace, built a hut, roofed with mud spread over sacks and brown paper, in front of it.

Harold Hobson and I built an oblong hut with boarded walls of packing-cases and a roof thatched with heather, which we stole one night from Limpsfield Common, where someone had cut and stacked it.

Another hut was made high up in a pine-tree where two limbs came out at the same level, with a boarded floor made of planks stolen on Sundays from the quarry where the stone-hewers had laid them to wheel their barrows on.

But the most wonderful hut was constructed by the Oliviers, who long kept its whereabouts a secret from my father and myself. We ranged *our* woods fruitlessly for months to try to find where the invading tribe of Reivilos (Olivier spelt back-

wards) had made their headquarters. We listened for their voices, we tried to intercept them on their way to it. But they were extremely cautious, and it was not until all the leaves had fallen, and then only by chance, that Edward discovered it.

When we first saw it we stood amazed at its perfection; it was almost magical and was invisible a few yards away. It was built in a part of the Chart woods where there was a profusion of heather and bracken growing underneath scattered young birch-trees, interspersed here and there with tall Scots pines.

One of these, the branches of which descended in sweeping skirts, had been chosen as the roof-tree, against the side of which the hut nestled, and the drooping boughs had been woven in to support the roof and walls. There were two rooms in it—one quite large—and the hut would hold eight or ten people comfortably. The walls were made of interwoven wattle, thickly thatched with heather and dead bracken. But the roof was its finest feature, for it was so strongly constructed that several people could lie upon it as though it were a heather mattress without any fear of injuring it. It was very thick and sewn together with string.

Below, in the smaller second room, was a bed of heather. It was lit by one window, cunningly placed between the natural pine branches, from which one could keep observation on the most likely direction from which intruders might come.

The Reivilos were not pleased that their secret had been discovered, but their inbred hospitality eventually won the day, and we were invited to visit them on several occasions—once, I remember, in the evening.

The four girls dominated my youth. Usually rather serious and always noble in looks and manners and in attitude of mind, they could be as unthinkingly cruel as savages. Sometimes they were savages. A great pastime was climbing, and they were bolder and with better heads for heights than I. Coming to the row of beech-trees that divided Limpsfield Common from the High Chart, one would see them in white jerseys and dark blue knickers, frocks or skirts discarded, high above one's head. One swarming sloth-like up a diagonal branch; another resting

99

among the topmost twigs; a third, getting ready to spring across a wide chasm between two trees, would be rocking herself to and fro upon a thin branch like the bob on the upright pendulum of a metronome, while the fourth was watching and advising. Suddenly the oscillating figure would let go, springing from her perch to clasp a branch from which she would hang for minutes over the abyss.

Sometimes they were cruel to me, for I often caused offence by tactless or insulting remarks. Once when we were all lying at full length during an interval in a game of cricket on Crockham Hill Common, I made some remark which Daphne took in bad part. She rose quietly, picked up a brick and, standing over me, threw it hard into the pit of my stomach.

My howls and groans brought wrinkles of disgust into the faces of her sisters. I crawled away from them on hands and knees, afraid that the attack might be renewed, and when I had somewhat recovered, went home. I was about twelve and Daphne fourteen. They were all aristocratic creatures; pride was the moving force of their lives; they felt contempt easily; pity did not come naturally, except for animals. Their minds were free; but though loving discussion of all things and eager to hear all sides, they were violently prejudiced and swayed by their emotions and the views in which they had been brought up. When these were offended they expressed contempt and disgust easily and believed the matter had been disposed of. Many of the chief motive forces in human society inspired disgust or contempt in them. Later, when these forces took hold of them, they found life hard to endure or to accept.

For a few days before one Christmas, Noel was alone at The Champions, and she asked me to help her get a Christmas tree. We went out and chose the tree and cut it down by daylight, but waited till it was dark before bringing it back. It was clear starlight and freezing hard. We dragged it through the woodland paths and then along the ice-bound high road, and hearing the swish of its spreading branches, passers-by called out to us cheerfully. Cutting the tree and taking it back was an absorbing

NOEL OLIVIER

adventure—but all the time I longed to kiss her, to touch her hair. I said good-bye to her just inside the white gates of The Champions, and the effort of self-control needed to prevent my expressing my feelings left me giddy and breathless as I walked away.

On several occasions Edward organised a New Year's party in the woods, and the Olivier girls, wrapped in furs and rugs, came to meet us and sit round a big bonfire. Edward would entertain us then with glasses of mulled wine and tell stories until suddenly the bells would burst out to ring in the New Year, and we would rise up and with many cries of "A Happy New Year" we would part and go our ways.

How Brynhild's eyes used to flash and sparkle in the fire-light! How lovely and romantic Daphne looked with her dark hair softly tumbling over her snow-leopard fur!

My relationship with them blew hot and cold. Sometimes we met every day; sometimes we did not see each other for months. What was true for the children, was true also for the parents. But Noel and I were linked by a closer feeling of com-radeship, for I was more interested than any of her sisters in the wild creatures and birds and in their anatomy and construc-tion. We collected skeletons; we stuffed birds; we skinned rabbits and moles and tanned their skins.

One spring and early summer we decided to get up before dawn and explore the woods together every morning and find out what we could about the wild creatures. Each of us tied a string to one of our feet and hung it out of the window. The first of us to wake up would hurry off and rouse the other by pulling the string, and away we would go through the mist at four o'clock in the morning. These expeditions were fruitful. Once we saw two stoats making rushes at each other, fighting or making love, and once hares almost tumbled over our feet in their love-making. We found where a heron roosted in a Scots pine in the middle of the woods, and we hoped he would establish a heronry. But our greatest morning was when we invaded a small pheasant preserve not far from The Cham-pions and discovered a keeper's larder. Half a dozen great cats

hung gibbeted there and rows of stoats and shrivelled weasels. The blue wings of jays shone bright among the sable crows.

This was a gold-mine for our museum, and we instantly began to rifle the larder, bundling together stoats' skulls, mummified weasels and, most glorious of all, cut off the tails from several rotting cats and brought away the skull of one as well. Thus laden we made off fast and soon scrambled over the wall of The Champions' garden and spread our loot out in the summer-house.

There we underwent a sad disenchantment. Many of our treasures stank to high heaven, and the glorious cats' tails disintegrated horribly when handled. Daphne joined us and examined our trophies with a contemptuous disgust which it was hard to bear.

Noel was made of strong stuff, but her family disapproved of her tastes and many of her early experiments in skinning animals or in dissection were made in the more sympathetic surroundings of the Cearne.

The winter after Edward had discovered the Oliviers' hut it was found by Colonel Warde's head keeper. The Colonel had the shooting from the Leveson Gower estate. When the Oliviers went there next they found it had been hacked to pieces and the supporting branches lopped off the pine tree. It was a wanton and disgusting act and quite arbitrary, for the keeper had no right to destroy it, since the woods were, and are, open to the public.

In January, 1907, there was a terrible earthquake in Jamaica. Scarcely a building was left standing in Kingston and a thousand people were killed. When three United States warships arrived with help, the Governor refused to allow the United States sailors to land. This incident led to his resignation. Olivier was appointed in his place and held the position for two terms.

The whole family went out to Jamaica for several months. Later they returned, Noel to go to Bedales, Daphne to Dresden, Margery to Cambridge. So there were absences, and then suddenly they would be back again more grown-up, with a

102

fresh beauty; or perhaps only the loveliness which was always theirs had been forgotten in absence.

One day, when I was idly scouting through the wood, I met two strange ladies: one very tall, florid and large of limb; her companion stocky, with short hair and eyes that twinkled behind bifocal spectacles. They came, viewed, and measured the field lying next to the Cearne. Then to my parents' dismay, they bought it and proceeded to erect a hideous house far larger than they needed. They were both qualified doctors, but whereas Amy Sheppard was an ophthalmic surgeon, who was to become famous, Frances Ede never practised, and there was indeed some mystery about her not doing so.

At first the great ragstone barrack of a house, which looked like one arch of an embattled railway bridge, was for week-ends only. Later Dr. Ede lived there during the week alone, and Dr. Sheppard joined her from Friday night to Monday. Both were passionately devoted adherents of the militant suffragette movement and of its leader, Mrs Emmeline Pankhurst.

They enclosed their acre and a half of meadow with wire netting and a barbed-wire fence eight feet high. But though they kept out such marauders as Harold and me, they could not keep out the rabbits. This failure infuriated Dr Ede. When rabbits were mentioned she compressed her lips and a look of steely determination came into her grey eyes. She purchased a ·22 rifle and spent every available moment waiting for rabbits, either in a sacking hide, or firing at them over the battlements.

She killed rabbit after rabbit, and often did she boast to me that the last of the Scearnbank conies had met its doom, but after a few days fresh evidence of rabbits was to be seen— carnations eaten, droppings noted or ears seen pricking up from the dew-soaked grass at dusk. Once again the war against the rabbits was proclaimed: the humane traps were set and the devoted markswoman waited motionless in long vigils before dawn.

Dr Ede and I had many interests in common, and I respected

her in spite of her absolute lack of imagination. My parents soon made friends with them and forgave them for building the house. Both ladies were, although unimpeachably respectable, rebels against constituted authority, and during the years which followed became more and more violent and prepared to follow their leader in any folly. Parties of suffragettes used to spend the week-ends at Scearnbank practising revolver-shooting! That is a fact which I can swear to.

The two doctors were perfect subjects for Edward's favourite art of flirtatious teasing. They had neither of them ever met with flippancy before and were for some time a good deal puzzled what to make of him, or how to deal with him. The fact that they were mystified and baffled, and took whatever he said literally, greatly increased Edward's amusement and delight.

They were also extremely generous and fond of giving us things from their garden, but their native delicacy about doing so took a peculiarly British form. "We have brought you some of our first tomatoes!" Dr Ede would announce nervously. "A shameless brag!" Dr Sheppard would cry joyfully. "Well I admit that it is a brag," Dr Ede would say more happily. "But I don't know why I should be expected to be ashamed." "As I said, a shameless brag," repeated Dr Sheppard.

Thus they were able to gloss over and avoid the tacit admission that they were both kind and generous neighbours and make themselves out to be boastful and competitive, a polite fiction which made things easier. They were infinitely kind and helpful to Constance in other ways, and when she almost went blind, in the year when she completed her translation of *War and Peace*, Dr Sheppard did everything possible to save what was left of her eyesight and refused to take a fee.

For several years in succession Constance and I used to pay a visit to Ernest and Minnie Black just after Christmas, when there was a family gathering of Black relatives at No. 4 Windlesham Road in Brighton. My uncle and his wife were ideal hosts for boys and girls. They were warm-hearted and kind, and I immediately felt cosily at home.

104

There were three servants: a cook and two housemaids and under Minnie's rule their lives were happy and absolutely secure. The house, in spite of being full of young people, was always spotless. Every room was swept, dusted and polished every day. The paint was washed at frequent intervals, there was no dirt whatever and no rubbish lying about. The price paid was that we all had to change our shoes when we came indoors.

In the hall, drawing-room and dining-room everything was always gleaming and solidly in apple-pie order in its right place. No books were lying open on the floor, no pile of encyclopaedias was propping a sofa with one leg off—in fact it was to me quite an incredible abode, and I still cannot understand how such homes are managed.

What was remarkable was that this perfection seemed to be combined with a good deal of liberty. On the ground floor and the staircase discipline reigned, but on the second floor we children and young people had a big nursery, over which was a range of attics, in which we could play our games and do what we liked.

But nevertheless, the perfection was irksome to me, and brought up in the confusion and muddle of The Cearne or the Spartan amenities of a workman's flat in Hampstead, I disliked perfection in itself. Looking back from almost half a century, I marvel that it could ever have existed and feel myself rather lucky not to have enjoyed it, for it is out of reach for all today, and the efforts to attain it would involve sacrifices of terrible and idiotic proportions.

A feature of our family gatherings was always a dance, which became more important every year as the children grew into eligible young men and marriageable maidens.

For my cousins the perfections of Windlesham Road were greatly mitigated by the proximity of The Huts. Some time in the late 'eighties or early 'nineties, Ernest Black and his partner Charles Edward Clayton had purchased some rough meadows not far from Henfield and about twelve miles from Brighton. The land was heavy clay; couch grass and oak trees flourished

there, but not far away the noble line of the Downs swept the horizon. Disused railway carriages were bought and converted into cabins with thatched roofs and bunks to sleep in.

It had been a place with happy sentimental memories for all the older generation of Blacks. For Ernest's children it made life worth living. All discipline was relaxed; the children could fish or bathe in a mud-hole where the water was solid with tadpoles, and there were blackberries, sloes and mushrooms to be gathered and an orchard full of apples. There it was that my cousins, Helen and Kenneth, played Indians under the benevolent but autocratic direction of Eagle-Spear, who in many ways was the counterpart of our elderly Westerham bank clerk, Sitting-Bull. Mr Sussex Hall was a Commissioner for Oaths who lived in Ship Street over his office. He was a rather fat little man in his sixties who pursued a large number of hobbies which were delightful to the young. He had, as a young man, been an amateur water-colour painter, but that love lay sleeping. More original was the art of knapping flints, which he carried to a neolithic perfection. Many of his arrow-heads, made without a metal hammer, were indistinguishable from the finest products of the late Stone Age.

His room in Ship Street was a mass of primitive weapons, flints, paint-boxes and brushes, model ships—in bottles and out of them—mummified hands from Egypt, shrunken heads from the head-hunters, jewels, swordsticks, old telescopes, things made of mutton-bones by Napoleonic prisoners, shepherds' crooks, fossils and the pelts of beasts tanned by himself.

With grown-up persons Mr Sussex Hall was a little *difficile*, and at 4 Windlesham Road he traded on his old and tried friendship with Ernest. He must have known that he was laughed at, in a most kindly way, behind his back, but he would have preferred to be only admired, and he demanded that his foibles be treated with respect.

With Minnie, he was always excessively gallant, and I think she often found it hard to prevent her twinkling eyes and smile from showing more than polite gratification. Mr Sussex Hall had a deep devotion for my cousin Helen, almost like that

of a Roman Catholic for the Virgin. In a moment of childish love and generosity she once gave him the coral necklace from round her neck. Eagle-Spear wore it always as his watch-chain. But as the years went by, the little necklace had to be stretched tighter and tighter to span the waistcoat. Finally it was too tight and he had it re-threaded and the coral beads spaced out. For Minnie, there was something irresistibly funny in this watch-chain. But I am a sentimentalist myself and can understand his feelings, and when I think of the little coral beads, spanning his old paunch, I feel tenderness and pity for the memory of Eagle-Spear.

Mr Sussex Hall was well to the fore at the dances at Windlesham Road; genial to the gentlemen and gallant to the ladies. But one year the dance was the occasion of an unforgettable and horrific scene of which he was the central figure.

Eagle-Spear either had come early or had dined with the family. Eager young people were still rubbing the French chalk into the polished nursery floor with the toes of their patent leather shoes. Annie Eastty had scarcely settled the ample silk skirts of her evening frock over the piano stool, and was beginning to turn over the music, when Eagle-Spear came into the room.

He was in tails of course, but somewhere there was a flash of crimson silk: a species of cummerbund perhaps, visible beneath the white waistcoat. The young crowded round him, and conversation turned on the always delightful topic of weapons—Damascus steel and the anecdote of Richard Cœur-de-Lion's competition with Saladin to see which of them had the best sword. Richard, it will be remembered, cut through an iron helmet at one blow: Saladin floated a piece of swan's down in a basin of water and cut it in two with his scimitar without wetting the floating feather.

Eagle-Spear, unwilling to be outdone by any of the heroes of romance, drew a beautiful little dagger from out of the scarlet cummerbund beneath the white waistcoat. It had a lovely stag's-horn handle and a delicately curved blade. Watched by all of his eager, youthful audience, he tore off a

strip of newspaper and began to emulate Saladin's trick, his object being to cut the paper clean without tearing it or knocking it aside.

The results were slightly disappointing, the paper was cut, but not cleanly severed, and half-way through it tore—or bent. Eagle-Spear, a little nettled, tried three times and then swiped quickly at the couple of inches of paper left.

Horror! The razor-sharp blade cut off the extreme tips of three fingers and a thumb, which flew away and fell on to the floor. Blood spurted in fountains, but Eagle-Spear, who must have been in agony, behaved with extraordinary courage, only calling out desperately: "Don't step on them! Find them! Keep away! Don't step on them. You damned little idiots, they'll grow if I can only find them and put them back!"

Kenneth, with more intelligence and *sang-froid* than the rest of us, did find two of them, but the others were trodden into the French chalk. Pressing the gory fragments to thumb and finger Eagle-Spear left the room to find a doctor. And then, after a decent interval for our nausea, wonder, sympathy and horror to subside, Annie Eastty struck up on the piano, and we buttoned our white gloves, took our partners and began to dance the polka upon the blood-bespattered floor.

The two tips of Eagle-Spear's fingers which had been replaced *did* grow. The others were never found, though we looked ghoulishly for them in the morning.

VI

CONSTANCE decided that I must go to school again. Once more I was to go to a day school, but we should have to move to London, leaving Edward at The Cearne. University College School was chosen in preference to St Paul's. The school was then in Gower Street, occupying the south block of University College buildings. It was a disagreeable institution. We were unattractive, smelly, inkstained boys, wearing frayed Eton collars and Norfolk jackets, knickerbockers or trousers, for in those days boys only wore shorts when playing football. And with two or three exceptions the masters were of much the same quality as the boys.

The two years I spent at University College School were coloured by an incident which occurred within two months of my arrival.

I joined the Cadet Corps, chiefly because I wanted to be a good shot with a rifle. My parents were mildly opposed to my doing so. After about half a dozen drills the entire corps went off for a field day, including the latest recruits, of whom I was probably the most awkward. We were dressed in grey uniforms—tunics, breeches, puttees—and were armed with carbines and bayonets. We met at Waterloo and took the train to some heathery common in Surrey or Hampshire. We were about an hour in the train. When I got out I was desperately anxious to empty my bladder, but it took me some time in the general hurly-burly to find the lavatory. When I did, it was so full I could not get in, and while I was waiting a bugle sounded and a large boy with sergeant's stripes shouted that we should fall in and pushed me away. I should, no doubt, have said I *must* go in. But I went where I was pushed and soon, in the cold air of a frosty morning, fell in. We formed fours and I found myself one of the inside pair as we marched off up a hill

and along a road over a bare heath without a tree or bush upon it.

The misery of that march was intense. I kept expecting a halt, an opportunity to fall out. Eventually with my bladder bursting, I made feeble efforts to fall out, but was kicked and pushed back into my place by my neighbours. Then my powers of retention failed and I began to wet my breeches. A warm flood ran down my thigh and my urine began to leak out through the folds of my puttees. After that I marched on stolidly, while my neighbours grinned and whispered. To crown my misery we were halted shortly afterwards and allowed to fall out. Later, in extended order, we lined a heathery crest and fired blank ammunition at an advancing line of cadets from another, and more important, public school. Retreats and advances at the double followed; we were kept on the move, and by the time I returned home I was dry, though smelly.

I never told either of my parents of this misfortune, and I simply went on, as far as possible, as though it had not happened, though I was acutely aware of it. My schoolfellows saw to that. Indeed I was reminded of that disastrous event almost every day for the two years that I remained at University College School. During the morning break a group would collect round me and Jack M— would swagger up and inquire "Done it again?"

It was impossible for me to laugh it off, and I never tried to do so. I followed my instinct to fight it out. No tactics could have been more imbecile, for my tormentors were ten to one and included boys much stronger than myself. Every day I fought some boys, being jeered at by the spectators, and usually retired ingloriously. Once a boy who boxed told me to challenge him in the gym. I did so, got the worst of it, but went on until the Gym master stopped us, and he then dropped out of the ranks of my tormentors and became a friend. But Jack M— never tired of baiting me. Once, using a Japanese trick, I threw him heavily down some stone steps and he retired badly bruised. But that was one of the very few occasions when I was not worsted.

Soon I dreaded school, and in particular every moment out of class. Lessons were an irrelevancy. I was waiting, keyed up for the fight which was coming. In two subjects, French and Latin, however, I did well. In French I was second to the son of a French Jewish hairdresser from the Tottenham Court Road. But when I moved into the lower Fourth, my Latin master was Gerald Warre Cornish. I liked him very much and began to learn Latin easily.

When my morale at University College School was at its lowest, Giblin suddenly reappeared. I do not know if he guessed something was wrong as he greeted me with his slow look and friendly smile, but he suggested that I should go along with him and took me to Snow's Chophouse, gave me a rump steak and shandy and I told him Gerald Cornish was one of my masters. It turned out that they had been friends at Cambridge. Later, after class, I told Gerald Cornish I had just seen Giblin and told him where to find him. Giblin and his friend Grainger had become interested in Japanese wrestling and the latter had brought over two or three famous exponents of ju-juitsu. They had fitted up a gymnasium in the basement of a house in Golden Square, where they gave lessons and held exhibitions. At the latter, Giblin sometimes took the part of the heavy man who could be thrown and reduced to helplessness by a Japanese of half his weight. Giblin took me to the gymnasium, and one of the Japanese wrestlers, called Miyake, showed me how to fall and taught me one or two simple tricks.

A few weeks afterwards the whole school was summoned to see an exhibition of Japanese wrestling in the school gym. It was a moment of immense pride when the great Miyake recognised me and spoke to me in front of the whole school. Giblin did not stay long in England, but went off on a pearl-trading venture to the Solomon Islands. But his kindness to me did a lot to restore my morale at a time when it was pretty shaky.

Yet school was not quite such a hell as I have described. For tucked away behind the gymnasium were two fives courts. I liked the game and became fairly good at it. Often, before going home after school, I would play until my hand, bruised

like a beaten bit of rump steak, ached too much for me to go on. And I would ride home on the swaying Vanguard bus filled with a normal schoolboy's contentment.

The other pleasure that school gave me was more highbrow. Flinders Petrie and his wife were neighbours and acquaintances in Hampstead, and, on their return from some fruitful dig in the Nile Valley, an exhibition of Egyptian sculpture and other finds took place in University College.

I went to the exhibition with two Jewish boys—V. I. Gaster and Klementaski—and all three of us developed an almost mystical passion for ancient Egypt. It lasted long enough for me to read through the first four volumes of Petrie's *History of Ancient Egypt*. Gaster read all the volumes and no doubt remembers their contents to this day.

My friendship with those two boys was typical of other friendships which I have made all through my life. For Gaster was certainly the cleverest boy in the school, and Klementaski not far behind him. Compared with either, I was a dunce at school work. Yet they liked me and sought my friendship, not only because I was on speaking terms with the great egyptologist and his history was on my father's shelves, but because I had a point of view which they had not met elsewhere.

I went several times with Klementaski to his house in Hampstead and it was my first introduction to a Jewish household. Among his many brothers and sisters, Alida, a girl with a thick mane of black hair, seemed to have most individuality. She afterwards married Harold Monro the poet, and carried on the Poetry Bookshop. Klementaski was killed in the 1914–18 war.

In the same Hampstead street as the Petries lived their close friends Professor Karl Pearson and his wife, who were also acquaintances of my mother. Karl Pearson was a tall, stiff man who wore one of those hard hats with straight sides and a flat top, and had a very blank and wooden face with thin, compressed lips. I often travelled to Gower Street with him in the mornings, as he was a professor at University College, where he carried out research on the theory of probability, which he attacked from the statistical angle.

On the bus, or in the newly opened Hampstead tube, Karl Pearson would acknowledge my existence with a faint nod, but no smile ever creased those severely compressed lips. I do not know if he could smile, but I never saw him do so as I watched him reading his morning newspaper between Hampstead and Warren Street.

Mrs Karl Pearson was a helpmeet worthy of him. Both were Rationalists and for some reason felt it necessary on that account to live up to stricter moral standards than the older type of puritan who faced the divine sanctions of brimstone and hell fire. The Pearsons loved Puritanism for its own sake.

On one occasion Mrs Pearson told Constance that she and Karl were worried about the little son of their neighbours, the Petries. "Karl and I fear that Egon is pleasure-loving." Egon Petrie (who dropped the *e* from his name when he became a famous 'cellist) was then six years old, an age when the love of pleasure is usually regarded with an indulgent eye. But to the Pearsons no pleasures were venial; they condemned hedonism whatever form it took and at whatever age it might raise its head.

Our move to London had coincided with exciting political events in Russia. They meant far more to me because I could visualise surging crowds in the streets of St Petersburg and Moscow, and the Cossacks mounted on their nimble little horses armed with double-thonged leaded whips, the nagaikas.

The ignominious defeats of Russia in the war with Japan had lowered the prestige of the Tsar's Government. Great unrest followed, culminating in a general strike and an armed insurrection in Moscow.

On Bloody Sunday, a peaceful procession of about two hundred thousand persons formed in St Petersburg to march to the Winter Palace in order to present a petition to the Tsar. It was headed by Father Gapon, a popular priest, whose movement among the St Petersburg working men had received some

official encouragement. Many in the procession were singing "God Save the Tsar." But the Emperor lost his head and, on his orders, the procession was attacked at many points by troops, who fired at the unarmed people. Several hundreds were killed and some thousands wounded. The events of Bloody Sunday enraged the Russian people and destroyed their faith in the Tsar. It was followed by the general strike and an armed revolutionary uprising in Moscow. Both were marked by the spontaneous emergence of workers' councils or soviets. About this time the crew of the Russian battleship *Potemkin* mutinied at Odessa. The Russian autocracy, after a short time, gave way to the popular feeling it had provoked, the Tsar promised a Constitution, and elections were held for the first Duma or representative assembly.

Soon after we settled in London I began to notice, from the top of the horse-tram on which I went to school, blue or red placards hanging up in many windows between Hampstead Heath and Camden Town. I do not think either Edward or Constance showed much interest in the General Election which was taking place, and no placard was displayed from the windows of our flat. But the result, a sweeping victory for the Liberal Party, surprised and overjoyed them.

Though in favour of Free Trade, they were little concerned with domestic politics, and their rejoicing was almost entirely because they believed that the foreign policy of a Liberal Government would be less jingoistic and more sympathetic to the movements for liberty abroad.

The first results of the Liberal victory were striking. General Botha became the first prime minister of a united South Africa and on his death was succeeded by General Smuts. Liberal sympathy for the cause of liberty in Russia was soon shown. It so happened that a deputation of members of the first Duma was in England and was to be entertained at a dinner, by the British Government. A few hours before the dinner, the news came that the Tsar had dissolved the Duma. The delegates in England had, therefore, no longer any status. Campbell Bannerman, the prime minister, decided that the dinner should,

nevertheless, take place and lifting his glass said: *"La Douma est morte, vive la Douma!"*

The Russian autocracy, which needed to borrow money from the Western democracies, was extremely sensitive to public opinion, and Campbell Bannerman's action was important.

At this time Constance translated a book by a young revolutionary called Feldman, who had boarded the *Potemkin* when the crew mutinied. His story was one of almost inconceivable incompetence and ignorance of ships and naval gunnery on the part of the mutineers. At one moment they wished to bombard the arsenal, but were persuaded by a petty officer that this was impossible without a large-scale map! I could not believe that British bluejackets would have been bamboozled on such a matter, but it did not occur to me that the fact that British bluejackets would have been less likely to mutiny was connected with their being less gullible than Russians.

One result of the new Russian constitution was an amnesty for many political prisoners and political refugees abroad. Most of our friends in England were too cautious to avail themselves of the amnesty, but David Soskice, typically enough, took the opportunity to revisit Russia. On his return to England he had lunch at a restaurant with my father and, for some reason, I was present. I was only a schoolboy of fifteen, but I was well grounded in Russian politics and I liked and respected Soskice, and what he had to say made a considerable impression on me.

He said first, that the old Social Revolutionary Party was, in his opinion, finished for ever. Its function had been to awaken the Russian people, but the Social Revolutionaries had degenerated into a band of assassins carrying on a Corsican vendetta with the police. What was, however, disastrous in his opinion was that a split in the old Social Democratic followers of Karl Marx had occurred and the majority party—the Bolsheviks or Maximalists (as he called them)—had now more influence. The Maximalists were, he said, recruited from bank-robbers, criminals and ruffians, and were a blend of Jesuits and American gunmen.

My father, feeling that Soskice was exaggerating, asked

many questions and was obviously interested. I sat quietly, absorbing what Soskice had to say as blotting-paper absorbs ink, but in my heart I was unconvinced. Soskice ended by saying that if Russia ever gained its freedom any Democratic party would have to deal drastically with the Maximalists, if it were to survive. His message was eleven years too soon for us to understand its importance.

About this time Constance was able to form her own impressions of the Bolsheviks. She was not completely impartial, for she was on terms of warm friendship with Vera Zassulich, who had assassinated General Trepov at a moment when trial by jury existed in Russia. There was no question of fact involved, but the jury liked the looks of Vera and detested the memory of Trepov, and so they acquitted her, and she left Russia on the day of her acquittal. It was the last time that a political crime was left to a jury. Though Vera Zassulich had sprung into prominence by assassination, she became a Social Democrat and a devoted adherent of Plekhanov (an ancient Social Democrat disciple of Marx) and lived with him in Switzerland, sending Constance all his writings, which my mother declared were the dullest in which man had put pen to paper. After the split in the Social Democrats, Plekhanov remained the leader of the Minimalists or Mensheviks. In 1907 there was a last attempt to re-unite the two wings of the Social Democratic party, and it was planned to hold a conference.

The first plan was to hold it in Finland, but the Russian Governor, General Bobrikov, forbade it. The delegates then set off down the Baltic, but the Swedish, Norwegian and Danish police successively forbade the projected conference. At last the delegates arrived in London, where, much to their surprise, they were allowed to land. They had exhausted their funds, but a building called The Socialist Church in Southgate was put at their disposal.

They next appealed for funds, and H. N. Brailsford, our friend and neighbour in Hampstead, was asked to help. It occurred to him to apply to Mr Fels, the proprietor of Fels-Naphtha soap. He was an American citizen of Russian origin

and an enthusiastic adherent of Henry George's proposal for a single tax, which he believed would cure all ills. Brailsford applied to Fels, who said, "I must consult my almoner," and summoned Lansbury from the next room. Lansbury approved, and Fels lent the necessary sum, with the proviso that it should be repaid after the revolution, when the Social Democrats came to power. Brailsford thereupon set off to The Socialist Church. He arrived when Lenin had been speaking for several hours and was just reaching his peroration. He was in an excellent humour, making little jokes which set the conference in a roar, for he had finally succeeded in his object of making any reconciliation with the Mensheviks impossible.

The news of the arrival of the money soon spread, and when Lenin had finished, one after another of the Menshevik leaders came up and thanked Brailsford most warmly. Lenin hung back and Brailsford could see one or two Russians telling him that he must also thank the bourgeois who came bearing such a princely gift.

Finally Lenin allowed himself to be persuaded and came and expressed his gratitude in rather a curt and unpolished manner. Towards the end of the conference, a meeting was arranged at which the delegates should meet various English people. I believe that this meeting was held in the drawing-room of Madame Félix Moscheles, but Brailsford believes it was a garden party and connects it with the name of Mendelssohn-Bartholdy.

Constance was present and was invited to act as Lenin's interpreter when he made a speech. She felt doubtful of her knowledge of the Marxian vocabulary in Russian—and indeed in English—so she put Fanny Stepniak, who had no such doubts, forward instead and Fanny translated.

Most of the leading Russian exiles were invited. Brailsford remembers how all shades of revolutionary theorists stood round Kropotkin, fascinated by his wit, charm and exquisite manners. Kropotkin was an anarchist and almost all of those present disagreed entirely with every word he said. Yet he was the man whom all the Russians liked the best.

Lenin himself made a very favourable impression upon Constance: she thought him a man of tremendously strong character, intelligent and humane in his outlook. But the other Bolshevik leaders struck her with dismay. Many of them were dishonest. There were bank-robbers and gangsters amongst them—men completely different in moral calibre from Stepniak, Nicholas Tchaykovsky and the older Social Revolutionaries. Her opinion of them was only slightly more favourable than Soskice's. Stalin was present, and was one of the bank-robbers, it being one of the very few occasions when he left Russia. Trotsky was at that period a Menshevik and was present as a supporter of Plekhanov. Constance had heard much of Trotsky from Vera Zassulich, who liked him and had befriended him. Constance may indeed have met Trotsky earlier through Vera. My memory is that soon after the departure of the delegates from our hospitable shores, they repudiated Mr Fels's loan on the grounds that he was a capitalist bloodsucker. There is no doubt, however, that the Bolshevik party repaid the loan after coming into power in 1917, when it was anxious to trade with capitalist countries.

Constance's opinion of the Bolsheviks, formed after inspection, saved me from the fate of being brought up as a young Communist. "What a set of self-righteous crooks!" was Fanny Stepniak's verdict after the conference. My mother, who had a Scottish horror of financial crookedness, was particularly disgusted by the contempt with which the Bolsheviks rewarded Mr and Mrs Fels for their generosity. It was interesting to observe that Fanny Stepniak and other Russians who regarded the Bolsheviks with contempt were not in the least shocked or disgusted by their attitude to Mr Fels. They all, apparently, felt that it was ridiculous for a capitalist to expect to be repaid for a loan contracted "on the honour of the party." Constance could not swallow this.

I wish I had been able to poke my nose into the meeting and see Lenin and Trotsky and Stalin. I did go to a number of political meetings, sometimes in company with H. W. Nevinson and Mrs Dryhurst, the Irish mother of Sylvia Lynd. Her

drawing-room was often filled with Sinn Feiners, Egyptian Nationalists, Armenians, Georgians and Finns.

The most striking of these political conferences which I attended with Mrs Dryhurst was some years later, when I was sixteen or seventeen and accompanied her to a Subject Races Congress held in the Caxton Hall. There was a sprinkling of Poles, Finns, Irishmen, Georgians and Armenians, but the vast majority of the delegates were coloured—Indians, Burmans, Egyptians, Africans.

The only speech I heard, which was not completely boring, was delivered by Cunninghame Graham. Looking like Charles I, with his aristocratic features and Vandyke beard, and exquisitely dressed, he held up a thin, carefully manicured hand and began his speech with the words:

"I am not one of those who tremble at the word—ASSASSINATION!"

There was a storm of applause, which prevented his proceeding for some minutes, and it was obvious that all the delegates, whatever the colour of their skin, were consumed with a passionate longing to commit murder. Although I was very uncritical at that age, it did strike me that Cunninghame Graham's remark was one of the silliest I had ever heard. He was in no danger of assassinating or being assassinated. He had no reason to tremble.

About the time of the Social Democratic Conference, Constance made a new friend among the older Russian exiles. Vera Figner was one of the group of Social Revolutionaries who had plotted the assassination of Tsar Alexander II. She had been arrested and condemned to life-imprisonment in the fortress of the Schlusselburg, which is built on an island in the river Neva in St Petersburg. There, living in a cell below the level of the water, she underwent ten years' solitary confinement. But although unable to meet, the prisoners developed a system of communication by knocking on the walls. One of Vera Figner's most horrible memories was when her neighbour, whom she never saw, slowly went out of his mind and

rapped out messages which told her of his insane delusions.

At the latter end of her twenty years' imprisonment Vera Figner was treated with less harshness, and she was finally released in the amnesty of 1906. She lived for a time in Finland and then came to England and was a frequent visitor at the Cearne.

She was forty-five, but looked over sixty—indeed she looked as though she had miraculously survived a mortal illness. The inward spark, the glow of life, had been killed; she appeared strong, stern and lustreless.

But this was actually far from the truth. She was all too emotional and she could not face seeing many people together, as she became over-excited. To avoid a breakdown she had to spend the greater part of each day alone and severely limit the number of people she saw. Soon after her arrival she nerved herself to give a public lecture, but it was a most exhausting ordeal for her.

One day a tall young man came to stay at the Cearne. It was Edward Thomas, and I soon discovered that he admired the work of Richard Jefferies and had been to Coate Reservoir, so we talked a lot about *Bevis*, *Wood Magic* and *After London*.

Before he left he suggested that during my school holidays I should come over to visit him and his wife and babies at Sevenoaks Weald, about ten miles away, where he was living in a small farmhouse. I did so. I took a large-scale map and had no difficulty in finding my way by footpaths through Chartwell and Ide Hill and then down into the weald.

Edward Thomas was spare and thin, with a beautiful sensitive face, and he had manners which were another expression of the same beauty. He was very friendly, obviously liked me and was interested in my conversation, and we never had any difficulty in finding subjects to talk about.

Mrs Thomas was a red-cheeked, round-faced young woman in spectacles, small and plump, and she was equally friendly, so I was at once at home with them and free from self-consciousness or shyness.

They were poor and lived simply, but I was used to that. In the evening, we all three had supper of bowls of bread and milk, nuts and home-made bread and Dutch cheese. I went early to bed and lay awake for some time—there were whitewashed walls, black oak beams.

Next morning, after breakfast of porridge and home-made bread and jam, Thomas suggested fishing, and we spent a little while assembling two rods and tackle, digging worms and mixing paste. Then we set off across the spring meadows. On the way we stopped at a cottage which he had just found for a Welsh poet he had discovered living in a common lodging-house in London. Thomas had read me some bits of a poem by him the night before. His name was W. H. Davies, and he had been a tramp and a beggar.

Davies was not visible, so we called out to him that we should return later. That afternoon we visited him, and he showed us his cottage.

It was almost empty: one chair, one table and one pail for water being all that was visible. Davies was a short dark man with eyes like stewed prunes, a coarse skin and a wooden leg with a sort of leather bucket into which his knee went and which was strapped round his thigh.

Although I had been struck by the poem Thomas had read me, I was not attracted by Davies because of his coarse skin and unprepossessing appearance. His own description of himself was a good one:

> "My face is large, my lips are thick,
> My skin is coarse and black almost,
> But the ugliest feature is my verse,
> Which proves my soul is black and lost."

I admire everything that Davies has written: his prose novels and memoirs are full of the charm of his ingenuous character, and his poems are indeed a magic robe and a burning crown for which all the human race might well be greedy, as he claimed. But at thirteen I could not see beneath the coarse, dark skin.

Later on, Davies came to stay with us at the Cearne, but he had by that time replaced his wooden leg with a cork one, of which he complained a good deal: it was far less handy than the wooden peg-leg to which he was accustomed. But in his new position as a famous poet it was necessary, he told my mother, to keep up appearances. To her secret amusement, he also confided that he was persecuted by ladies of title. In a way this was true, but the truth was not quite what Davies thought it. For he was a curiosity and as a result got a number of invitations to lunch or dinner from fashionable hostesses. To Davies an invitation from a woman could mean only one thing, and though something of an amorist, he was rather scared of the number of women (many quite elderly) who seemed to be chasing him.

Unfortunately, my father found he could get on better with Davies if he had him to himself. So all the poet's later visits to the Cearne took place when Constance and I were away. I greatly regret this, as he could have taught me much, for it is not from the sophisticated that we learn the most.

Davies was fond of my father, and after he had moved to Sevenoaks he used to walk over, in preference to coming by train or bus, in order to keep himself fit.

Next morning, I set out with a packet of sandwiches, given me by Mrs Thomas, and returned home. This visit was the first of many which I paid to the Thomases.

My later visits to them at Berryfield Cottage, Steep, above Petersfield, were numerous. One of them was combined with visiting Noel at Bedales school. Later, when I was in London, I used to meet Thomas and have lunch with him, usually at Eustace Miles's health food restaurant near the corner of what is now William IV Street.

Eustace Miles was a vegetarian lawn tennis champion, and at his restaurant Edward Thomas used to order nut cutlets and spinach sprinkled with plasmon powder. I derided his vegetarianism and maintained that it was the cause of his suffering from dyspepsia. He did not in the least resent the elementary and repetitive teasing of a schoolboy.

As Edward Thomas was one of the poets I have known whose work I most admire, it is perhaps worth recording what he said to me about poets. He thought Robert Frost the finest of his contemporaries; with de la Mare second. He said Rupert Brooke was a real poet, who would go on to greater things. He was the most catholic of all the critics of poetry I have known: he admired and appreciated *all* the poets of the past I had ever heard of, could pick out their best work and praise it, and I cannot remember his disparaging any poet worthy of the name. Although he had been forced into being a hack writer, a grub-street author of something like a score of books, he remained sensitive and completely free from jealousy. And he only needed the liberation given him by the war to become a great and original poet himself. I never heard an ill word spoken of him.

About this time I went with my Mother to see Eleanora Duse, in *La Dame aux Camélias*. The effect she produced on me was overwhelming, and I can remember her face, her voice, her gestures far more vividly than the actresses I saw a year or two ago. No doubt this was partly because she was the first great actress that I ever saw, possibly the only great actress I have ever seen.

Every moment that Duse was on the stage I was living more intensely than I had ever lived before. I was transported out of myself, caring nothing that I was a boy of fourteen and not a man. For those wonderful hours nothing mattered but that supremely tragic woman, and it was happiness enough to have seen her and heard that wonderful voice.

Afterwards, in a daze, Constance and I went round to the stage door and waited for her. Across the road was another theatre, the stage door of which was surrounded by a throng of exquisitely dressed young men, in shining top hats, morning coats, striped trousers and spats. The play over there was *The Spring Chicken*, and they were waiting to see Lily Elsie. There were scarcely half a dozen of us waiting for the plainly dressed and tired-looking Italian woman.

Duse and Lily Elsie both came out together, so that the first thing that Duse saw was the heroine of *The Spring Chicken*, all frills and flounces, parasol and picture hat, being fêted by an adoring throng of gilded youths on the opposite side of the street. Then she looked round and saw us and burst out laughing, waved her hand and thanked us very prettily and graciously, but when she had got into her cab and was being driven away I could see her fall back against the cushions to laugh again.

I was at this stage morbidly sensitive, and the impact of real tragedy was as overwhelming as that of Duse's interpretation of the dying consumptive girl. An old lady dearly beloved by us all had died suddenly, while staying with her daughter who was expecting a child. Shock and grief were disastrous, and when the baby was born it proved to be mentally deficient. Though not an idiot, its intelligence never developed but was arrested. My mother explained to me this tragic story: mother and child were close at hand, and I wandered away alone into the woods, thinking the matter over and seeing clearly for the first time the insane cruelty of cause and effect. The intensity of one great sorrow had bred another more terrible and lasting. As I thought it over, it seemed to me that the world in which such things were normal and natural was not fit to be lived in: that life in such an environment and on such terms was unendurable, and that I should be wise to be quit of it.

"Suicide is the answer," I said to myself, and I drew my keen little black-handled Finnish knife and looked at it. "Only drive that in between your ribs and you will be free of all sorrows," and I lay for a long time undecided, holding the knife in my hand.

In Hampstead Constance found many old friends. Chief among these, and near neighbours, were the poets, Ernest and Dollie Radford, whose house was always open to me and whose three children soon became close friends.

The Radfords lived in a charming little house in East Heath

124

Road, looking directly over Hampstead Heath towards High-gate. In shape it was much like a chest of drawers: a dining-room and kitchen in the basement, a drawing-room on the ground floor and three floors of bedrooms upstairs. But if the house was small, it was always overflowing with people. Dollie and Ernest had multitudes of friends and so had their children. At tea-time the drawing-room was always full of poets and poetesses, artists and musicians, and it was seldom that the family sat down to a meal without laying one or two extra places for friends who had dropped in or had to stay on because they were in the middle of an aesthetic discussion which could not be interrupted.

This was delightful; but they could ill afford it, and Dollie was hopelessly impractical in business matters. So while I loved their hospitality, later on I sometimes felt a little worried by it.

Dollie was as small as her name suggests; she had pretty brown eyes and short, curly brown hair, and though she was the mother of a grown-up son, she was still a very attractive and vivacious creature.

It was impossible not to like her. It is true she had her foolish moments, but she was usually aware of them soon afterwards. Indeed, her gay silliness was one of her chief charms, as she was seldom *purely* silly: it was almost always mixed with so much fancy, such sudden spurts of imagination, and so quali-fied by little gusts of laughter at herself that one would have had to be a very hard-hearted and humourless person to resist her. Constance loved her dearly and so did I. She had an intense love of life, the bubbling vitality of a child.

Ernest was a great contrast to her. He was a heavy, tired man, rather corpulent, going bald and with a noble forehead. Usually he seemed only half-awake, and most visitors must have thought him unconscious of the sparkling conversation and bursts of laughter going on all around him.

As he lay extended on the sofa, he sometimes actually went to sleep, but more often his eyes, like a cat's, were only half closed, and a faint sardonic smile curled his lip. Occasionally

he exerted himself to write lectures on architecture or poetry, which he delivered—quite where I don't know. Sometimes he kept to his study upstairs, but often enough he occupied the sofa, observant, but usually ignored by most of the visitors. Once when some rather conventional Hampstead ladies were having tea, and Dollie was secretly longing to be rid of them, he unexpectedly remarked:

"That reminds me, madam, of something which was said when I was in the lunatic asylum . . ."

The ladies left soon afterwards. But sometimes he would talk freely and most interestingly of the lunatic asylum, seeing no reason to conceal the experience.

Ernest soon took a liking to me and I to him, and at one time I used to go round to the Radfords' to play chess with him. Though scarcely anyone realised it, he had more brains than the rest of his family. Or perhaps I should say he had once had. When I knew him clouds and mist often obscured his mind— and then suddenly they would disappear, revealing what he once had been. But I was one of the few who noticed when this happened.

His brilliance as a young man was repeated in some degree in his son Maitland, who was one of the most amusing talkers I have known. But Maitland's mind was more superficial than his father's; he was too easily delighted with a paradox and apt to think that a good joke clinched an argument.

Maitland was a very gifted young man. He was rather short, but beautifully proportioned, and held himself well. He had a straight nose, blue eyes and fair hair which grew thin early in life. He was an indefatigable dancer and a most beautiful diver. He could ride a horse, sail a boat, speak well in public and set a company in a roar of laughter. He might have been one of the young men to whom, in Lord Birkenhead's words, the world offered a host of glittering prizes. What was the reason that he did not distinguish himself? I think it was because he adopted a profession to which he was not naturally suited when he decided to become a doctor. Because of his varied interests he was slow in learning and bad at examinations. He

failed in one after another, and when, after eight years instead of the usual five, he qualified, his first brilliance was gone. The hard facts of life were not really for him: his medium was ideas —and the more airy they were, the better he dealt with them.

I was still a schoolboy when Maitland awoke in me an appreciation of the ballet. Neither of my parents knew anything about dancing. Constance was, moreover, prejudiced, regarding it with something not far removed from puritan disapproval. Tolstoy had declared it a false and artificial form of exploiting the sexual appetites of the rich, and she would not have disagreed with him. Dancing on the points, she would say, was *not natural*, and even Edward would think that ballet dancing was disposed of by that statement.

Maitland loved the ballet, and it was with him that I first went to the Palace Theatre to see Maud Allan, Pavlova and Mordkin, then to the Empire and the Coliseum to see Genée and Kyasht. By that time I was becoming as fond of ballet as Maitland himself. Thus when the Russian Ballet came on its first visit to London I went as often as I could and took the ballet more seriously than the theatre. Later it was Maitland who first persuaded me that the post-impressionist painters might be serious artists and not playboys.

One week-end I went down to the Cearne alone. Why my mother did not come with me I have no idea, nor why my father was also absent. But alone I was, with only Li Whale to look after me, when I had an unexpected visitor, an old friend I had not seen for some time. It was Ford Hueffer, who was urgently anxious to see one of my parents—Constance, I believe, on some matter concerned with Russian translation.

He was disappointed and put out by having made the journey from London for nothing, but was quite delightful to me. He stayed to tea, and then I walked back with him to Westerham. He had been cheerful at tea, but in Squerries Park a mood of melancholy stole over him, and he sang me one melancholy song after another, some French, some German, ending with

the Westmorland folk-song *Poor Old Horse*. Ford's voice was not bad, his ear was good, and the expression he put into the words of the horse's cruel master was pathetic in the extreme:

"You are old, you are cold, you are deaf, dull, dumb and slow
You are not fit for anything, or in my team to draw.
You have eaten all my hay, you have spoiled all my straw,
So hang him, whip, stick him, to the huntsman let him go."

And in the most unhappy voice Ford broke in to say something like this:

"I am that poor old horse, David. I am old, and I am cold, David. And I am no longer fit for anything. They do not pity me, David, but throw me aside. . . ." and then he began to sing the verses over again:

"My clothing was once of the linsey-wolsey fine.
My tail it grew at length.
My coat did likwise shine;
But now I'm growing old.
My beauty does decay,
My Master frown upon me.
One day I heard him say:
'Poor old Horse, Poor old Horse.'"

And then Ford continued:

"The world is cruel to the old, David. It is very cruel to me . . . once I was a brilliant young poet, a famous writer . . . now I am no more use to anyone and they kick me, now they have got me down. . . . Poor old horse . . ."

I took Ford's hand in mine and squeezed it. I was in tears and, seeing this, Ford wept also; then brushed his tears aside for a moment to look at his watch and make sure that he was not late for his train.

I said that we all loved and admired him; we hurried on and as we reached the outskirts of Westerham, Ford wiped the last of his tears away and began to tell me some cheerful story. For several years I felt a particular tenderness for him when I recollected this scene, and I defended him fiercely from my father's cynical criticisms.

Both my parents seemed very heartless when I told them about Ford's visit. They were frankly amused and did not even appear to regret that poor Ford should have had his journey for nothing.

But now, forty-five years later, what do I make of this extraordinary display of self-pity by a man who could not have been more than thirty-five? I may be quite wrong, but I don't think Ford's visit was because he was in despair and wanted my mother's advice at a critical turning-point in his life. There were many such turning-points and this may have been one of them. But my impression is that he had come down on business of some sort, and I think the emotional display was because he was genuinely moved by the song he had been singing and improvised a suitable part to play—in fact, he dramatised a fleeting but sincere emotion. I have never known anyone else behave in such a way—but I can imagine Dickens doing so.

Not long after this episode, Ford realised one of his ambitions and became the editor of a great literary monthly, which could bear comparison with anything of the kind which had ever existed in our history. The first number of the *English Review* appeared in December, 1908, and its contributors included Thomas Hardy, Henry James, Leo Tolstoy, Joseph Conrad, H. G. Wells, John Galsworthy and W. H. Hudson.

For a year or two Ford was to become an outstanding figure of literary London: he was arrayed in a magnificent fur coat;—wore a glossy topper; drove about in hired carriages; and his fresh features, the colour of raw veal, his prominent blue eyes and rabbit teeth smiled benevolently and patronisingly upon all gatherings of literary lions. He went to parties, and he gave parties at his flat in Holland Park Avenue, and I was privileged to attend two or three of them, the youngest person present.

At one, all those who were invited were poets who had to compete for a crown of bay-leaves by writing *bouts-rimés*. I did not know by any means all of the celebrated figures present at this contest, but they certainly included Ezra Pound, who had

just appeared in literary London, wearing one ear-ring, which was considered very scandalous by certain ladies. Dollie Radford won the first prize and looked very much like an Italian painting in the crown of bay-leaves; Hilaire Belloc won the second prize, Mrs Gordon Woodhouse afterwards played the harpsichord.

There were many others present, more distinguished, for it was Ford's greatest period, when he could get hold of anybody. The poor old horse was by no means in a state of decay, but was wonderfully well groomed and, to use a forgotten idiom, was feeling his oats.

One of Ford's protégés whom I first met at Holland Park Avenue was a rather short, thick-set man called Stephen Reynolds. He lived in the flat above and kept a Great Dane, a glorious aloof beast, brindled almost like a tabby cat. She terrorised the neighbouring butchers, entering their shops, helping herself to prime sirloins or legs of mutton and making off for home. Often a butcher followed on her heels and presented a bill which Reynolds could ill afford to pay.

He soon transferred his allegiance from Ford to my father and was for a time a fairly frequent visitor at the Cearne. This was before he went down to Sidmouth and, after living with a family of fishermen called Woolley, wrote a novel called *A Poor Man's House* about the lives of two Devonshire fishermen, which was a great deal talked about.

Success rather went to Reynolds's head, and he and Bob Woolley were later to be seen being lionised at many parties, dressed in blue jerseys and blue serge trousers. Edward got rather tired of the seriousness with which Reynolds took himself, and W. H. Davies told this story about them in his book of reminiscences *Later Days*.

"On one occasion Stephen Reynolds came to lunch. . . . On this occasion, Reynolds launched into a long account of Bob Woolley, which bored everybody present, and Garnett had to head him off with the remark:

"'You live with two fishermen, but some day a man will live with *three* fiishermen, and what will you do then?'"

This cruel remark was made at the Mont Blanc Restaurant in Gerrard Street, where my father lunched on Tuesdays with his friends. Hudson, Norman Douglas, Edward Thomas, J. D. Beresford were fairly regular in attendance. Conrad, Galsworthy, Belloc and Davies, who lived in the country, came when they were in town. Tomlinson, Muirhead Bone, Stephen Reynolds, Perceval Gibbon were occasionals. I went there four or five times when I was a schoolboy of fifteen or sixteen, and I remember on one occasion choosing to sit between Edward Thomas and W. H. Hudson, because they were both particular friends of mine.

Fifteen years later I was going up in the lift at Leicester Square with my face a foot away from that of a thin tall man whose face bore the marks of a certain unselfish distinction, when he smiled and said politely:

"I believe you are Mr Garnett's son." I told him that I was. "I used to wait on him and his friends at the Mont Blanc and you came sometimes when you were a boy."

I met Marius often after that, as for many years he had a job at the Gourmet in Lisle Street; he always told me what to order, and I never had cause to regret it.

While I was still at University College School, Edward wrote his first serious play, *The Breaking Point*. I don't know what led him to put so much effort into writing for the theatre, rather than writing novels or stories, for which it always seemed to me he was better qualified. He had little or no experience of the stage, was not an enthusiastic theatre-goer and did not greatly appreciate the technique of the theatre for its own sake. In fact, whereas he was an expert on the novel, he was only an amateur of the theatre. In particular he was not completely at ease in writing dialogue—though I should add that he had a far better notion of it than I have ever had.

The subject of *The Breaking Point* is the destruction of a sensitive girl by the conflict between her father, with whom she is living alone in rural retirement and whom she loves, and her lover, who is a married man separated from a selfish and malicious wife.

The girl finds herself with child, but dare not tell her father and vacillates. Finally, when the clash comes between the two men, she rushes out and throws herself into the river. The theme is thus an indictment of male egoism, and at first sight the play might appear, on this account, to resemble Ibsen. But it lacks any touch of the strange and fascinating poetry of the Norwegian. It is simple, savage and direct, with the uncompromising brutality of Brieux. If it were well acted the effect upon the audience would be terrific. Conrad, who wrote a very long and devastating criticism of the play in a letter to Edward, emphasised this:

"I don't think, my dear fellow, you have realised the firmness of mind necessary to an audience who would face your play. If the phrase weren't idiotic I would say that the play is too concentrated. It hits one exactly like a bullet. You can see it coming—I admit—but that doesn't make it easier in the least. On the contrary it prolongs the agony and brings on that feeling of helplessness which I think is fatal to the effect of the play.

. . . But don't think for a moment we remain indifferent. The effect is produced only too well. The effect is nightmarish. . . . We are flung into the middle of a situation that is already gone *too far*."

Edward sent *The Breaking Point* to a manager called Trench, who was running a season at The Haymarket. He promptly accepted it, but a licence was refused by the Censor of Plays, acting for the Lord Chamberlain. Plays were continually being censored in those days, but the authors and managers for the most part accepted their fate philosophically and said nothing about it, but tried again.

Edward was, however, a fighter. He was filled with fury, which changed at moments into the joy of battle. In this it was rather the Yorkshire side of him than the combative Irish that appeared. He counter-attacked the Censor for his frivolity, his immorality and hypocrisy. He thundered that the function of the stage was to discuss serious subjects, to reform manners, and not to cater for the frivolous and lewd—yet the Censor, Mr Redford, a former bank manager, very seldom refused a

EDWARD GARNETT

licence for a play exploiting doubtful situations for the benefit of the box office.

Edward would have been more effective if he had been less indignant. He was the aggrieved party, and he would have won public sympathy far more if he had appeared coldly amused. Nevertheless he made Mr Redford extremely uncomfortable and it was not long before a new appointment was made—of Charles Brookfield, the author of *Dear Old Charlie*, precisely the kind of play against which Edward had thundered. All Edward's friends were mobilised and came loyally up to scratch. There were letters to the papers, deputations, remonstrances and petitions. The play was published. For a time Edward's attack seemed to be going well. Then came the Stage Society performance at the Haymarket Theatre.

The actress available was an ambitious young lady, who had come forward to advertise herself—but who insisted that the advertisement would be incomplete unless she wore the most fashionable clothes obtainable: thus she ran out to meet her lover in Tor Wood dressed as though for Ascot. The lover presented fewer problems, for he was a capable, though elderly actor. The only thing against him as a seducer who had to hold the sympathy of the audience was that he looked over fifty and that his husky voice made one think of whisky.

Edward suffered tortures at the rehearsals, but he was, as I have recorded elsewhere, almost the bravest man I have known, and never was his courage more necessary. Constance and I sat in a box, and Conrad's cruel words proved exactly true. We could see it coming, but that did not make it easier in the least. The play hit one exactly like a bullet, and the wretched audience flinched as the ridiculous travesty of Edward's play proceeded. The agony was prolonged and the effect was nightmarish.

The Breaking Point has always puzzled me. It requires a strong will to read it, as the situation is harrowing and exasperating. Yet nobody could say it failed in its effect—and yet what was Edward's intention? It seems at moments that his object was to punish his audience.

The feeling of punishment is certainly what remains, and the feeling also that it fails as a tragedy because the girl is tied to her father to a degree unlikely in real life. My emotion at the Stage Society performance was an agony of sympathy for Edward; only secondly an agony which I had to sit through.

The material result of *The Breaking Point* being first accepted and then censored might seem very bad luck for Edward. But neither he nor Herbert Trench had any illusions about its making money. The lasting effects on Edward's career were more unfortunate.

Had it been given a normal run and proved a failure, it is just possible he might have given up writing plays and taken to writing stories. But his natural obstinacy was aroused by the infuriating experience; the notoriety had made him known as a playwright and he went on, at intervals, writing other plays.

In the second place it made him more than ever a rebel against authority. But the whole episode helped him, I think, as a discoverer of new talent: it added to his natural sympathy and patience, and he never hesitated to take up the cudgels for the writers who were being persecuted in the twenties when Joynson Hicks was Home Secretary, not only out of principle but because he knew how it felt to be censored.

At intervals, through my adolescent years, Edward would write a new play. Two of them were produced with some success by the Manchester Repertory Company, which was then managed by B. Iden Payne, whose wife Mona Limerick was the star actress.

The first of these plays, *The Feud*, I saw when the company had a short season at the Coronet Theatre in Notting Hill. It is a simple, straightforward and exciting story of love and hate in the setting of an Icelandic saga. Any faults were concealed by excellent acting. So on that occasion I was frankly thrilled and not racked by sympathy or excoriated by the author's treatment of his subject. Yet I suspect that what Conrad said of *The Breaking Point* was also true of *The Feud*. The play is too concentrated. There should have been a secondary interest of almost equal importance to the savage theme of a blood-feud

lying across the passionate sexual attraction of hero and heroine.

Another play by Edward, *Lords and Masters*, was published under the pseudonym of James Byrne, as he was afraid of the principal character being identified by mutual friends. It was produced successfully by Iden Payne at Manchester, but I never saw it performed.

Edward also took the theme of *La Celestina*, which is more like a novel in dialogue than a play—it is enormously long and there are twenty-one scenes—and adapted it into a play called *The Spanish Lovers*. The original work was by Fernando de Rojas and was first published in 1499, but Edward worked from a French translation. His version was produced at the *Little Theatre* and I enjoyed it, though I longed for a break in the play, with a sub-plot and a change of mood.

Edward's last play was *The Trial of Jeanne d'Arc*. He spent many years studying the subject and finally wrote his play and was sending it to the managers when Shaw announced that he had completed *Saint Joan*. Not only had Shaw pitched upon the subject on which Edward had been working for years, but he also picked the same actress—Jean Forbes-Robertson—whom Edward wished to see as the Maid. She, however, did not throw Edward over, but took the part of Jeanne in two or three performances at the Arts Theatre in Great Newport Street. She was ideally cast; the play was a moving and historically accurate reproduction of the trial. Yet the same fault of concentration and lack of a counter-plot made the performance emotionally exhausting. So did the innumerable and unnecessary changes of scenery.

VII

MANY of my clever friends have told me how they escaped from the misery of school by rising rapidly to the top and becoming members of the privileged sixth form. I was not clever and had to escape by other means and I did so thanks to my stupidity. School was numbing my faculties. I could not memorise what a sine and a cosine were. I simply could *not be bothered* to attend or to remember. All I knew was that the trigonometry master had a glass eye, and that in his class there was an eery flavour of uncertainty and horror. I knew, partly from observation, partly from intuition, that he was on a knife-edge balanced between sanity and madness. He might, I thought, forget that he was teaching a class and suddenly start going to bed, taking his clothes off one by one, folding them carefully, kneeling down in his underwear to say his prayers . . .

Needless to say, he never did behave in such a way, but by a sort of sixth sense I was aware that some ghastly breakdown of the sort was not far off. And sitting, glued with horror to my seat, I never listened to a word that he was saying about cos, sin and tan. In algebra, I spent my time forecasting when old Cocky would crack his jokes and which one it would be. I was usually right.

My inability to learn anything at school frightened Constance, who began to believe my stupidity was abnormal. So she decided that it was useless leaving me at school, and took me away, just as I was beginning to like Latin and get the hang of it, because I liked and admired Gerald Warre Cornish.

Leaving school was an immense joy and relief. In future I was to attend a "cramshop" in Red Lion Square and prepare to pass the London matriculation. At the London Tutorial College I was treated as a rational being and there was no attempt at social life outside the classroom. The result was

that I began to learn rapidly: at the top of the ramshackle building I started zoology with "Flatfish" Cunningham. His other students were preparing for the Intermediate examination. I listened to his lectures and found no difficulty in understanding them, and I invariably passed the matriculation in both zoology and botany, just as I passed it in French. My troubles were in mathematics and English. I had hopes, one day, of seeing the point of mathematics: I knew there was a point. But what a fraud English seemed! What a dreary waste of time to learn about gerunds and gerundials and synecdoche and litotes (or was litotes that fossil like a squashed woodlouse?) and hyperbole (or was that something like a parabola and part of conic sections?).

It was in a revision class of only three or four at the Tutorial College, that I first noticed a brown young man with a head of luxuriant black ringlets. I wondered what he could be and finally decided that he was probably a Madagascan. I had been reading Robert Drury's account of his experiences as a slave in Madagascar in the early eighteenth century, and I was therefore anxious to meet a native of that island. However, when I asked him shyly in the passage if he were not a Madagascan, he seemed a good deal surprised and laughed, showing white and regular teeth.

"No, I'm a Bengali," he said. I am afraid I may have shown slight disappointment, and he seemed still more surprised when I remarked:

"I suppose that's somewhere in India, isn't it?"

He replied with faint asperity that it was, and that Calcutta was the capital of Bengal. I knew almost nothing about India except what I had picked up from Colonel Meadows Taylor's *The Confessions of a Thug*, and as I did not think thuggee was the best subject to start off with, I asked him if he would join me for lunch at the A.B.C. in Southampton Row. We ate poached eggs on toast, and I explained about Robert Drury and the Madagascans, whom it was clear he regarded as savages for whom he had no wish to be mistaken.

He told me about Bengal and, suddenly remembering that

Bengal tigers are the finest in the Zoo, I thought it probable that my new friend must be a compatriot of Little Black Sambo. However, to refer to that would have been as bad as talking about Thugs. This first meeting was the only one when I was consciously tactful. After that, I said anything which came into my head, even if it was disobliging, and our friendship prospered accordingly.

My dark friend's name was Dutt. The following afternoon we went at my suggestion to Holborn Baths for a swim. It was a wet and stormy day and Dutt lit a cigarette holding the match in the hollow of both hands, telling me that a Highlander had taught him the trick in India. I joked with him about Highlanders, on the assumption that he did not much care for British soldiers in India. It was obviously a surprise to him that I should take that for granted.

I invited him to come to tea in Hampstead later in the week, but he failed to turn up, and later I got a letter saying he had caught a chill swimming and inviting me to tea the following week at 140 Sinclair Road. The English weather, he said, was as formidable as the bayonets of the Highlanders.

I felt penitent and a few days later went off to find Sinclair Road in the wilds of Shepherd's Bush. When I reached No. 140 I rang and knocked, but nothing happened. At last I pushed open the door and went in. A door opened at the top of the stairs and in the darkness I heard a curious chortling noise. The voice continued to chortle until I called out, when it answered, "Who is that? Please to come up," and then, in louder tones: "Miss Collins, Miss Collins, Miss Collins."

I went up the dark narrow stairs into a wave of hot air laden with strange smells. Some were sweet and oily like those in a cheap barber's shop—sweat and dirty towels and bay rum. Others were clearly compounded of spices: cloves, cinnamon, pepper and sandalwood. An ugly and obese old Hindu was standing in the dark recess of the landing. I explained why I was there and he continued in an agitated manner to call for Miss Collins. He was very dark and wore rusty black clothes cut so

as to suggest a dignitary of some uncertain position in a dissenting church.

At last he understood what I wanted and I went up to a room where I found Dutt and two other young men, who were engaged in looking out of the window. As I entered I was aware of a young white woman with a fiery red head and flying blouse-strings, dashing down to meet the old man, three steps at a time. She was the remaining member of the household.

Dutt introduced me to his two companions, Narajan Pal and Ashutosh Mitter. Narajan, or Nanu as he was always called, was a handsome boy of my own age with very charming manners. He was the son of the old man on the stairs, Bepin Chandra Pal, who was one of the minor Indian Nationalist leaders of the period.

Mitter was older than either of the others; taller also and more muscular. He was not handsome, but dark-skinned with rather rugged features. There was a transparent honesty in his face and in his character, which was extremely pleasant. Boxing gloves were lying on the floor. We picked them up and I sparred a little with Dutt, who had a craze just then for learning to box.

Tea was brought in on a tray, so that I should not have to make conversation with Bepin Chandra Pal and Miss Collins, and as there were only three chairs, I said I would sit cross-legged and tried to do so. But Mitter frowned and pulled me up by my hand saying, "No more nonsense," and made Nanu fetch another chair. Dutt remained squatting and flashed his large eyes at us, relieved that I should be making a good impression on his friend Mitter, who was usually very reserved and almost unfriendly. After that visit I soon saw them again and took great pleasure in their company. We met in London and once or twice I asked all three to come down for a week-end to the Cearne, when my parents were away.

One of these visits was in the middle of winter. There was a very hard frost, and we walked along the road from Kent Hatch to Crockham Hill to look at the "unknown comet" which swept right across the night sky, its tail spreading

faintly visible over an immense arc of perhaps forty-five degrees.

All three of my Indian friends were lively and innocent young men, always full of jokes and leg-pulls, little excitements and enthusiasms. Very soon I learned their states of mind and the problems which worried them. Dutt had given up attending the Tutorial College soon after I met him and was going to a dramatic school as he wanted to be an actor. He had been sent over by his parents to read for the bar, but the idea was repugnant to him.

There were more Hindu barristers in India than ever could be wanted. If he became a barrister pleading in the Courts, he acknowledged the validity of British law and British institutions—and he wished to oppose and repudiate them. His elder brother was in prison, for he had made the bomb which had been thrown at an unpopular English magistrate at Midnapore —a tragic fiasco, as the magistrate escaped unhurt and two innocent Englishwomen were killed. This affair had set Dutt profoundly against terrorists and terrorism at a time when the awakening nationalism of India was expressing itself in a spasmodic series of murders.

Lord Curzon had been Viceroy a few years before and, on his advice, the Government had partitioned Bengal—a division which, since Indian Independence, has been repeated in the partition between Bengal and Eastern Pakistan. However, when Curzon introduced partition it was regarded as a subtle British move to weaken the largest and most educated Hindu community and was violently resented by the Bengalis. Several unfortunate Magistrates, Collectors and Police Superintendents were, as a result, assassinated by young Bengalis anxious to prove themselves the equals of the Russian Social Revolutionaries. I had been brought up to accept acts of political murder and violence with sympathy bordering on admiration; I had known and respected at least two eminent assassins, and I should have thought it particularly disgraceful to resent the murder of Englishmen by Indians, since I was myself English and to some extent shared the guilt of British imperialism. Of

course I took for granted, without investigation, that British rule in India must be bad, exactly as most British boys of my age took for granted that it was good.

In some way I felt that I expiated this supposed guilt by showing that I had no racial feeling and that, at least, was perfectly genuine. But also I was ready to applaud a series of senseless, wicked murders of honest and honourable men working in the interests of the Indian people. And I am afraid this callousness was due to a lack of sense of reality quite as deep-rooted as my lack of racial antipathy.

I was not in the least shocked by Dutt's brother making a bomb, but I was rather shocked and puzzled that the accidental deaths of two innocent ladies should have disgusted my friend so profoundly with terrorism that he would declare: "Killing an honest, honourable man who is doing his best, killing him because of a general situation for which he is in no way responsible, cannot be right—and brave and innocent boys are sacrificed to commit what are really crimes and do harm, not good."

Dutt had decided that the best thing he could do was to devote himself to art and so help to make Indians admired and respected. He had been to see Granville Barker and Beerbohm Tree acting. Tree was in Dutt's opinion our finest actor, and he proposed to model himself upon him. His ambition was to learn in England and to return to India and there raise his own company touring about and acting Shakespeare and Molière, Pinero and Shaw—all of which would have to be translated into the Bengali vernacular. And he might write plays himself. This was a large programme and I sometimes wondered if my light-hearted young friend had the least aptitude as an actor.

Nanu Pal's views at that time were not so clearly defined. But he was more sympathetic to the Indian revolutionary movement than Dutt, perhaps from a natural reaction against his father's extremely cautious position.

Mitter had been sent by his parents to study at the bar, but he had got off the boat in Italy and had gone to Zürich, where he studied natural science for a term or two at the University. His parents had then cut off his funds until he went to England

and studied law. He was enthusiastic about the professors at Zürich. His attitude to the Indian Terrorists was that they were frivolous. The Indian people, he declared, had an immense amount to learn from the West. Only when they had got rid of the clouds of superstition, vanity and wishful thinking in which they existed and become, instead, educated realists, would they be able to achieve the independence they hoped for. Until then their superstition and ignorance would make them the prey of ignorant demagogues. The first lesson Indians needed to learn, he said, was self-respect, and the vice he hated most in his countrymen was the moral and physical cowardice which made them cringe to an Englishman and then console themselves with all sorts of nonsense drawn from the Vedas about the past glories of Indian civilisation. The Vedas were said by such Indians to provide proof that the Hindus had invented aeroplanes and flown in them three thousand years ago. Also wireless telegraphy was known to them. Such statements made Mitter feel positively sick.

In fact Ashutosh Mitter was a remarkably level-headed and intelligent young man, who was, however, more likely to be taken in by the dogmatic pseudo-science of Haeckel and Marx then by the chauvinism of the religious nationalists.

At the Tutorial College I met another Indian student, who was being coached in zoology with the object of passing his first medical. One day, after dissecting dogfish, we were told to draw diagrams of what we saw. All the students drew the streamlined outlines of their fish—except Mr Rao. When his diagram was shown up it was seen to consist of a drawing which might have been the result of a game of heads, bodies and legs—for connecting the head and the body was a long thin neck into which poor Rao had been at pains to squeeze the gills and arteries.

"Flatfish" Cunningham stared for a full minute at this extraordinary production and then asked Rao gently why he had drawn it in that way.

"How else could I show which part was *really* its neck?" replied Rao.

That answer has always seemed to me extremely illuminating. Rao had not drawn it wrong out of stupidity, but out of idealism. He knew the dogfish *had* a neck, but since it was not recognisably one by human standards, he felt it better to make it conform to the ideal.

Later I came to realise that Rao's instinct in this matter was deeply representative of the Hindu mind and it is possible that this attitude of mind goes a long way to explain why Indian literature is so extraordinarily meagre a birthright for a people numbering hundreds of millions who have enjoyed a lettered civilisation for almost three thousand years.

And here, perhaps, I should say that soon after meeting these Hindus they had persuaded me to read *Sakuntala*, the Bhagavad-Gita, and any translations I could find of the Mahabharata and Ramayana. I also dipped into the Upanishads. Although at the time I was strongly disposed to think as highly as possible of the Hindus, I was unable to persuade myself that Hindu literature was anything but miserable in the extreme—the product of an unimaginative people, hag-ridden by religion and living in the dark ages.

One day, when Dutt came to tea with Constance and me in Hampstead, he suggested taking me on to meet some friends of his who lived in Highgate in a house called India House, which belonged to an old Mahratta called Krishnavarma, who lived as a political refugee in Paris, out of harm's way.

Krishnavarma, like many of his countrymen, had read Herbert Spencer and had adopted that prime bore as his gospel, just as the Social Democrats had taken Marx as theirs. Krishnavarma, in the security of Paris, produced a paper called *The Indian Sociologist*, which was what is generally known as a seditious rag. All the Indians I met made merciless fun of Krishnavarma: he was nevertheless regarded by the British authorities as the leader of a most dangerous, seditious movement. Of all this I, and everyone else in England, was soon to hear much more.

Dutt and I walked to Krishnavarma's house over Hampstead Heath. It was dark by the time we reached a quiet house standing

back from the road in Jubilee Crescent. Dutt pushed open the gate and we were greeted by a man standing in the garden. Dutt recognised him and was recognised, and we passed in. Later he explained, with some amusement, that the sentinel had been put there because he was a man they did not trust or want to have at the meeting inside.

Inside the building were about thirty Indians, almost all very young men, for the most part students who, like Dutt, had been sent to study law and had made about as much progress in it as he had.

At my entrance there was some surprise. Nanu came forward and welcomed me and stopped a young man, Vinayak Damodar Savarkar, and introduced me to him. He was small, slight in build, with very broad cheekbones, a delicate aquiline nose, a sensitive, refined mouth and an extremely pale skin, which was almost as pale as ivory on the forehead and cheekbones but darker in the hollows.

Soon after my arrival we trooped into the dining-room and Savarkar, after addressing the company in Hindi, stood up and began to read aloud. As I could not understand what he was saying, I looked about the room without paying much attention to him. The sight of those brown men, some sitting round a long table, others leaning against the walls, all listening intently to the staccato voice of the speaker, was very strange to me. When I was with Dutt or Mitter I could forget they were Hindus and I was an Englishman, but at this meeting I felt alone. My race and colour did indeed create a gulf between me and these brown men. But the consciousness of this gulf did not dismay me. On the contrary, I rejoiced in the sense of freedom which it gave me. In this company I could be myself and say whatever came into my head. There was no question of my feeling shy and, at that age, I was always feeling shy. Now I was delivered from that burden, simply because I did not know these people's standards. Whatever I did, or was, would be strange to them. I felt exhilarated. I had embarked on an adventure of my own finding; there was nobody to guide me; nobody to feel ashamed of me. It was a new departure.

144

DAVID GARNETT AND FORD MADOX
HUEFFER AT ASSMANNSHAUSEN

AN INDIAN, NARAJAN PAL,
VINAYAK DAMODAR SAVARKAR
(from left to right)

Meanwhile, how strange they looked. One older man near me was bearded and wore a fez; the others were bare-headed with their black, oily ringlets and black eyes: some sparkling with fun and life, others like dry, black olives. And, looking at them, it was impossible not to classify them as higher and lower racial types, judging them physically by European standards. There were those with sensitive, delicate features and those with coarser negroid lips. Aryans and Dravidians, perhaps.

Then I looked at Savarkar and thought that his was the most sensitive face in the room and yet the most powerful. I watched how he spat out his words, with almost convulsive movements. And, from looking at him, I became aware that he was actually reading aloud in English, not in Hindustani. His accent, his mispronunciations, the strange rhythm of his staccato delivery had deceived me. What a wool-gathering fool I was! But it was a relief to have made the discovery for myself. I listened then attentively and made out that he was reading about a battle in which an Indian general called Tatia Tope had been defeated by English troops and Sikhs.

Savarkar was, although I did not know it, reading aloud a chapter from his extremely propagandist history of the Indian Mutiny called *The Indian War of Independence of 1857 by An Indian Nationalist*, which was secretly printed a few months later. When he had finished his chapter, the greater part of the audience went into an adjoining room and someone put a record of Indian music on the gramophone.

A woman was singing in a high falsetto voice. As I listened a picture formed in my mind. The air was hot: the darkness was like a tent: the stars shone like holes in the ragged cover of the night. I thought of pomegranates: the brown skin broken to show a jewelled seed, pale nipples of garnets breaking through the brown rind. The ripe pomegranate was the symbol of the unseen woman singing, while all about her swayed the king cobras, their coils rising above the cross-legged circle of musicians. For the first time I realised that there were Hindu women as well as lively boys and obese men.

Another Indian song followed, and another, and then Dutt

was telling me that the next record was of *Bande Mataram*—an Indian hymn, proscribed at that time. After that, the man in the fez came up and with a teasing look at me insisted on putting on a record of *The Cock of the North* "as a compliment to our guest, who must want to hear some real music and cannot be expected to enjoy our barbarous tunes." This was tiresome of him, but I said nothing. The man in the fez—I learned that his name was A.A.—then put on a record of Harry Lauder.

This was a bore, and I turned and said so to my neighbour, a tall young man with a most gloomy expression, who stood leaning against the door-post. Without replying, he walked rapidly to the gramophone, stopped it and put on an Indian record. I thanked him; he smiled and resumed his station, leaning against the wall in a Byronic attitude. Presently Savarkar came in, talked to me for a while and then joined in the singing. Soon afterwards A.A. came up and began to talk to me with a roguish twinkle in his eye.

He began making personal remarks of a joking kind about my youth and my looks, which embarrassed and annoyed me, and I was uncertain for a moment or two how I should take them. Without my realising it, all the Indians were listening to us. By a strange chance my reading of Indian literature enabled me suddenly to turn the tables. Simply because he was wearing a fez, I guessed he was different from the others, and I suddenly asked him what race he belonged to. He replied that he was a Tamil.

"That explains why I have been so puzzled by you," I replied. "For the Tamils, you know, are the descendants of Hunaman, the divine monkey who helped Ram to conquer India and I can tell your monkey origin in the witty remarks you are making at my expense, which are such a contrast to the greetings I have received from everyone else."

This produced roars of laughter on all sides and I was henceforward safe from A.A. For whenever he tried to make a remark at my expense, I would hold up a finger and say: "No more monkey tricks or monkey conversations." A.A. of course laughed himself, but he did not like it and soon decided to let me alone.

One other figure I noticed during that visit to India House:
a short thick-set young man, very dark, with protruding eyes
and short fat fingers adorned with several rings. He was, I
divined instantly, an unpleasant fellow, and directly he spoke
to me I knew that I was right. Like Savarkar he was a Mahratta.
Later it turned out that he was a police spy. Shortly afterwards I left and, saying good-bye to Dutt, walked back alone
across Hampstead Heath. I had entered a new world of my
own discovery.

One morning at the Cearne, opening the paper, I read the
news that Sir Curzon Wyllie had been assassinated at a soirée
for Indian students at the Imperial Institute by a young Indian
called Dhingra. A Parsee doctor, who had flung himself
between the assassin and his victim, had also been killed.
Dhingra had been overpowered before he could commit
suicide. The name Dhingra meant nothing to me. But I thought
it extremely probable that some of my acquaintances were
implicated and I wandered down under the great beech tree
at the end of the garden as I thought the matter over. Curzon
Wyllie! Was it possible that the Indian student thought it was
Lord Curzon? Or was that too idiotic?

Edward suddenly approached me, the newspaper in his
hand, looking pale and shaken. He asked me if I knew
Dhingra; was he one of my friends? Did I know anything
about him or about this assassination? It was obvious that
Edward drew a very sharp distinction between Indian and
Russian terrorists. Not that he was ever an advocate of violent
measures.

I was able to reply quite truthfully that I had never heard
Dhingra's name before and knew nothing whatever about him.
But I went up to London that afternoon to find out.

Naturally enough my friends were in a fine frenzy, and as
soon as I had got hold of Dutt and Mitter I heard all the details.
Dhingra, it turned out, was the Byronic young man I had met
at India House, who had stopped the Harry Lauder record at
my request. Mitter was furious at the frivolity of the assassination. Bepin Chandra Pal was scared and angry because Nanu

had been to India House. Dutt was calm and matter-of-fact. None of the three had known Dhingra intimately: Savarkar and some of the others were his friends.

One result of this assassination was that India House was closed and its inhabitants dispersed. When Dhingra came before the magistrate he asked to be allowed to read aloud a statement. This was refused. I met Savarkar shortly afterwards, and he gave me a copy of Dhingra's statement and asked me if I could get it published. That was easy. I took my first and only journalistic scoop to Robert Lynd, than on the staff of the *Daily News*, and it appeared in that paper next morning. Savarkar was extremely pleased. Curiously enough, after being deprived of his statement, Dhingra had been unable to express himself nearly so well or quite to the same effect. It occurred to me that someone might have written it for him and that he had not bothered to learn it by heart. If so, I guessed who the author of it was and realised that he was an accessory. In due course Dhingra was tried for murder and hanged. During the trial seditious pamphlets with photographs of the martyr who had struck down one of the oppressors of his country, and the patriotic statement which had been suppressed, began to circulate among the Indian students in London. I strongly suspected that Dhingra had been briefed to assassinate Lord Curzon, or at all events someone more important than Sir Curzon Wyllie. But I never obtained, nor tried to obtain, evidence bearing out any of my suspicions. My friends were from that time forward kept under close watch by Scotland Yard, and there was usually a detective hanging about, watching their lodgings or following them in the street. It was an easy matter to shake these detectives off in the tube railways.

After India House was closed by the police, Savarkar went to live over a small and extremely dirty Indian restaurant in Red Lion Passage, where Dutt, who had quarrelled with Mr Pal, joined him. I arranged with the proprietor, a large old Jew called Jacobs, to have lunch there five days a week for four shillings a week, paid in advance, and forfeited if I did not turn up.

As a result I saw a certain amount of Savarkar and was more than ever struck by his extraordinary personal magnetism. There was an intensity of faith in the man and a curious single-minded recklessness which were deeply attractive to me. The filthy place in which he was living brought out both his refinement and also his lack of human sympathy, both characteristic of the high-caste Brahmin. The windows of the room which Dutt and Savarkar shared as a sitting-room, looked across the narrow, filthy alley of Red Lion Passage—one of the dirtiest slums in London. In the room opposite lived an appalling slattern with four young children. Often she was screaming, frequently drunk, sometimes one could see her through the open window, lying insensible upon the floor.

Dutt often spoke of her and her children with horror and pity. But Savarkar was indifferent to her existence and indeed oblivious to his environment. He was wrapped in visions. What was his vision then? I cannot say, but I believe it was that India was a volcano, which had erupted violently during the Mutiny and which could be made to erupt again, and that every act of terrorism and violence would beget further violence and further terrorism, until Indians regained their manliness and their mother country her freedom. All the sufferings involved were but a fitting sacrifice to her.

Eventually Savarkar was persuaded to leave England and go to Paris, as another assassination, in which his younger brother was compromised, had taken place in his native city, Nasik.

Dutt stayed on in Red Lion Passage for a time, but left in peculiar circumstances. He was on friendly terms with Mr Jacobs, and one day the old man, chaffing him about learning ju-juitsu, asked to be shown some wrestling tricks and declared that Dutt couldn't throw him. Dutt did throw him. Mr Jacobs got on his feet again, apparently none the worse and Dutt went out to buy some cigarettes. When he came back, twenty minutes later, Jacobs was dead of heart failure. Dutt packed his bag and went at once to new lodgings. But, before this accident, he was involved in a fiasco in which I played a minor part.

Spain had embarked on one of her intermittent attempts to occupy and subdue a part of the Moroccan coast opposite her shores. This adventure was gallantly resisted by a leader of the Riff tribe called Abdul Krim. Savarkar had recently been reading the life of Garibaldi and had been struck by the part which he had played in the South American wars of liberation. It seemed to him that experience in foreign wars might turn out to be a useful military training for young Indians. He therefore persuaded Dutt and another young Bengali to join Abdul Krim's forces. Just how this was to be achieved was not explained. However, it seemed to them that they had better go armed, since the Riffs had probably no rifles to spare. I therefore lent Dutt the Winchester rifle which Galsworthy had given me. It was, as I had proved, inaccurate at any range over forty yards and ammunition for it was almost unobtainable in Europe. Nevertheless, Dutt was glad to set off with it to Gibraltar on his way to join Abdul Krim.

When the two volunteers reached Gibraltar the Customs detained my rifle. The two imitators of Garibaldi went on to Algiers, but found it impossible to reach the Riff and, becoming quickly discouraged, returned to London. Some months later I succeeded in getting my rifle returned from Gibraltar, thanks to the good offices of Thos. Cook & Son. When it turned up I was surprised to discover that a Browning automatic pistol had been sent back with it. Dutt begged me to keep it. I noticed, however, that the serial number, by which it could be identified, had been filed off. I asked him why and was told that the pistol was one of a batch, some of which had been smuggled to India, and that its connection with the others might be traced. When, however, I took the pistol to pieces to clean it, I found the serial number on the barrel had *not* been removed. The whole episode began to make me critical of these amateurish revolutionaries and terrorists. Nevertheless it did not lead me to draw back in my association with them, but only to rely more on my own judgment and to trust them less.

When I was seventeen I passed the London Matriculation in January and had therefore to wait until the following October

before I could be admitted to one of the Colleges of London University. Constance decided that I had better not be hanging about in town and I was despatched to Letchworth to live with my aunt Lucy Cowlishaw and her husband Harry, the architect. I shall describe my experiences there later; it is enough to say here that one morning, while I was at Letchworth, I opened the paper to read that Savarkar had been arrested on his arrival at Victoria Station from France. I immediately went up to London for the day and saw Nanu. He and Dutt told me the whole story. Some years before, Savarkar's elder brother had printed some seditious songs and had been sentenced to six years' imprisonment by a Mr Jackson, at Nasik.

Savarkar had sent out pistols to India, and Mr Jackson had been assassinated while attending a performance at a Hindu theatre. Many people were arrested, including the assassin. Savarkar's younger brother had been caught concealing arms in the thatched roof of his house. But the chief feature of the case was that Savarkar's emissary, when arrested, had turned king's evidence. He was the fat Mahratta I had met and greatly disliked, at India House and I was disgusted to hear that Savarkar should have trusted him.

Dutt said that he wanted no more to do with Savarkar or any of his group, and he asked me if I could find somewhere for him to live outside London until he received money from his family which would enable him to continue studying acting.

After telling him I would do my best to find him a temporary home, I went to Bow Street, where I understood Savarkar was up before the magistrate. I did not see Savarkar, but found myself being given a searching questioning by Inspector Parker of Scotland Yard. I realised immediately that it would not do to try to be clever. My best line was the truth. But in my answers I exaggerated my ingenuousness. I explained I was a science student who had met Indians in my classes, had visited India House and had become acquainted with Savarkar. Seeing he was in trouble I had come along to see if I could help in any way. When and where could I see him?

Parker's attempts at grilling me broke down before my

truthfulness. Finally he told me that as Savarkar was only a remand prisoner I could see him any morning at Brixton Gaol. When I left Bow Street I felt convinced that Parker had classified me as a young fool of no importance—and he was quite right in doing so. I was only eighteen and certainly looked innocent.

Next morning I went to Brixton Gaol. The prison lies at the end of a long cul-de-sac. There was a big door for vehicles with a smaller door in it for men. The visitor to the prison rang a bell and a warder unlocked and opened the smaller door, and the visitor stepped in. The warder immediately locked the door, took his particulars, and walked across to unlock an inner door of steel bars, and the visitor found himself in the prison proper. It was obvious that the warder's chief duty was to see that the outer and inner doors were never unlocked at the same moment, since there were frequently prisoners passing inside. There was sufficient space between the two doors for a lorry or a Black Maria to stand while they were both shut.

I took in all this at a glance; the strength and weakness of this mediaeval system were instantly apparent to me, and I thought over the weakness of the system as I waited with others in a room. The weakness was the time-lag before the warders in the prison could render help to the forces of law and order outside the gate. Presently we were shepherded along a passage divided into a series of open compartments with narrow-mesh steel wire separating the visitor from the distraught prisoner he had come to see.

The vehement jabber of these distracted creatures, who seemed to be trying to combine whispering with talking at the tops of their voices, was horrible. Presently I came to the compartment where I was to see Savarkar. It was empty. I examined the steel mesh netting. A moment or two later he strolled in and was very much surprised to see me.

He was perfectly calm and at his ease. I discussed his defence and offered to collect money for it, and to do anything I could to help him. All he wanted at the moment were some clean collars: the size of his neck was only $13\frac{1}{2}$—the size of a schoolboy.

152

From the point of view of the Government his arrest was peculiar and required careful handling. They had evidence of his connection with the murder of Mr Jackson at Nasik, but they were not prepared to charge him with it. For the murder had occurred while Savarkar was in London and he ought, therefore, to be tried in London. If he were tried in England on, let us say, an incitement-to-murder charge, he would, if convicted, get a sentence of two or three years. If he were tried in India, it would be another matter. The authorities were therefore trying to extradite him to India, but to do so they had to dig up, or manufacture, evidence of crimes committed while he was in India, carefully avoiding reference to the crimes he might have committed in London. This took some time, and while the case was being prepared, Savarkar had to be brought up at Bow Street week after week and remanded, bail being refused.

Eventually the Indian authorities dug up some speeches that Savarkar had delivered in India several years before, and for which they had had ample opportunity to prosecute him at the time. They then applied for his extradition on that evidence only. The evidence was thin, for the speeches had been delivered at a time when the political atmosphere in India was entirely different. The speeches, which had not been thought worth prosecuting him for at the time, had become seditious as the ferment of unrest increased in India.

I wrote a short letter on the subject, which was printed in the *Daily News* under the heading *Past Offences*. Meanwhile, I went practically every week to Brixton Gaol to see Savarkar, taking with me clean collars and handkerchiefs and I collected a few pounds for his legal defence.

Finally, the time came for me to leave Letchworth and I returned to London, sending my luggage by train and walking all the way as far as Finchley, starting about nine o'clock in the morning and getting home to Hampstead about six o'clock in the evening. I had meant to walk the whole way, but my heel chafed and the temptation of the electric tram was too great.

Next morning I went down to Brixton and learned from

Savarkar that the documents from India were on the way and that it would only be two or three weeks, at most, before the case came up for trial. There was not the slightest doubt how it would go. I hesitated, waited until the warder walking up and down the corridor was out of earshot and said: "Why not try and escape? I have an idea how it might possibly be managed."

Savarkar said he had been thinking of it, but had decided he would have more chances of success on the way back to India, but if I had a plan he would be glad if I would work it out. When I had done so, the necessary money would be forthcoming from C.C., with whom I could discuss it freely. I asked Savarkar a number of questions about prison routine and then went down to the Cearne that afternoon to think things out.

Savarkar was taken every week to Bow Street for the formalities of a remand, always in a taxi and not in a Black Maria. He was accompanied by one, or sometimes two, detectives. His going up for a weekly remand had become a routine matter and he was taken from the prison at the same time, within two or three minutes.

The essence of my plan was that he was to be rescued at the prison gates, or within a few yards of them. A watcher would note when the taxi which was to take him to Bow Street drove up. A car would then drive up to the prison with supposed visitors, who would overpower the detectives, and Savarkar would jump in the car, which would drive off with him. The essential feature of the rescue was that the rescuers should not seek to avoid arrest, or to escape themselves. They would have to deal with the two detectives and the taxi-man, but there would not be time for help to arrive from the prison, owing to the routine of the two gates.

At first I thought I should have to find both rescuers and cars, but I came to the conclusion that it was impossible for me to do so. Before I came to this decision, I had, however, asked Harold if he could drive a car and if he could find out about hiring one, and had asked Mrs Dryhurst if she thought there were any members of Sinn Fein in London who

154

might be ready to make a disturbance. She promised the utmost secrecy and thought she might find the right men. But, when I thought the matter over, I was doubtful if Sinn Feiners would come up to scratch for the sake of an Indian. Finally, I told her they would not be wanted.

Discussion with C.C. was more fruitful. He said there were two men in Paris who would willingly go to gaol for long periods in order to rescue Savarkar. But if they were brought into England, they would be closely watched.

I decided that the best plan was to bring them into England on a yachting trip, land them early on the morning of the rescue, drive them straight to Brixton, rescue Savarkar, drive back with him, embark him and sail to France. C.C. also undertook to provide the car for the double trip.

My intention was to arm the rescuers with bags of pepper and loaded truncheons. I discussed the plan with Savarkar who approved it. The time-table was worked out. Instructions were sent to A.A. in Paris to charter a boat. I then had to decide on the route from Brixton prison to the coast. This I did in considerable detail, spending a large number of days bicycling over alternative routes. My chief difficulty was to avoid level crossings and country towns: the level crossing at Uckfield, was a particularly annoying one. Finally, I decided on a route.

I bought a female disguise consisting of a motoring hat and veil, then commonly worn by female motorists, for Savarkar. This was to be in the car with a cloak, and he was to put them on as soon as possible. I was to go over to Paris and return with the rescuers, remaining in the car while the rescue took place and acting as a guide on our return to the coast.

During the weeks of preparation I lived at the Cearne and went up and down to London as necessary. I saw C.C. as rarely as possible. We met three times, coming alongside each other in separate hired boats at the Kensington end of the Serpentine on which he often rowed for amusement. The period of preparation was one of intense strain; I was only eighteen and was well aware of my inexperience and unsuitability for the practical tasks I had taken on myself.

A week before the date fixed for the attempt, all was complete on my side, except that I had not found a watcher to observe when the detectives' taxi drove up to the prison. But rather than employ an Indian, who would be certain to arouse suspicion, or a European whom I could not trust, I decided to dispense with him and trust to police routine. Nor did I know the precise details of where C.C. was getting his car, but I trusted him. I then told my parents I was going for a few days' visit to Letchworth and went to London. That night I crossed second-class to Dieppe and reached Paris in the morning. A few hours later I kept my rendezvous with A.A., whom I had scarcely seen since my first visit to India House, and we had lunch together. He told me the two rescuers were perfectly prepared to come, but that he had taken no steps to hire a boat. He thought that for an Indian to have done so would have aroused suspicion. The excuse was an afterthought and I did not believe him. But I did not tell him that I realised it was a betrayal.

After lunch we drove to the Bois de Boulogne, where we met the rescuers—both of them men I had met before and believed to be brave and honest—a great contrast to A.A. They were extremely angry when A.A. admitted that he had disregarded the orders sent him and had taken no steps to get a boat. I said I would get one next day. We went back to a house, where I met an elderly Indian lady who was deep in their councils, and had supper there. Then I drew about two thousand francs from A.A. and went out into the summer twilight of Paris to find a boat. Paris was extremely beautiful that night. I had not slept on the way over and I was tired and angry, but for a little while the beauty of Paris went to my head and I walked down towards the river. Suddenly I exclaimed that I was glad A.A. had let me down. I would find the boat, and the greater part of the execution of the plan would be mine. I had walked down to the Quais, in the vague idea that I might see a boat floating on it which would miraculously be available and solve my needs. Looking over the parapet at the water I realised that I had no respect for the Indians, who had revealed

themselves again and again as hopelessly incompetent. But for a little while I was drunk with pride. I realised for the first time that I was a man. I had imposed myself on these enemies of my country, who had put their lives at my disposal, an English boy of eighteen, because my leadership might be better than theirs. On what a wonderful night and in what strange circumstances was I alone in Paris. For an hour or two I walked about along the border of the river and asked myself why was I there? By that time I cared nothing for Indian Nationalism and my feeling for Savarkar was personal. I could not endure to see a man with such intense vitality spending his life in prison. I shared none of his ideas and I wasn't a terrorist. Then my intoxication and vainglory vanished suddenly.

"I'm wasting my time here," I said to myself. "The job has got to be done. I must go to a port. Which shall it be—Calais, Boulogne or Dieppe? No, Havre," I decided. I left Paris in the very early morning on the first train for Havre and reached it in the afternoon. After an hour or so looking round, I saw an old sailor washing down the deck of a pretty little cutter. I walked aboard her, along a plank, and told him I was looking for a boat in which to go for a week's trip sailing in the Channel with some friends. He was a delightful moon-faced old man, and, when he understood what I wanted, he began to swear, almost crying with vexation. If only I had come the day before I would have met the owner of the little cutter. He would have let it to my friends and have gone with us. He was an Englishman, a retired Colonel in the army. He had left for a couple of weeks in Paris. If I could postpone my trip. . . .

I drew a deep breath. That was an escape!

I asked him then if he knew no fishermen and said I had always wanted to sail in a smack. After a lot of reflection he remembered that *le patron* Cornu was in port. Together we set off, and half an hour later we were on board a big smack with M. Cornu and his wife, wearing sabots and determined that her man should not be swindled. It was a big, strong, extremely untidy boat, which had sailed to the Newfoundland Banks. They had just refitted her. M. Cornu agreed to take

me and two friends for a week's sailing trip, to provision his boat and provide the crew for the sum of £40. We argued for some time about details, I gave him four hundred francs on account to provision the boat and then, suddenly, the life almost went out of me, for I was dropping with exhaustion. Fortunately we had to seal our bargain with a drink and we drank black coffee with a generous measure of Calvados in it. That just saved me from collapse. I gave the old chap who had introduced me to Cornu a tip and, going to the station, caught a very slow train to Paris.

There were eight French soldiers in the compartment and they shouted songs all night long. It was my third night without sleep. I reached Paris at dawn. The streets were being washed and there was the smell of fresh bread coming from a few bakers' shops. I was dazed with fatigue and went straight to A.A.'s hotel in the Rue de la Boëtie. The concierge seemed to be expecting me: there was a note, she said, left the previous night by a small boy. I took it and went up to A.A.'s room to find him luxuriating in what looked a most comfortable bed. He made no move to get up.

"Thank goodness you've come. I've had an awful time. Your father's here and thinks I've kidnapped you—"

"I've got the boat all right," I muttered.

"But it's all off. It's impossible. Your father's here. He's going to the French police."

For a moment rage overcame me. I don't know what I said, but I heard A.A. exclaim: "Don't bring the old man's grey hairs with sorrow to the grave," and the idiocy of this remark made me burst out laughing. A.A. gave me my father's address, and I handed him the balance of the money I had not spent. It gave him visible satisfaction to receive it.

"Now you can go to sleep again," I said, hoping the contempt in my voice would penetrate, and I walked out. Before going into the street I remembered the note I had been given and opened it. "Don't let the ship sink for a ha'porth of tar," I read. I had not the least idea what it meant, but it could not matter now. Later on I discovered that Mrs Dryhurst had asked

Maude Gonne, the Sinn Feinn leader, to find me and give me this warning. I walked along the street, saw a baker's, bought a roll and ate it. What should I do? Go to Germany to study botany at Heidelberg? Just walk off and leave my father to set the police on A.A.? It would serve Edward right for interfering, and it was pleasant to think of A.A. being frightened out of his skin.

However, I must warn C.C. and tell Savarkar. I could not just desert them. So I got into a cab and went to the address A.A. had given. I arrived just as our friends were having breakfast and Edward and I exchanged one look with the message: "Whatever we have to say to each other must be postponed until we are alone." So with British phlegm I asked if I could join them at breakfast, drank as many bowls of coffee as I could and ate up all the *croissants*. Finally my hostess realised that I was famished and cooked me an egg and I ate that. Then I had a wash and brush up; we said good-bye and went off to catch the train for London.

On the way to the station I almost said to Edward: "Isn't it rather silly to miss the opportunity of seeing Paris? We may never both be here again together. Let's go to the Louvre." What he would have made of that remark in the circumstances I don't know, but the impulse vanished as quickly as it had come.

In the train we did not speak until a little while before we reached Calais, when he asked me whether I was carrying a pistol.

"I'm not quite such a fool as that," I replied. "I have no intention of ever shooting anybody."

Directly we got on the boat at Calais, I saw that my plan would not have come off in any case. It was blowing a gale and M. Cornu would certainly not have put to sea. A French submarine had sunk just outside the harbour and rescue operations were impossible, but there was a cluster of naval vessels anchored where the submarine had gone down, with seas breaking over them. Edward and I stayed on deck and got rather wet. Edward was violently seasick; for some reason,

although I am a very bad sailor, I felt not the slightest qualms. Probably I was too tired and strung up to be sick. Watching Edward hanging over the leeward rail, I felt no pity for him. Only when we were in the train, bound for London, did I ask how he had found out. I had gone to see Mrs Dryhurst and had told her I should not want any Sinn Fein help, the day before I left for Paris. As I was leaving her house, Harold Hobson's sister Mabel had come in and I was hardly out of earshot when Mrs Dryhurst had told her all she knew about my activities and that I was just off to Paris. Mabel had reported it at home and the Hobsons had thought it wise to inform my parents. Constance had taken to her bed with a migraine and Edward had set off to find me. When we got back to the Cearne, Constance was still in bed. I went into her room, spoke to her, and went to bed immediately myself. I did not wake up until early the following afternoon; then I sent off a warning to C.C. Half an hour before the rescue was timed to take place I went to Brixton prison and saw Savarkar. The moment he saw me he knew that the plan had miscarried. But as I told him the details, he was already trying to console me for my failure. There was not a single sign in him of reproach or bitterness, or even of shock. I told of the situation I had found when I arrived in Paris; that it was obvious that A.A. did not want him to escape, but to keep hold of the party funds. Then I described how I had gone to Havre and found a boat, and how I had been frivolously betrayed, but that in any case the weather would have rendered the plan impossible for that particular week.

Then Savarkar said something like this:

"It does not matter whether one wins or is defeated, whether one succeeds or fails. Care nothing about the result so long as you fight. The only thing that matters is the spirit.

"You have done wonderfully and there was no reason why you should have done anything at all. Do not worry about me. I shall escape somehow. I have a plan worked out already, in case your plan failed."

The warder called out that time was up. A few minutes later I was let out of Brixton prison. As I walked slowly down towards Brixton Hill, knowing that I had seen Savarkar for the last time, a taxi passed me. In it there was one detective. I looked at my watch: it was three minutes to the time I had fixed for our car to appear.

It was clear that, in spite of the rumpus, Scotland Yard had not yet heard the news of my activities. But they did hear later on, and when Savarkar was taken to the Court for final judgment and to the ship where he was handed over to two detectives sent out from India, he was, I was told, handcuffed and very heavily guarded.

The end of the Savarkar episode left me exhausted, not only physically and for several weeks I stayed at the Cearne, wandering far into the woods with a book under my arm and then lying down under a tree and dozing or dreaming away the morning without opening a page.

Sometimes a band of titmice came near and I watched them; sometimes a red squirrel sprang out to fall lightly from bough to bough above me. But I looked at them with tired eyes; my experience with A.A. was soaking in, and digesting its lessons was a slow and painful experience. For look at it how I could, I saw that I had played a fool's part in the affair.

In the first place it was not my business to intervene. If the Indians could not run their own terrorist movement efficiently, what good could an English boy do by helping them? Would they expect Englishmen to run their country if they ever drove the British out? Nor did I believe in terrorism and I was already sceptical as to what might be achieved by it. Why was I risking my future for a cause in which I did not believe and for a man who had made so many and such gross mistakes? I was a fool—and the romantic and altruistic emotions which had led me to involve myself were folly. But I was so tired that I could not bear to think about the subject any more.

The Oliviers were away that summer, but their cousin Ursula had come back from Moscow for a visit, and she and

her bosom friend, Lenotchka Goncharov, were staying at The Champions. My depression turned to an agreeable sentimentality in the presence of the two girls, with whom I went on excursions to the river at Tonbridge.

One day I opened the paper to find it full of the story of Savarkar's escape. On the arrival of the liner on which he was a prisoner at Marseilles, Savarkar asked permission to have a hot bath. After soaping himself all over he managed to squeeze through a port-hole and drop into the sea. It was over half a mile to the nearest land and, as Savarkar was swimming, he was seen and recognised from the liner. A boat was lowered. Savarkar was a good swimmer and reached land just before the boat, but he was exhausted. He had asked for a car to be waiting, but A.A. had once again disobeyed orders and there was no help at hand. In desperation Savarkar rushed up to a French gendarme and asked to be taken to the Commissary of Police. At that moment the sailors and detectives came up and, seizing him, told the gendarme that he was a thief and took him by force back to the ship. The gendarme took no action and made no attempt to stop them.

There were soon interpellations in the French Chamber and Jaurés's protests forced the French Government to demand Savarkar's restitution. The British Government proposed arbitration and the case was finally tried at the Hague Tribunal. The decision was that, as the French policeman had not protested, the French Government could not raise the matter later. It was an unfortunate precedent for international law.

By the time this decision was reached, Savarkar had been sentenced to life imprisonment in the Andaman Islands. He was let out some fourteen years later, when Lord Olivier was Secretary of State for India, though I never found out if he had intervened and given orders for his liberation. Vinayak Savarkar is today one of the leaders of the Indian extreme religious Nationalists—the Hindu Mahasabha. He was arrested at the time of Gandhi's assassination, but later released for lack of evidence. I have never communicated with him since I last saw him in Brixton Gaol.

VIII

I HAVE skipped over much in order to put the story of my relations with my Hindu friends into a coherent story. But many friendships of a more enduring nature had been made during those years, and to these I now revert.

I met H. G. Wells for the first time when I was about thirteen or fourteen, when he was brought over two or three times to the Cearne by Sydney Olivier and his daughters. I can see him now as I first saw him, a small figure, bouncing along like a rubber ball between the tall figures of Edward and Sydney, each a head taller than he was, like a boy walking between two men, and all three walking in quite different ways. Edward walked in a long, casual, lurching stride, H.G. positively bounced with ill-suppressed energy, and Olivier strode with aloof dignity, apparently unaware of his companions, to whom he was really listening attentively.

On another occasion Wells was brought by the Olivier girls alone, and I walked back with them, H.G.'s liveliness and activity dominated all of us, and I remember his instant response to Brynhild's sparkling eyes and flashing smile. But any attraction they felt for each other was suppressed and its expression averted when he played a violent game of rounders after tea.

Wells was, at the time I first saw him, an active figure in the Fabian Society and, when a clash arose between him and the Webbs, my father joined the Society purely in order to vote for Wells and Wells's supporters, when they put up for the Executive Committee. A month later, when Wells had been defeated, Edward resigned.

Constance was quite indignant with him over this: he was not a Socialist and had no business to pretend to be one merely

in order to take part in a fight; but Edward only laughed and left his defence to Maitland, who supported Wells.

H.G. had already caused uneasiness among the conventional owing to his lack of respect for the taboos attaching to sexual desires and, at one moment Lady Olivier forbade her daughters to read *The Sea Lady*. I remember that Brynhild and Margery poured out their indignation to Edward.

But a little while after I had left University College School, Wells moved to Church Row, Hampstead, and the scandal of *Ann Veronica* broke. The row was prodigious and a considerable portion of it reached my ears. In his *Experiment in Autobiography* Wells explains that, like many of his characters, the heroine of *Ann Veronica* was suggested by an actual young woman, who is represented as taking the initiative in sexual relations with a demonstrator in Zoology, a typically Wellsian hero. My memory is that the outraged parents of this young woman attempted to destroy Wells, who became the target for a fantastic social persecution. He was turned out of his club— the Savile—and he and his wife were cut and boycotted, in particular by many Socialists who were afraid he would fasten the label of Free Love for ever to the movement.

Shaw, unlike the Webbs, who hated Wells and seized the opportunity to try to destroy him, was one of the few of the leading Fabians to behave with common sense: he urged all concerned to hush up the scandal. But it was too late.

Olivier, though remaining most friendly with Wells, wrote to him at this time a moderate and sensible letter, saying he would rather Wells were not seen in public in the company of his daughters. This letter was the cause of a strange scene at the very height of the scandal. I went one day with Brynhild to an exhibition of paintings in Bond Street. After we had been there some time, she suddenly caught sight of H.G., who was hiding from us behind some pictures on a stand running down the middle of the room. Brynhild called out to him in her clear voice and H.G. turned and fled like a rabbit. But he took refuge in a cul-de-sac, and Brynhild and I followed

BRYNHILD OLIVIER

and ran him to earth. Her cheeks were scarlet as she held out her hand and her eyes flashed more than ever as she said:

"I won't let you cut me, Mr Wells, so don't ever dare to try to do so again."

I don't think I ever saw her look lovelier than she did at that moment. She held H.G. in talk for five minutes and forced him to look at some of the pictures with us. I could see H.G. was pleased and, at the same time, uncomfortable and longing to get away.

Wells's temporary social eclipse and his move to Hampstead led to our seeing much more of him than we otherwise should have done. Edward and Constance and Dollie Radford went fairly often to dinner at Church Row and, on one occasion, Constance came back glowing with gratification at the compliments that Arnold Bennett had paid her translations of Turgenev, to which, he declared, he owed much in learning the art of a writer.

I only went once or twice to tea with the Wellses and remember being rather flabbergasted at the energy and noise H.G. put into some of the games he made us play. There was rampageous bumping round a table and knocking over of chairs when I had expected to sit around, on my good behaviour, listening to highbrow conversation. And then I was dragged into a nursery where a little war was in progress and saw H.G., in a whirlwind of tactical enthusiasm, ousting his small sons Frank and Gyp from the peaceful enjoyment of their toy soldiers.

I don't think Wells took much notice of me then: but a year or two later, meeting me by the Hampstead Fire Station, opposite the Tube, he said, "You are following exactly in my footsteps and I suppose later on you'll throw up biology to write novels." For curiously enough H.G. had taught biology at the Tutorial College, Red Lion Square, before "Flatfish" Cunningham and had taken his B.Sc. after being a student at the Royal College of Science, South Kensington, where I had just started work. Indeed the first version of *The Time Machine*

had been published in *The Phoenix*, a monthly magazine of the Royal College of Science students.

One afternoon when I arrived with my mother at the Radfords' a little late for tea, we found in the drawing-room a very large man sitting on a small hassock in the attitude of Rodin's *Le Penseur*, captivating the company by his parlour tricks. Constance was greatly charmed by him, and I asked him to come down for a week-end to the Cearne and he at once accepted.

Godwin Baynes was then twenty-six, a medical student taking his finals at Bart's. He was about six foot three in height, so broad-chested and strongly built that he did not seem a tall man but a well-proportioned hero of antiquity. He was indeed an athlete of some distinction—had rowed twice in the boat race against Oxford, each time in the winning boat, and was also in the crew which defeated Harvard. He had wrestled with Hackenschmidt, the Russian strong man, and had lasted for three and a half minutes against him.

Godwin had a big-featured, fresh-complexioned face with dark hair already touched with grey, a rather clumsily made mouth with a dark moustache, the points of which he was at that time inclined to twirl up like those of the Kaiser. His eyes were hazel and, like those of a large and kindly dog, often held a puzzled expression.

His charm, like that of the mastiff and the St Bernard, was to a considerable extent the result of his size, his splendid health and magnificent physique. He was open-hearted, warm, affectionate and generous. Having escaped from a strict nonconformist upbringing at home, with prayers muttered into the seats of the chairs before breakfast, he had become an enthusiastic neo-pagan and I myself was just ripe for the neo-pagan revelation.

What and who were the neo-pagans? Perhaps the best idea can be got from the following lines from Rupert Brooke's *The Great Lover*:

These have I loved:
>   White plates and cups, clean-gleaming,
>   Ringed with blue lines, and feathery faery dust,
>   Wet roofs beneath the lamplight; the strong crust
>   Of friendly bread . . . [, etc.]
>   And oaks; and brown horse-chestnuts, glossy-new;
>   And new peeled sticks; and shining pools on grass;—
>   All these have been my loves. . . .
>   Nor all my passion, all my prayers have power
>   To hold them with me through the gate of Death.

Those lines give a truer picture of Godwin than of Rupert Brooke himself.

But now and then, when the joy of life and the love of white plates and gleaming conkers flagged for a moment, Godwin looked puzzled, and when he discussed things seriously he left me puzzled too. He, who was so good at learning everything and was so universally successful, got into a complete and hopeless muddle when he tried to think.

Godwin was musical and had a magnificent voice. He had studied at Dresden to become an opera singer, but had thrown it up in a revulsion against the life of the stage and had then decided to study medicine. Our friendship with him blossomed rapidly, and he became a very frequent visitor at the Cearne, and often we slept out in the woods with Harold.

Not long after our first meeting he told me he had fallen in love with Rosalind Thorneycroft, a cousin of the Oliviers. Their marriage was delayed for some time, until Godwin had qualified and settled down in practice. But I soon met Rosalind and became great friends with her. Her beauty was cool and flower-like and it seems to me that it has changed little in the last forty years.

It was in the summer of 1909, when I was seventeen, in the summer holidays after haymaking time, that the Olivier girls and I decided on a bicycling picnic to Penshurst. Godwin and Maitland were with us. When we reached Penshurst we found a little road crossing the river Eden, and above a narrow old

bridge was a wider pool with yellow water-lilies, in which we bathed. Near by was a little weirhouse over the river.

I was enchanted by the place and came back there alone with camping things. When I had been living there a week Godwin came back and joined me, and then the Oliviers came with Harold Hobson and Dorothy Osmaston, a lovely blue-eyed girl who is now Lady Layton.

I had been quite extraordinarily happy there while I was alone. After the others had joined me, there was a wet evening, and we left the river and went up to a farm on a hill, where the farmer let us sleep in a haybarn.

It rained again next day. I had not learned to be a social animal and, living largely in a dream, could not bear to accept or acknowledge the reality.

It rained: the meadows were wet; the weirhouse was full, the roar of the water prevented conversation, and suddenly all the others were talking of going to a pub in Penshurst.

I did not try to stop them, but saying, "I shan't go," I went off to collect sticks from the willows dry enough to burn. My refusal was practical as well as emotional: the others had the money to stay at the pub. I had not, for I had always less money than any of my friends.

It turned out later I had misunderstood the proposal, but they found my behaviour exasperating. "Come along," said Godwin to Harold, "we can't leave him," and picking up a long strap they came planning to lasso me and drag me along by force, in joke of course.

Just as this took place a pair of new arrivals strolled up and followed Harold and Godwin, vaguely wondering what was afoot. One of them was Walter Layton. The strap was thrown over my head and shoulders, my arms tightly pinioned by Godwin and Harold. Suddenly my unhappiness exploded into a moment of blind fury. I whirled upon them, broke loose and hurled myself upon the nearest of my persecutors.

A moment later I saw that I had a total stranger by the throat and was trying to strangle him. I let go and, still shaking

with passion, I apologised and told him I had attacked him by mistake.

He walked away, upset and puzzled—it was a comic incident—but no one laughed and Godwin, appalled at his clumsiness, stood bewildered. The only person who understood that there was a misunderstanding was Brynhild. She came up, pushed Godwin away and explained they only intended to have luncheon at the pub. I was overcome by my stupidity and I went with them, but I was bitterly ashamed of my behaviour. No one spoke of it, but the attempt to overlook it was not the best way to cure it for the future. I realised I was a savage and an embarrassment to my friends.

The following night, just after we had all retired to sleep, there were gay shouts of greeting and we emerged from sleeping-bags and tents to find two young men from Cambridge had come to join us. They were Rupert Brooke and Dudley Ward.

Rupert was extremely attractive. Though not handsome, he was beautiful. His complexion, his skin, his eyes and hair were perfect. He was tall and well built, loosely put together, with a careless animal grace and a face made for smiling and teasing and sudden laughter. As he ate in the firelight I watched him, at once delighted by him and afraid that his friendliness might be a mask. What might not lie below it?

Dudley Ward was, in comparison, prematurely old, and if Rupert was a trifle incalculable, a creature of moods and laughter, Dudley was a good and patient Dr Watson, but a Dr Watson with brains.

Someone suggested bathing. Noel and Daphne joined us, and we went upstream to our lily pool and put a bicycle-lamp in the grass by the edge of the river-bank, so as to know where to jump from into the darkness. Then, one after another, we took running dives into the unseen river. It was exciting—the moment of doubt before one struck the water, and then swimming rapidly out of the next diver's way. The smell of new-mown hay, of the river and weeds, the curious polished smoothness that fresh river-water leaves on the skin . . . all

heart-aches were purged and healed and an immense happiness and gratitude to my friends filled me. Soon we were sitting round the blazing fire, Noel's eyes shining in welcome for the new arrivals and the soft river-water trickling from her hair down her bare shoulders.

And on the white shoulders, shining in the firelight were bits of duck-weed, which made me love them all the more. The moon rose full. Soon we crawled back into our sleeping-bags and slept, but Rupert, I believe, lay awake composing poetry.

Dorothy and Walter Layton had gone back to her home, the evening before, to get engaged to be married. But we lingered, and on Sunday morning the rustics of Penshurst came down and leant in a line upon the parapet of the bridge, staring into the pool in which we were to bathe.

"Come on," said Daphne. "They're not going to stop us."

Nor did they. We bathed, ignoring them, and Noel, not to be put off from her high dives, picked her way along the parapet between the rows of wrists and elbows, politely asked for standing-room in the middle, and made a perfect dive into the pool. With florid expressionless face, the nearest labourer shook his black Sunday coat-sleeve free of the drops which had fallen from her heel.

That afternoon we lay in the meadow, playing first with grasses—swiping at plantain heads—and then Rupert, teasing us, taught us the trick of playing fast and loose. We plunged a pencil into the central coil of his rolled-up leather belt, but when he pulled the belt free, the pencil was never in the loop after all. Brynhild was a long while puzzled by this mystery, knitting her lovely eyebrows over it in thought. When at last she understood it, she was mightily indignant that Rupert should have taken her in so easily.

One result of my friendship with Godwin was that he soon discovered I was suffering from septic tonsils and got me a bed in Bart's Hospital, where they were enucleated.

This was a turning-point in my life: my general health improved immensely, and my intelligence rapidly developed.

At all events a few months after the operation I succeeded in passing the London Matriculation examination. I had achieved the miracle of getting seven sums correct, solving five algebraical problems, and writing an English essay, up to the required standard, on the comparative advantages of town and country life.

I passed in January and had to wait until the following October before I could start at any of the colleges of London University, and so I was despatched to Letchworth. There I was to be coached in mathematics and physics two or three times a week by a schoolmaster living in Hitchin.

There was at Letchworth a remarkable lady with a battered brass ear-trumpet, called Miss Lawrence, who died in her nineties while this book was being printed. She was one of those ladies, more numerous in the first decade of the twentieth century than today, who confidently expected to change the nature of the world by the expenditure of a few thousand pounds, which would enable the theories of philosophers to be put into practice. Like Scythrop, when he peopled Nightmare Abbey with venerable Eleutherarchs, she planned to call into existence a confederation of illuminati, who would go forth like Scythrop's "Seven golden Candlesticks with which I will illuminate the world." All that was lacking was the Abbey, for, odd as it may seem, the Pethick Lawrence family did not own a Nightmare Abbey. She therefore decided to build one and my uncle, Harry Cowlishaw, was chosen as its architect. Hence, indeed, the presence of the Cowlishaw family at Letchworth.

The result was in all respects extraordinary—a building which was very beautiful, but unlike anything ever built before. Its central feature was a horseshoe arch of cloisters with Swedish marble pillars, in which the community lived and ate during the day and in which they slept on canvas hammocks let down from the roof at night.

At one end of the cloisters were grouped rows of cubicles, in which the members of the community might find privacy, bathrooms and lavatories, and a small meeting-room, beyond

which was a lovely little open-air swimming-pool. Behind the cloisters were kitchens with gas stoves, larders and a furnace-room. In the roof was an organ which could fill the whole building with its sound. Above the cloisters wound an openwork tower, which led to a promenade over the roof, and there was a last climb to what I think of as Scythrop's own tower, in which the poet-philosopher who inspired the community, had he existed, could have looked up at the heavens and down over the First Garden City. Next door to the Cloisters was a neat and comfortable little house in which Miss Lawrence had her conventional abode.

I no sooner had been taken over The Cloisters by its architect than I decided that I must live there, and my uncle, with his invariable good-nature, proceeded to arrange it for me. Fortunately he was one of the few people who could make himself audible to Miss Lawrence. I was introduced to the lady, whose wild and strange smile suggested that she secretly thought she was a gullible old woman, but that she had discovered it too late to do anything about it.

I stood on my toes and feebly bellowed into the much contorted ear-trumpet and she shook her head and laughed. But I liked her and she liked me and the upshot was that I could live along with the Illuminati for twelve shillings and sixpence a week, until a worthier recruit turned up.

I greatly enjoyed life at The Cloisters. One slept in a canvas cot, swinging a couple of feet off the floor, sheltered from rain or snow, but in the open air. In the morning one hauled up one's bed, either had a hot bath or a plunge in the swimming-pool, collected a breakfast, which was eaten sitting raised up behind a vast slab of rose-coloured alabaster. The interlocking shadows of the cloister arches patterned the floor, and shafts of sunlight fell from the roof through its open louvers. Those breakfasting at the table looked like a painting of the Last Supper.

There was space, leisure, beauty and food (though not wine) provided for the neophytes who were to go forth as the twelve golden candlesticks to illuminate the world.

Who and what were the members of this community? Alas, the faces and characters of most of those young men were always dim—illuminati of very low candle-power. One of them was so dim that I once took the trouble to find out how he came to be there. It turned out that he was a professional. He had come from another community in Surrey, where he had been made to work harder and had failed to give satisfaction. Before that he had been in yet another community and Miss Lawrence had already spoken to him of the desirability of his going for further study to a community in Canada.

There was an earnest young man who believed in primitive Christianity, but the only member I liked was a robust fellow with a hearty laugh, a red face and a good deal of tawny hair, called Stanley Potter. He was an anarchist, who enjoyed life, refused to be a wage slave, and was confident that if Miss Lawrence got tired of supporting him he could always earn a living by making sandals and rucksacks and selling them to other cranks.

He had been reading Kropotkin and it was perhaps because of his influence that Miss Lawrence had set her young men to plant a field with wheat grown on Kropotkin's principles. Those, I need hardly say, were not derived from experience in growing wheat anywhere, but were deduced from what he declared was the Chinese practice in growing rice. The principle was that each seed should be sown separately and each plant given individual attention throughout its growth.

It was February or March when I went to The Cloisters; for an hour or two each day, four or five of the dim candlesticks would press separate grains of wheat into the roughly ploughed and harrowed clay field, each grain being about a foot from its nearest neighbour.

If not very much of the field got sown, one would have supposed that the young plants would gain by greater individual attention later on. But though they came up, so did couch grass, watergrass, wild oats, docks, thistles and every other weed common in cornfields.

April was the testing time and, alas, by May it was obvious

that Miss Lawrence's Candlesticks were not industrious Chinamen, that wheat was not rice, that Hertfordshire was not in the delta of the Yangtze Kiang and that the sea of docks and thistles which extended over the unsown portion of the field was equally unbroken over the little belt devoted to growing wheat on Kropotkin's principles. I was living in Nightmare Abbey as it might have been after the death of Mr Glowry.

But where was Scythrop? Alas, his seat in the tower was empty and there was no madeira in the cellars! I occasionally went up the tower to sigh over the mysteries of a text-book of physics or mechanics, but no poet-philosopher ever came up to disturb my meditations. Only on Sundays was there any sign of a guide or *guru* who was to inspire and send forth the evangelists.

He was a Man of God, a second-sighted dissenting Scot from the New Hebrides, who gave an address to everyone who would come to hear it in Letchworth. He chose to speak in front of a glass screen put up to shelter him from the weather, so constructed that his short figure was silhouetted against a wooden cross supporting the glass panels. At the crucial moment—in every sense of the word—of his sermon he would fling his arms out along the horizontal limbs of the cross, would gasp out: "I have come to you" and then, still holding his arms out as though crucified, would let his head fall forward in a moment of simulated unconsciousness, or death. Then the organ would peal forth and the audience would struggle out while one or two of the Candlesticks walked round with collecting-boxes.

Looking back on it, I wonder that Miss Lawrence should have permitted these unpleasant scenes, but there was the extenuating circumstance that she could never hear what her spiritual adviser said.

At the end of May or the first week in June, while I was still at The Cloisters, I got a letter from Noel saying that Rupert Brooke would like me to visit him in Cambridge and suggest-

ing that I should write to him at the Old Vicarage. I did so and received an invitation. When the day came I got on my bicycle and rode off through Baldock and Royston. In the queer way in which places have affected me all my life, one bit of the Baldock–Royston road was photographed for ever in my memory. I have driven over it hundreds of times since and very frequently something stirs in my mind and takes me back to my first sight of it.

Rupert was extremely friendly and a feeling of his unhurried leisure and yet of his pursuing his own purposes impressed me: it was the flavour of Cambridge in those days and contrasted very favourably with the vacant idleness alternating with despairing and hurried labour which had been my portion up till then.

One of the first things I noticed in the Old Vicarage was a photograph of Noel in a silver frame on the table. I did not remark on it, neither did Rupert mention her.

Rupert could not have been more delightful. He was quite free from airs of superiority, which it must have been difficult to avoid with such a half-baked creature as myself. And he was quite free, also, from any affectations such as I noticed later. Instead, he was easy and kind, hospitable and yet happily preoccupied with his own work.

We went about midnight—for I had arrived rather late—to bathe in Byron's pool. We walked out of the garden of the Old Vicarage into the lane full of thick white dust, which slipped under our weight as we walked noiselessly in our sandshoes, and then through the dew-soaked grass of the meadow over the mill-wall leading to the pool, to bathe naked in the unseen water, smelling of wild peppermint and mud.

I slept well and heavily, for I was tired, and it seemed only a moment before I was woken up in the early morning by shouts and cries outside and by Rupert's coming to my room to say that some friends of his had come out from Cambridge for a bathe. There were three of them, and one was to become a lifelong friend: Geoffrey Keynes, eager, lean and in a hurry. We ran along to the river and bathed, diving again

175

and again off the bank and swimming up and down the pool. Though several years younger than the others I was not shy, and Geoffrey and I must have talked to each other, for I can remember him clearly and have always felt that our friendship dates from that first meeting. Our visitors did not stay to breakfast, which we ate in the garden. Later Rupert gave me his poems in manuscript and I sat reading them slowly and picked out one or two that I liked better than the others. He was modest and sincere when we talked about them.

In the afternoon Rupert had to go in to Cambridge and it was arranged that I should paddle down in a canoe after tea to Cambridge and meet him there and that he should take me to dinner with Lowes Dickinson.

The Old Vicarage garden was unkempt and trailed off into an orchard with overhanging trees by the water and a little summerhouse, derelict under them, with paintings by Duncan Grant in it. For some reason I lost track of the time and was late in starting, and I had to drive the canoe down the narrow winding river at a great rate. It was Saturday afternoon and the river was crowded with punts and parties of townspeople. The result was that I slopped a lot of water into the canoe and arrived rather wet, but Rupert welcomed me, and we went together to Lowes Dickinson's rooms in Gibbs.

I suppose he was not more than middle-aged, but he already had that curiously dark skin, the forehead rising to a bald head, the deepset hidden eyes, the nose with two or three hairs sprouting up stiffly an inch or so from its tip. Why, I always wondered, did he not have them removed? Though, to be sure, imagination boggles at his visiting a beauty specialist. And then, as Morgan Forster says, suddenly the gleam came which lit the whole face and transformed it when he was interested—and with Goldie to be interested was to be in sympathy.

After dinner we came back up the river by night, after arranging that Goldie should bring an American friend to the Old Vicarage for lunch.

Next morning, Sunday, we again had an early bathe, followed by breakfast outside. The weather was lovely and we

lay about and talked and read until, about half-past twelve, we were disturbed by a servant coming to lay the table in the garden for lunch. Rupert had all his meals out of doors in fine weather.

We were lying on the grass reading, when a tall and extremely solemn gentleman in a dark suit, cut for the City rather than for an English June, came into the garden. Rupert rose from where he was lying and went to meet him.

The strange figure was Dickinson's American visitor. Dickinson had told him how to reach Grantchester and, after saying he would be at the Old Vicarage before him, had rushed off without saying where he was going. The American had attended a service in King's College Chapel.

All seemed natural enough and Rupert made conversation as best he could—but where was Goldie? After waiting for about three-quarters of an hour, Rupert decided that we had better start the meal without him. We did so, but we had scarcely sat down when the American had a comment to make of some urgency.

"I notice that you do not like the formality of a grace—and I quite understand it—for so long as we thank God in our hearts all is well. At home I felt myself that a grace whether in Latin or English was too formal, and we tried many forms in the family circle. Finally, I introduced the custom of bowing our heads in silence and holding hands round the table. We found it very beautiful. Shall we do so now?"

He held out one hand to Rupert and another to me and we stretched across Goldie's empty seat to hold hands. I did not dare catch Rupert's eye and he gave me a vicious pinch as we clasped hands.

We were all three silent for what was, for me, a period of intense internal strain—and then the agony of suppressed giggles subsided as the American began briskly asking questions about Cambridge and I could drink a glass of water.

Still there was no sign of Dickinson and our meal was over before he crept into the garden looking very odd and ill, and

when he began to apologise, we noticed his teeth were chattering violently and his face was smeared in places with black mud.

Rupert fetched him some lunch and then while we sat round anxiously he described his misadventure. The morning had been so lovely that hearing his guest wished to go to chapel, he decided on a bathe in the river at Grantchester before coming to lunch. He had no bathing dress and leaving his clothes and spectacles upon the bank, he had plunged in naked. But he had only swum a few strokes when he heard the sound of female voices—a boatload of townspeople were approaching. Goldie was on the far side of the stream from his clothes and decided to hide in a belt of reeds while they went by. He waded through the reed-bed and behind its shelter began sinking further and further into depths of black mud. The punt came up abreast of him and there to his horror it remained, while the girls and young men in it proceeded to have a picnic lunch.

The longer he remained hidden, the worse Goldie's position became. The stigma of an eavesdropper overhearing a flirtation was added to that of nudity and indistinct vision prevented his getting an accurate notion of what the people in the boat looked like and their accents did not encourage him to throw himself upon their mercy.

So there he stayed, having finally reached mud bottom, and felt himself slowly congealing. The water, which half an hour before had seemed so warm and limpid as it lingered among the lily pads, grew chill as the hand of death upon his chest, and still the girls giggled and the youths idly pursued the paths of dalliance. And to Goldie further delay began to seem like death. At last the crumbs were shaken into the river, hair was tidied, the punt unmoored, and slowly, slowly off it went—and out crept the shivering figure of the watching satyr from among the reeds.

Goldie was extremely funny in telling the story, for he saw the full humour of his position as a naked Pan. But what added to the humour of the whole narrative was the attitude of his audience to this event. For while Rupert and I were amused

178

and yet concerned that Goldie might have got a serious chill—Rupert I think fetched him a blanket and a glass of hot milk early on—the American's feeling was one of relief on Goldie's account, that he should have had such a lucky escape from such a dreadfully damaging situation, to which he had so imprudently exposed himself. Had a don been seen naked upon the Sabbath—of all days—it would, he surmised, have caused a scandal so great as to lead to his having to give up his Fellowship.

These conjectures only made Rupert and me laugh louder, and we finally abandoned ourselves to a *fou rire*. When Goldie and his guest departed, I am sure the American told him that we were very thoughtless and irreverent boys and I should have been amused to hear Goldie's defence of us.

Many were the expeditions taken with the Oliviers, and often enough they were impromptu. One hot day at the end of June we bicycled to Tonbridge and took a boat up the river, bathed and picnicked and bathed again, and dusk fell among the hayfields.

"Don't let's go home."

Prowling about we found a Dutch barn half full of hay; we mounted and slept there; in the morning early we climbed down, got aboard our boat and drifted downstream, then stopped, lit a fire and made our breakfast.

What circumstances made such an impromptu outing possible I don't know—probably parents were away. To fall asleep within a yard or two of a lovely girl without a thought of trying to make love to her was natural to me at eighteen. It was simply part of the social climate in which I was brought up and had nothing to do with innocence or its reverse, not a matter of morality but of manners.

One June evening we bicycled for most of the night about the lanes round Hever, listening to the nightingales, comparing the song of one bird with another.

One day in mid-winter, with scarcely any preparation, the four Olivier girls decided to walk with Maitland and me to

Dover—ninety miles away. It was cold, windy weather, but it did not rain. We started late and the first night came on us when we reached Wrotham, where I remembered that Perceval Gibbon was living. Gibbon was a journalist turned author; a lively, dark little man, who had discovered the code used by a pair of celebrated thought-readers, the Zanzigs.

We descended, unexpectedly, upon Gibbon and his wife, and they appeared delighted to give us all supper and to put up some of us while the rest found lodging in the inn down the road. Gibbon had never seen so many lovely girls together and was dazzled by Brynhild's eyes. I think he may have shown his feelings, for several times afterwards the Oliviers used to refer in a particular tone of amused denigration to "that poor Mr Gibbon."

From Wrotham, we mounted the side of the unspoilt, rather desolate North Downs. We followed the Pilgrim's Way for some miles, a lane bordered by hedgerows that declined into a grass track along the side of the open grass downs, with here and there old chalk-pits half-hidden under masses of Old Man's Beard where we sat and ate our lunch.

I was foolishly wearing cheap boots and nail after nail came up through their soles. My feet blistered and when, four days after starting, we tottered, exhausted into Dover, I had thrown my boots away and was wearing slippers.

Dover proved a disappointment and we caught the first train to London, but we were pleased with ourselves for having reached the object of our pilgrimage. It was not the walk that mattered but the company and the talk. Conversation, if I were walking with Margery, would be a sort of scared teasing on her side, or else, if she were at ease, talk about the personal aspects of ideas—for example, that one must believe in the teachings of George Moore because Keynes and Shove did so. Not having been to Cambridge, a conversation at cross purposes resulted before I learnt that she was not speaking of the author of *The Confessions of a Young Man* but of G. E. Moore, the philosopher.

With Brynhild and Daphne conversation was far more

likely to be on the ideas themselves and their practical application. Brynhild, quick-witted and eager, Daphne noble, but inclining to be censorious. I usually found myself agreeing with Brynhild and disagreeing with Daphne.

Noel talked much less than her sisters and listened and thought more. She was their superior in intelligence and her superiority became more noticeable with the years. Margery and Daphne became muddled and extravagant, a touch of madness making inviolate their idealism. Brynhild remained bright and intelligent, but superficial. Noel alone of the four developed a mind which was courageous, realistic and profound and grew into a woman as wise as she is beautiful.

We talked of books and ethics, possibly politics; all long-forgotten nonsense: but the companionship of flushed cheeks, sparkling eyes and lovely, rippling tresses of dark hair through four grey winter days was happiness.

IX

MY parents could not afford to send me to Cambridge. Had I gone there I should have studied Genetics under my mother's old friend, William Bateson. But the question was where could I get a good and cheaper scientific education?

I don't know what advice my mother got, but the decision to send me to the Royal College of Science was the right one. Letters were written and I was told to go for an interview with Professor Farmer, head of the botanical department. He was a tall, eager man with severe, blue eyes and a straggling moustache, and though I went into his room speechless with shyness, I emerged full of enthusiasm and confident that I should achieve wonderful things as an economic botanist.

Meanwhile Ford had heard that my mother was worrying about my education and wrote: "Send him to me for a few years, Connie, and I will teach him to write like Flaubert." This offer was not considered seriously and I missed the opportunity of becoming a feather in Ford's cap. It turned out, however, that Violet Hunt was acquainted with the wife of Professor Adam Sedgwick, who had given up being Professor of Zoology at Cambridge in order to become Professor at the Royal College of Science, occupying Huxley's chair. Ford therefore wrote to say that if I would turn up at South Lodge, Campden Hill, at three o'clock one afternoon, Violet and he would take me to call on Professor Sedgwick.

South Lodge was a pleasant house with a garden and Ford, who was suffering from a number of financial embarrassments, had gone to live there with Violet Hunt, who was chaperoned by her senile mother of eighty. In order to make things even more respectable in the eyes of the world, Ford and Violet persuaded first Ford's sister-in-law, Mary Martindale, and then his old mother, Mrs Hueffer, to join their establishment.

With this unimpeachably respectable background, Ford and Violet did not hesitate to be seen everywhere together. From the strictly conventional Edwardian point of view this was foolish. Violet had something of the Elizabethan pirate in her, and refusing to keep quiet, organised rounds of social visits for them both as though bent on singeing Mrs Grundy's beard. On such an expedition I was to accompany them. Meanwhile, I waited while Ford genially showed me the pictures by Violet's father, Alfred Hunt, in the drawing-room and the dining-room.

Then Violet descended, smartly dressed, and soon afterwards we set forth in a hired open carriage to leave cards and pay formal calls. Such behaviour does seem, as I look back on it, extremely peculiar, as it positively invited gossip and scandal among the censorious. However, I was quite unaware of there being any particular social significance in our odd excursion as we trotted off.

Violet Hunt was a thin viperish-looking beauty with a long pointed chin and deep-set, burning brown eyes under hooded lids. There was a driving force within her, which I afterwards recognised as insatiable ambition.

Edward rarely met her except at funerals. Before going to Hudson's funeral he opened a copy of the *Daily Mail*, for which she had written an intimate article about "Old Huddie's" devotion to her, with a description of her having forced her way into the bedroom where he died and having seen a spot of blood on the sheet. Edward was somewhat disgusted by this, but he had scarcely arrived at the funeral when Violet Hunt came up to him.

"Oh, Mr Garnett, we never seem to see each other except on these sad occasions . . ."

Edward cut her short with: "Perhaps one of us two will be the next, so let's make a self-denying ordinance. I will promise not to come to your funeral, if you will promise not to come to mine."

The open carriage trotted down Church Street and away we bowled: Ford with his top hat upon his knee, Violet Hunt, all

183

veils and tocque and parasol beside him, the card-cases at hand, and the innocent young man sitting opposite them with his back to the cabby.

We turned away from the Albert Hall into Kensington Gardens, went down one side of the Park and bowled away merrily towards one of the squares off Sloane Street, where Ford descended, rang the bell and left cards. Then we were off again. At the next stop Ford said he thought he would wait outside with me—he was sure it would be better. So Violet alone descended and went in.

While we were waiting Ford said to me: "You feel shy, David, but when I was your age, I was so shy that I would crawl through the hedge rather than pass a labourer on the road and have to reply, if he said it was a fine day, when he passed me. It's terrible feeling shy, but you get over it in time."

I don't think Ford had completely got over it that afternoon, but Violet had made up her mind to drag him around Kensington and he could not stop her.

Our next port of call was off the Cromwell Road at the Sedgwick's, and we all went up to find a very smart, rather young Mrs Sedgwick and one or two ladies and gentlemen taking tea. It was quite evident from the interested stares given us that the ladies had heard of Ford's connection with Violet and were somewhat surprised at his presence. Ford, I think, was inwardly happy. Soon afterwards Adam Sedgwick came into the room and all my attention was focused upon him. He was of medium height, rather stout, a deep red in the cheek like a Margil apple, and there was a delightful mixture of urbanity and bluntness about him which, if it did not set me immediately at ease (that was impossible because I was already regretting having allowed myself to be dragged out on this idiotic excursion), gave me a gleam of hope for the future.

Soon he got up and came and talked to me and led me over to the window and then, after a few minutes, Violet and Ford arose and we departed.

After that we drove to the house of the popular novelist Miss Netta Syrett and I waited alone outside in the carriage

184

while Ford and Violet went in. I don't quite know why I sat there. It would have been easy to have got out and gone home by bus; however, I waited till they came out, thanked them warmly and then went off home.

But there were some months to wait before I could go to the Imperial College. Constance realised that I was wasting my time, that a change of scene was desirable and so decided to send me to Germany. Either Juliet or Ford wrote to a great-aunt living in the little town of Boppard on the Rhine who found a widow of a major in the Prussian Army who was willing to take me as a paying guest.

I travelled alone from Tilbury to Rotterdam and then transferred to a small Dutch paddle-steamer, which went slowly up the Rhine, calling at every town or village on its banks. The journey was delightful: the weather, hot and sunny; I ordered myself a bottle of Niersteiner to drink with my meals, was kindly treated by an English lady with a son at Eton, and gazed about me exactly like Brown, Jones or Robinson upon their celebrated tour.

Boppard is a clean little town with white-washed houses and slate roofs. There is no mediaeval castle frowning over it in romantic splendour, but there is a very agreeable little water-front with an avenue of pleached lime-trees, behind which the restaurants and hotels overlook the great river. Further back the town is traversed by the railway, then the terraced vine-yards rise up steeply, and behind them there are the forests covering the Hunsruck mountains.

The Heiders lived in an extremely ugly brick-and-slate house between the main road and the railway, on the outskirts of the town. White dust rose and settled whenever a motor vehicle went past. But the house had a garden, at the end of which was a summer-house looking over the railway line, above which the first vineyard rose at a sharp angle. When trains went by the garden was filled with smoke and smuts.

I was met and conducted home by Ferdinand, a young man whose face was like a firm little bladder of lard; his eyes were a colourless grey-blue and his hair a colourless grey-brown.

The Heider family consisted of an ancient grandmother, her daughter the Frau Major, and two sons, Wilhelm and Ferdinand. Wilhelm was a lieutenant in the infantry, a professional soldier, garrisoned at the neighbouring town of Coblenz, but frequently able to get leave. Ferdinand, who was to be a solicitor, was just starting his year of military service as a cadet. Both brothers were usually in uniform.

The Heiders had two servants—girls under twenty—who retired to the attics about midnight when their work was done and rose about five o'clock in the morning. When Ferdinand or Wilhelm sat in the little summer-house at the end of the garden there was a small handbell beside them on a tray. After a little while one of the young men would pick it up and ring it and Luise would pop up the basement stairs and hurry to attend him.

"Bring me a box of matches," he would say without looking up.

Half an hour later, when he was puffing his cigar, he would tinkle it again, and Luise would breathlessly reappear.

"Bring me a glass of water," and walking carefully so as not to spill a drop, she would bring a single glass. If another was wanted, he would ring again, for the water was cooler so than if she had brought a jug.

It was not long before I was in difficulties with the Heiders. One of the first subjects which the Frau Major raised was religion. Did I wish to accompany the family to Mass? Or was I a Protestant, in which case I could attend the Lutheran Church?

Instead of cheerfully saying I was Church of England and so I should not go to either, I replied that I was neither. This stunned the Heiders for fully twenty-four hours, during which they observed me carefully and marshalled their forces. The entire family eagerly took part in the cross-examination which followed and continually broke off for rapid discussion among themselves.

Was I a Catholic? Was I a Protestant? Was I a Jew? Unfortunately, I did not recognise the word and was not ex-

pecting the question, and my reply: "What is a Jew? *Was ist dann ein Jude?*" failed to convince and appeared like an admission. A rapid-fire discussion followed in which Ferdinand, with legal acumen, pointed out that David was a Jewish name and Garnet a semi-precious stone.

These points were put to me. I admitted the name David was Jewish and explained it was that of my maternal grandfather, but I flatly denied that Garnett was Jewish or that my name indicated that I was a Jew.

"But are you not a Jew?" the Heiders yelped at me in chorus. "If you are not a Jew, why do you read Heine?" asked Lieutenant Heider.

I did not even know that Heine was a Jew—he appeared from his poetry to have had a Catholic upbringing—so I could not understand the relevance of the question. I replied, that he was a great poet—but, suddenly my patience broke, and I pretended not to hear any of the further questions which were addressed to me and shortly afterwards left the table, at which the Heiders were shrieking like a flock of jays which have discovered an owl in a holly-bush. I was furious with them; they were furious with me. For though I did not look like a Jew, I did not appear to be a Christian. It is possible that they would have told me to leave if the rumour of Ford's arrival had not spread: *Der berühmter Dichter* was to visit his most noble great-aunt, and I was summoned to attend. Whatever lies Ford may have told us about his German relatives—and later on he wrote a book to prove he was a Russian, with no German blood—his great-aunt was socially vastly superior to the Heiders and had invited me to tea. So my persecution as a Jew was called off.

Frau Goessen lived in a stucco villa with a slate roof and an Italianate tower on one side of it, but it had a pleasant garden at the back with a cedar shading the lawn and an agreeable view over the Rhine. An ancient dame lay in a bath-chair and Ford was standing beside her. According to Violet Hunt, Ford and she had left London because of his debts. No doubt a good proportion were to his tailor, for he was exquisitely

187

turned out in a summery tweed suit, with a mourning band on his arm, thoroughly well brushed and shaved, with grey spats and a scented handkerchief; infinitely better dressed than any German in Boppard and he was genially making agreeable conversation, with a tea-cup in his hand and showing the rabbit teeth in his shark's mouth.

He was, as always, most friendly and affectionate to me, and later, when we took leave of the old lady, I strolled with the *berühmter Dichter* along the front, where we found Violet Hunt. We sat and listened to the band and drank a bottle of Niersteiner and Ford smoked a cigar and fanned himself with his scented handkerchief. Then the steamer was seen labouring upstream and Ford and Violet went aboard on their way to Assmanshausen-am-Rhein, after inviting me to visit them there a week later.

When I got back, I found that the Heiders were bursting with questions. How long had I known Ford? Did my parents know him? And who was the lady in his company? Acting upon Ford's own axiom, that "truth is relative," I made satisfactory replies.

A rather confused account of this period of Ford's life is given by Violet in *The Flurried Years*. The truths contained in that book are relative also and from it the inquiring reader will learn that Violet was always chaperoned by a Countess, and that Ford was acquiring German nationality in order to assume the family title, which was in abeyance, and take possession of the family estates, which were in Chancery.

The truths of Violet Hunt's book are distorted doubly, as she was re-shaping what were originally inventions of Ford's to suit the picture she tried to give of herself.

But Ford's great-aunt stood high enough in the hierarchy of Boppard and the Heiders were overawed by my merely being invited to tea with her. Just before my month at the Heiders was up, we were, however, at cross-purposes again. A letter suddenly arrived from Maitland saying he was accompanying a girl who was joining a party of friends staying at Mayence, and that he proposed dropping in at Boppard and

going for a walking-tour of two or three days with me in the district before rejoining her.

I was beginning to learn some worldly wisdom, so I said nothing of Maitland's companion, but merely told them that my friend Maitland Radford was coming, and that I proposed to go off with him for a tour of three or four days. The Heiders were at first impressed, then, like cattle in a field into which a dog or cat has strayed, came snuffing round to find out about the strange creature, and the conversation took this turn.

Was my friend a nobleman?

No.

But the nobility alone had double-barrelled names, and this was particularly the case in England.

No. Anybody could have a double-barrelled name in England, and, in any case, Maitland was not his surname, but his first name; he was called after his mother, who was a Miss Maitland.

As we said, it is a family name, and they are of noble birth.

No, I'm afraid not.

What is Herr Maitland Radford's first name?

Maitland.

But what saint is he called after?

The only first name he has is Maitland; there is no other. (In this I may have been inaccurate.)

There was an appalling silence, a wave of horror ran through the assembled company, while I wondered what I had done to cause it. At last the Frau Major asked severely: "Is there then no Christ?"

The horror of the Heiders at Maitland's having been given a name not on the official list was so great that the Frau Major tried to forbid our projected walking-tour, or my leaving Boppard with him, but I told her I was leaving anyhow.

That day was a Saturday. In the morning a truck of coal arrived and the coalmen, instead of carrying the sacks into the coal-cellar, emptied two tons of small coal onto the pavement and into the gutter outside the front door. It appeared that they expected a tip if they carried it to the coal-cellar and as

the Frau Major had two young maids at her orders, she was not going to be blackmailed by coalmen.

Anna the cook, aged about nineteen, and Luise, about sixteen, thereupon set about carrying two tons of coal round the house to the coal-cellar. It was a very hot afternoon and rather damp and airless, as it often is in the Rhineland. Those two girls shovelled the coal into a basket and carried it between them. They worked from lunch-time until long after dark and before they went to bed they swept and scrubbed the pavement with buckets of water so that there should be no trace of coal-dust in the road on Sunday morning.

Ferdinand and Wilhelm sat in the summer-house at the end of the garden smoking. On one occasion Wilhelm rang the bell and the girls, coming in with the basket of coal, wavered like over-beaten horses, and set it down.

But the Frau Major, who was watching them closely, gave a sharp order and a moment or two later came waddling out to the summer-house. I did not hear what was said, but I imagine her sons accepted her apology, for she waddled back to the house and came back with two glasses of cold water on a tray. Wilhelm and Ferdinand were, it must be remembered, in uniform, so it would not have been fitting for them to wait upon themselves.

Next evening Maitland arrived and we had dinner together at a charming restaurant, looking out across the river under the branches of the pleached lime-trees. When we had finished our coffee after a dinner which was a welcome change from the continual plum-soup with vinegar, boiled sausage, sauerkraut and dumpling of the Heiders' table, Maitland and I sauntered off for a walk round the town. There was a band playing and, at the sound, Maitland pricked up his ears. "They are playing waltzes," he said. "It's an open-air dance."

He was right and we strolled in. I caught sight almost at once of Anna and Luise. The sweating coal-heavers of the night before were now fresh and pleasant girls in their best frocks. A few moments later we were dancing with them.

Next morning, when I was packing my things, which I was

sending as luggage in advance to Heidelberg, Luise stole into my room pretending to make the bed. The pretence was, however, a thin one, and soon I was holding her in my arms and had undressed her down to the waist and was kissing her breasts, when there was the sound of the bell being rung in the summer-house. Luise, in a panic, slipped out of my arms, made herself decent in a moment and ran out of the room. I never saw her again.

After despatching my luggage, Maitland and I set out on our little tour. Turning our backs on the dusty white road which runs for miles along the shore of the Rhine beside the railway line, we climbed above the vineyards, soon coming to the forest and lovely upland meadows bright with wild Canterbury bells and viper's bugloss and groves of foxgloves on the edges of the forest. Up there was a different world of tinkling cow-bells and peasants, whose German sounded not unlike the speech of the older generation of Sussex labourer.

"Millish zoo drinken, Brood, Booter und Honey," the peasant had to offer at the Wirtschaft where we stopped for lunch, and when we asked our way he pointed:

"Zee muss gayand by der Strome droo dry Dale'n."

On we rambled, Maitland swinging his stick, taking in the German landscape certainly, but translating it all into bright, gay, intellectual terms and speedily forgetting it as he remembered some anecdote, at the close of which his eyes blinked rapidly and his head jerked again and again nervously as though he were swallowing a couple of pills, before he permitted himself to laugh outright.

According to Violet Hunt, "two very young men faring on foot to Switzerland—dear Dollie Radford's son and his friend, David, the son of Edward and Constance Garnett. The beardless future author of *Lady Into Fox* stayed to breakfast with us and passed onward down the Rhine."

I parted from Maitland after we met Ford and Violet, but I stayed a night at Assmannshausen in a little hotel near their big one. After tea Ford and Violet and I climbed up to the fantastic, hideous Germania statue, commemorating the Franco-Prussian War, which, with any luck, has since been

destroyed. A vast Valkyrie stood brandishing her sword at the distant Vosges, from behind what she mistakenly believed to be the safe barrier of the Rhine.

We walked all round Germania and came down to dinner. Next morning Ford and I had our photograph taken together and then crossed the river and went for a stroll along the banks of the river from Rudesheim. And Ford, in the most excellent spirits, began to tell me stories.

"My family has lived hereabouts, you know, for very many centuries, probably from the time of Charlemagne. When I was a small boy I used to go and stay with my grandmother, who lived in a house on the end of the bridge, by the fortress of Ehrenbreitstein. They used to send me upstairs to play by myself in the attics. And those attics were full of *hats*. There were hats there of every size and shape and of all periods in German history—from the slashed cockscombs of the Minnesängers, right down to the eighteenth-century three-cornered hats and top hats and panamas.

"You see my family had the hereditary right to stop anyone who crossed the bridge and ask him for his hat. Bismarck put an end to it when they asked him for his. But, of course, most of the hats were military. You see, the *Grande Armée* crossed that bridge in 1812 on the way to Russia: no wonder the attics were full of shakos!"

"Half a million of them, I suppose," I murmured, thinking of the hatless regiments marching on to Moscow.

Ford chuckled, but decided on realism. "No they didn't take them all . . . they only took one from each company . . . usually the Colonel's . . . sometimes only a drummer-boy's . . . but I shall never forget those great attics full of shakos!"

He dismissed the subject with a curiously charming smile, in which his mouth lost its fishy look.

A car approached and Ford waved to it. Inside there was a gentleman who seemed surprised and startled, but raised his hand a little vaguely in return.

"My dear friend, Prince Metternich," explained Ford. "When his grandfather divided up Europe he kept the Johannisberg vineyard for himself, a couple of acres which grow the best hock in the world. The field next to it gets half an hour's less sun and is only very moderate. Remind me to tell the head waiter and we'll have a bottle for lunch. . . ."

I didn't remind him and the waiter brought Rudesheimer, which was quite good enough for me at that age. Twenty-one years later I found out that what Ford said about Johannisberger was an absolute and not a relative truth.

As we turned back from our stroll I caught sight of a small raft of logs coming down the river and noticed that, unlike the great pine-rafts from the Black Forest, on which there are houses and whole families afloat, this smaller affair was of beech-trees. I pointed it out to Ford, who shook his head and said in melancholy tones:

"All those trees are floating down the river to ruin the digestion of the British working class."

I suppose my look of astonishment was satisfactory, for Ford said even more lugubriously:

"Those trees are not sawn up for timber. They are distilled into acetic acid to make vinegar, of a kind guaranteed to give you a stomach-ache—only for export. It is a greater danger to the happiness of the British people than the German Fleet will ever be." Was that absolute or relative? Who knows?

An hour later I bade a fond farewell to Ford and Violet and boarded a steamer, which took me as far up the Rhine as Mayence, where I joined Maitland and his companion. I had dinner with them and saw them off by train to Paris.

The two or three weeks which followed were the happiest I spent in Germany and gave me a far more agreeable picture of the country than I had got from the Heiders and that dreary ditch the Rhine, the charm of which for me faded rapidly and for ever.

I went first to Heidelberg and put up at a large first-class hotel. After taking a room, I went into the beer hall on the ground floor. Almost immediately a girl of about twenty came from behind the bar and sat down and talked to me. She might have been a younger sister of Brünhilde—fair, blue-eyed, loose-limbed and jolly. I was attracted by her, told her all about myself and invited her to come to the Black Forest with me.

I think she liked me genuinely, but it took me four days

to discover that I could not see her outside the hotel, that she would not come to my room, and that however prettily she discussed spending a week's holiday with me, she was not actually going to come during the only week available. In the intervals of talking to her I spent a good deal of money sailing small boats on the Neckar, which is swift and dangerous and I was lucky not to capsize. Finally, I paid my bills, bought my ticket to Freiburg-im-Breisgau and realised, as I got into the train, that I had only about ten marks left.

I was expecting to find some money at Freiburg. But Constance's letter ran: "Your Father and I think you ought to be able to return to England on what we have already sent you." I was in an awkward predicament. My first action was to go to the police station. I had to wait half an hour before being given an interview, at which I was told that unless I committed some crime the police were not concerned with me, but the inspector suggested that I should pawn or sell some of my possessions. The only article of value which I had was my gold signet ring with the Singleton crest, which my grandmother had left me in her will. A pawnbroker offered me five marks for it, so I walked out without replying to him.

The only person in Germany who might possibly lend me money was Ford, so I went to the Post Office and succeeded in ringing up his hotel in Assmannshausen. Luckily the manager could understand English well. I explained my situation, and he told me that Ford and Violet had just left for Bad Nauheim, but that he would take immediate steps. It was dusk. I bought some bread and ate it and then wandered round till I found a lodging house where I got a dirty bed in a filthy room for one mark. I did not undress and spent a somewhat disturbed night, owing to a drunk man next door, who talked about small sums of money for hours. He was voicing my own worries.

Next day I went to the Post Office as soon as I decently could and found a hundred marks waiting for me. How I blessed Ford! I wrote to him at once and by the same post to Constance, demanding my fare home and a pound or two over for the journey. Ford's hundred marks would last me for the

week's tour through the Black Forest which I had set my heart on.

I was alone, and I enjoyed my walk far more than if I had been with even the most charming of companions. The weather was perfect and, as I climbed up into the hills from the lovely old town of Freiburg, I decided to sleep out. The first short day took me to the neighbourhood of the Feldberg, where I slept in a forest full of ripe whortleberries, which I went on picking and eating until it was too dark to find any more. I slept soundly and happily and walked on next morning, meeting not a soul; only some large birds flitted from the top of one pine tree to the next and the morning sun shone sweetly through their trunks. After an hour or two the trees fell away and I found myself coming out on the sides of the Feldberg, covered with bilberries so thickly that before I had climbed to the top of it my shoes were full of juice.

There was nobody to be seen, not a building of any sort in sight—only ridge after ridge and, far in the south, the gleaming points of what must have been the Alps. But when I turned to the north I found the smooth hill fell away in a rocky precipice, at the foot of which was a tiny black lake. I hurried down to it in high spirits, found it surrounded by rowan trees and boulders and, taking off my clothes, plunged in naked. It was deadly cold and, when I had swum about fifty yards, I was seized with terror and swam back quickly. Who could tell what evil spirit or monster might not be hiding in that bitterly cold lake to drag me down?

Scared and breathless, I dried myself on my shirt and soon went on. That evening I came to a very pretty little lake, Titisee, a pleasant and simple holiday resort with one or two farms, a Wirtschaft, and some sailing boats for hire. I could not resist sailing for an hour or two before the sun went down, and supped and stayed the night in the Wirtschaft. Next morning I got on the road early and travelled south-east; the country was at first duller and more populated. But later I travelled over a plain with rich fertile fields, in which they had started harvesting, but to my surprise all the harvesters were women—great

deep-bosomed, brawny, red-brown creatures throwing up the sheaves of corn on to the top of the wagon drawn by four white bullocks—and further on great solid brown wenches, who stopped mowing to wave at me and laugh to each other as I passed. In the whole of that landscape there was not a man to be seen and I began to wonder into what strange country of the Amazons I had come.

When I got to the village I found the explanation. Every house had a long glazed window looking out into the street and sitting behind these windows were the men. Most of them were bald, with white and wrinkled features, nervous and short-sighted creatures, who were busy with screwdrivers and little hammers in assembling cheap alarm clocks out of bits and pieces. I wondered what the married life of these strange villagers was like.

A few miles further on the fields ended and I struck through a black pine-forest and came out into a small open valley, without a single building or human being in sight. I rushed down into it from the woods, found a stream and followed it. Suddenly the stream disappeared, falling down into a curious long rocky cleft in the limestone. There were steps down and I climbed down about fifteen feet and followed the stream between two steep and precipitous banks. Suddenly I heard voices talking and felt afraid. I was at a disadvantage at the bottom of this little canyon if the speakers were evilly disposed. The voices went on, but what they said was indistinguishable. As soon as I could find a way up the side I climbed out and looked rapidly about me. There was nobody in sight, and no spot in that open landscape in which anyone could possibly be concealed. The black pine-forest from which I had come out was half a mile behind me and the open field stretched for a mile or more in front.

It was clear that the voices must have come from people in the canyon ahead of me, and yet as I stood there I had the sensation of being watched. So I followed along the edge of the canyon looking into it. I could see nobody, and nobody could hide there unseen. I could no longer hear the voices and a

quarter of a mile further on the cleft petered out and the stream emerged to flow bubbling down the valley.

I was old enough to have some control over my imagination, but I felt uncomfortable and walked as fast as I could on my way up the road, which led over the side of the valley. It was planted with rowan trees in berry and I remembered that they had magical properties in Celtic fairy tales and legends.

As I got to the top of the hill, I heard a series of continually repeated squeals, which gradually grew louder. I laughed at my fears and forced myself to go on, but I was scared. I reached the top of the slope and saw the cause of the squeals—the ungreased axles of a farm cart drawn by two or three bullocks.

In my relief I went up to the cart, on the edge of which a man was sitting, and called out: "Guten Tag!"

But he looked straight through me with glazed eyes and realising that he was drunk I hurried on to get to the village, where I hoped to find supper and a bed. I reached it just as dusk was falling and stopped the first person I could find—a woman—and asked to be directed to the Wirtschaft. She gave a meaningless laugh, showing her gums and horrible decayed teeth. She was an idiot and as I turned from her she began to jabber meaningless words. The next inhabitant—a man—was also an idiot and so in despair I knocked at the door of a house. A dark woman opened it, but she was horribly diseased and, scarcely waiting to question her, I beat a retreat. Two or three hideous children had collected and followed me, chattering to themselves like monkeys. The place was vile and I hurried from it deciding to sleep out in the forest as soon as I had put a good distance between myself and the village of syphilitics.

For some way the road ran straight between tall and sombre pines, but already my spirits were rising, and I felt happy to have escaped. Presently a pathway into the forest tempted me, and I plunged into a young plantation of trees. It was already dark, and I could go no further. I dug a hole for my hip, ate the lump of rye bread and the piece of chocolate I had left and lay back to go to sleep.

I had scarcely closed my eyes when the most appalling caterwauling of wild cats arose near by. I had seen one of these fierce creatures being carried in by a forester, who had trapped it in the Hunsruck mountains, and knew how formidable they were. But I knew also that no wild animal in Europe will attack a sleeping man. My fears were all gone and I only wished that my eyes could pierce the darkness, so that I could see the great grey wild pussies fighting and making love. Soon I was asleep.

Next morning I rose up feeling happy, but cold and stiff and hungry, and the events of the day before seemed like a nightmare. I set out through the forest and after a mile or two came to the edge of it. A few fields away in the morning sunlight was a house built of shingles, with a verandah facing me. I walked towards it, and, as I drew near, a great white and brown St Bernard dog and a large white cat came out to meet me. I spoke to them and stroked them and they accompanied me back.

A young woman came out, gave me a smile, and I asked for some breakfast. "Are you really hungry?" she asked and laughed at the vigour with which I said I was and explained that I had slept in the forest.

A quarter of an hour later I was eating an omelette, coffee and cream, stewed whortleberries and cream, hot rolls, butter and honey, while the St Bernard and white cat sat one on each side, watching me eat. It was with difficulty that I persuaded their mistress to accept one mark after she had wrapped up some bread and sausage for me to take with me.

Everything went well for the remainder of my tour. I stopped for a day at Schlucksee to go sailing, and lost my heart to two young gnome-like children in green shorts and red caps who sailed far out into the lake together.

Next day I pushed on down the watershed of the infant Danube, reaching Donaueschingen about midnight and finding it a boiling turmoil of German artillerymen on manœuvres.

In the Wirtschaft there was scarcely standing room; tired soldiers were resting, others were drinking, others singing,

But a kind girl noticed me among the soldiers and asked what I wanted. When I said a bed, she told me I could have hers, she would not be able to get any sleep that night.

So I climbed into her truckle bed in the top attic under an oleograph of the Virgin and another of St Sebastian full of arrows. When I woke it was broad daylight; the town was empty, and the tired girl looked up from scrubbing the floor to bring me a scratch breakfast. Her face was heavy and she was not pretty, but I blew her a kiss as I went away, and she smiled and nodded.

My time was nearly up and I knew it would be wise to keep some money in reserve in case what Constance sent was insufficient. So I took the train back to Freiburg and back to England via Rotterdam. I got home with a box of Dutch cigars, which I gave to Edward who did not smoke them, and fivepence halfpenny.

X

THE first post-impressionist exhibition was held in 1910, and all our friends in Hampstead were eagerly talking about it. Maitland went and liked many of the pictures, but most of us regarded them as monstrosities or freaks painted by men without talent in order to get themselves talked about.

I went and, being completely uneducated in visual art, only liked those which resembled pictures I had seen before. For some reason the exhibition included Manet's impressionist picture of the bar with the barmaid reflected in the glass. I liked that. Then there were pictures that were easy to appreciate, Seurats and Signacs, and I genuinely liked several Gauguins in a shame-faced sort of way. But I remember fiercely denouncing the Matisses. Nellie, being a painter, simply declared that she was fascinated, that she could understand some, but had not completely understood others. But she was practically alone, among the people I met, in not taking a moral line.

For ninety-nine out of a hundred people the paintings were either shocking or not shocking. And it is interesting to know why. It was because for the mass of us the visual arts were taken for granted to be either interpretations of literature, or else comments upon the real world, which did not greatly differ in kind from the comments made by poets and writers.

When we first looked at Cézanne, Van Gogh, Gauguin and Matisse we were baffled because we were unacquainted with any literary equivalents. The more literary the paintings, the readier we were to accept them. It was just possible for me to appreciate Gauguin's Tahitians because I had read *Typee* and *Omoo*.

By October, when my first term began at the Imperial College of Science, South Kensington, the lesson I had been

trying to absorb all the summer since the failure of my attempt to rescue Savarkar had been learned and was forthwith translated into action. I went off alone and bought myself a bowler hat. I was determined to look like the most presentable of my fellow students and not to handicap myself by being eccentric in appearance, or behaviour.

In one way that bowler may be regarded as a badge of cowardice. But in another it was an act of courage for, by its purchase, I defied my parents, and though they did not say anything, I knew that they felt I was betraying them by wearing it. Edward had never worn a bowler hat in his life, and nothing would have induced him to do so.

The first-year men of the Royal College of Science and Royal School of Mines worked together. For certain social and snobbish reasons, of which I was unconscious, I fell a good deal into the company of the miners, but I was almost unknown to my fellow students until I became involved in a "rag". For some weeks London had been plastered with the face of a certain American, Dr McCara, whose vibratory Pulsocon provided a form of self-applied mechanical massage guaranteed to cure many illnesses. Dr McCara was to demonstrate the amazing properties of his machine at the Albert Hall.

This threat to their future livelihood was naturally resented by all the medical students of the London Hospitals, who suggested that the Royal College of Mines would be a handy base of operations from which to invade the Albert Hall. Secret preparations were made and I only learned of the rag shortly before the meeting, which I attended with several acquaintances in the idlest spirit of curiosity.

I got a seat in the middle of the hall. Dr McCara was at first constantly interrupted and, fairly soon, lost his temper and it looked as though the occasion would be the dull baiting of one man by many, when there was a startling interruption. A young curate suddenly rose from the stalls, climbed onto the platform and politely asked the Doctor's permission to address "these misguided young men". To my amazed delight I recognised a friend, a most popular figure at the Royal School

of Mines called Guttentag, or Gut. He was a noted poker-player and not always the soberest of youths.

I have never seen a better impersonation of an idiotic curate. His speech, in which he severely rebuked us, was listened to in exemplary silence. At its close he appealed to us, as Englishmen with an inborn love of fair play, to give Dr McCara five minutes' patient hearing. It was perfect parody.

Roars of applause followed and then we patiently allowed the Doctor to proceed for his five minutes. When, however, he produced a cripple who threw aside his crutches, a storm of catcalls broke out. An aged clergyman—possibly a Dean—got up to try to stop us. No doubt he thought that if a youthful curate could keep us quiet for four or five minutes, he would exercise an even greater influence. He was mistaken. We listened and then to his dismay we howled him down.

Suddenly a signal was given: we jumped up and rushed out of the hall, letting off intolerable stink-bombs as we did so—for the chemists had lent a hand.

Our next problem was to collect a coffin, which some bright spirit wanted to float in one of the fountains at Trafalgar Square. I do not know whose coffin it was supposed to be—whether McCara's, or merely a symbol of the medical profession in general, or of one of the London Hospitals in particular. It had been hidden in the Common Room in the New Building. But the big iron gates were unexpectedly locked. I realised at once how to open them and shouted instructions to the mob surrounding me to seize the gates and swing in rhythm and called out: "Pull—Push." In a few moments the doors gave and we got in.

Collecting the coffin, we formed a column and set off to the Chelsea Palace. I had by this time assumed a position of authority and when we reached the music-hall I slipped in and asked for fifty seats. But the police were already with us and chased me out into the street.

A march to the West End followed, in which my friend Gimson and I were in the second rank. At Dover Street the police swarmed out into Piccadilly, seized our coffin and began

to break up our procession. Gimson and I shouted orders that all were to mix in the crowd and find their way to Trafalgar Square, but a rush of policemen followed and all the leaders except myself were arrested. I dodged one policeman and was being chased by a police inspector when we were overhauled by a bus, which I boarded. For a few moments he continued the chase. The conductor was on top, and I stood on the running board, four yards from my pursuer and laughed at him as we drew away. Two hundred yards further on I rang the bell and alighted, but the fun was over and, after dropping into Gambrinus's and quenching my thirst with a couple of dark Munich beers, I went home.

I have described this evening in some detail because the part I played in the later stages of the rag made me known among my fellow-students. From that time onwards I was on friendly terms with the sporting set as well as with the serious students. It was an escape from my birthright as a rebel and a puritan. I had decided that I very definitely did not want to accept that inheritance. But it turned out not so easy to get rid of as I imagined. Indeed, two years later when another "rag" was organised at the Albert Hall, I played a traitor's part. A dock strike had been dragging on for many weeks in Dublin, and bitter passions were voiced by the dockers' leader Jim Larkin. As the strike was on the point of collapsing, he came over to England to address a mass meeting at the Albert Hall. Harold and I had decided to go to hear him when, sitting in the Students' Union, I overheard plans being laid to break up the meeting and to cut off the electric light by a raid on the switchboard in the cellars of the Albert Hall.

I wanted to hear Jim Larkin and it was obvious he had a right to put his case, so I did not hesitate, but went to the telephone and rang up an American labour sympathiser, called Gaylord Wilshire, who was in touch with Larkin. When I got hold of him, I reported the intentions of my fellow students.

At first my warning was not taken seriously, but by the time of the meeting there was a large number of stewards

inside the hall and a big body of police outside. When Harold and I tried to get in we were stopped and turned away, and we only got in because Harold caught sight of Jack Squire, then a Socialist poet, and appealed to him. Squire vouched for us to a steward at the door, and we were allowed to enter and took seats in the middle of the hall.

Jim Larkin was an Irish labourer of magnificent physique, considerably over six feet in height. Soon after he began to speak there was a noise outside, one of the doors was burst open and three Royal School of Mines students flung themselves into the hall. A dozen stewards were waiting for them. The first two men were collared, and the third was picked up off his feet by four men and thrown with a shattering noise through the glass swing door. It was one of the most brutal and imbecile actions I have seen. The other two students were marched out and, seeing the fate of their friend, made no more resistance.

On the spur of the moment Harold and I jumped up and walked out of the hall into the corridor. I had some idea of intervening and Harold, who had seen some friends in one of the boxes, was anxious to join them.

In the doorway there was splintered glass and blood, but the interrupters and stewards had vanished. Harold went to join his friends and I looked about uncertainly for a moment. Suddenly a little steward rushed at me brandishing a piece of lead piping in his hand—a weapon with which he could have split my skull with one blow. For some moments I dodged to and fro and did my best to explain that I was not trying to break up the meeting. My explanations seemed only to enrage him further and our dodging continued, as I knew it would be fatal to run. Finally he got hold of me by the sleeve and hit at me twice, giving me a nasty crack on the shoulder. Then, when it seemed this nonsense might end in my being knocked insensible, Maitland appeared from nowhere and rushed up shouting at my aggressor. I can still see the little rat, his grey face twitching with passion, facing Maitland and me. For a few moments he persisted, asking Maitland who he was. The

answer, "a doctor and a member of the Fabian Society," had no effect—but Maitland's anger had been roused by the behaviour of the stewards, and he spoke his mind. We were not free of the little man, however, until Maitland invoked the help of some well-known Socialist, who was wearing a steward's badge, and under his protection I went back into the hall.

The interruptions had roused Jim Larkin to fury. He walked up and down the platform like a caged tiger and his tremendous voice roared out angrily. Once the the sounds of fighting somewhere outside the hall penetrated, but Larkin roared a little louder, telling us of the infamies of the Dublin employers and the corruption of the city fathers. The only words of his I remember were when he spoke of Augustine Birrell.

"They've sent Mr Birrell to us, and they tell us he is a joker. But we don't want jokers in Ireland. We've had too many of them cracking jokes while the dockers and their children starve."

Larkin was the greatest orator I heard until Winston Churchill began to voice our thoughts in June 1940.

Next morning the Students' Union was full of young men with bandaged heads and others who limped. Only about half a dozen had got into the Albert Hall. The man who had been thrown through the door—a South American—was in hospital: luckily his face had not been cut. But the main battle had been between students and police outside the hall. One mounted policeman had been pulled off his horse and thrown over the parapet of the Students' Union and had fallen through a skylight, landing astride the bar below. The barmaid had promptly given him a glass of brandy. He was uninjured, but thought he had done enough and stayed where he was until the fighting was over. During the fight, a mounted inspector had taken his foot out of his stirrup and had laid the scalp of his attacker open with the spur of his boot. This was thought very badly of by the student concerned.

As I sat among my wounded friends, I wondered how they would take it if I told them I was ultimately responsible for their injuries. Though defeated, most of them had enjoyed the

fight and saw nothing to regret in it. I was, however, disgusted by the violence of both sides. I did not regret the part I had played. Jim Larkin had a right to speak and I owed no allegiance to the sporting set who had hatched the plot to break up the meeting.

But the memory of the little man, swiping up at me with his bit of lead pipe as I side-stepped him, was what made the most impression. He was such a perfect example of the spirit of evil, which revolutionists call out of the abyss with promises of Heaven upon Earth. And though I sometimes went on advocating revolution after that, I had the picture of that little man tucked away in the back of my mind.

Crosby Hall was a mediaeval building in the City, which was demolished and re-erected in Chelsea on the embankment. Shortly after it had been rebuilt, one of the Women's Suffrage Societies gave a dance in it. To my astonishment I received a card inviting me to attend with a party of young people, all of whom were to be dressed as *Nègres Enflammés*. The dress would cost about two guineas and the invitation was signed with the names—unknown to me at that time—of James and Marjorie Strachey.

I had not got two guineas. However, thanks to Maitland's persuasions, I went to the dance dressed, not as a *Nègre Enflammé*, but as a Rajput prince, wearing a pair of white cotton jodhpurs, a white tunic with a cummerbund of gold and a turban of purple silk with a narrow border of gold thread, which I had borrowed from a Rajput Kumar of my acquaintance.

Once in the great fifteenth-century hall, open up to the roof, and looking about with trepidation, I caught sight of many familiar figures. In my state of mind they were like lifebelts in a stormy ocean. But I could not cling to them; I had to swim by my own efforts.

Brynhild came by flashing a bewitching smile, and Maitland departed in her wake. The Oliviers were there, Godwin Baynes, the Thorneycrofts—and then I noticed a strange, tall

figure, made taller still by the very tall hat of a Persian Magus and long oriental robes. Altogether he, with his hat, must have been nearly seven feet high. He had hollow lantern jaws and a slightly bewildered air of astonished amusement. I went up to him at once and hailed him with delight, without the shyness I felt for more ordinary persons. It was Adrian Stephen, whom I had met once before and knew from the first moment of meeting that we were friends.

Adrian had extraordinarily innocent eyes: he looked through them at the passing scene like the child in Hans Andersen's story of the Emperor's New Clothes—as though he could not believe what they saw. Then, aware of the inadequacy of words, he caught one's eye and either made a most horrific comic grimace, or laughed.

Near Adrian stood his sister Virginia, tall, slim, with flowing draperies and long hair—a striking beauty, mysterious and lovely. Then, suddenly, she precipitated herself across the floor to greet a female friend.

I was still standing near Adrian, engaged in desultory conversation with him, when James and Marjorie Strachey suddenly appeared and danced a *pas-de-deux* down the centre of the hall. They were, alas, the only specimens of the much-heralded *Nègres Enflammés*.

James's dress was based on Bakst's design for the negro slave danced by Nijinsky in the ballet of *Scheherazade*. That is to say, he was chiefly grease-paint from the hips upwards, but wore full Turkish trousers of blue gauze or butter-muslin, cut low enough at the waist to reveal his navel. On his head was a black astrakhan wig, and round his neck a big gold or silver-gilt necklace in the form of a cobra with jewelled eyes.

Marjorie's dress was more modest, but scarcely less striking. Together they were certainly the most startling pair in the hall, not because of their dresses, but because of a serious, almost religious intensity in both of them which was lacking in everyone else. Adrian and Virginia were at least as striking a pair, but they were content to be disinterested observers of strange customs.

James and Marjorie, on the other hand, were inspired by a mysterious sense of duty, they felt that they represented something in which they passionately believed. The temple servants of an unknown religion, they came bounding down the centre of the floor, to end up breathless but secretly jubilant. I was thrilled, but had no idea what it was all about. Nor had anyone else. Yet it was a part of what we were all doing: breaking the fetters of convention which had held our parents' generation prisoners.

At large dances the advantages of being one of a big family is immense. Its members can gossip with each other until outside contacts are made, or shyness has worn off. The only child, on the other hand, walks awkwardly across the slippery floor, simply because he is too embarrassed to stand still any longer, but half-way across the waxed expanse he realises there is nobody on the other side whom he can go up and talk to. He is at the mercy, also, of hostesses who lead him up and introduce him to the wrong lonely maidens.

Everywhere I looked in Crosby Hall, there were groups of people I knew, but my old friends had their own partners and their own budding romances and not one of the girls I knew wanted to have me treading on her toes all the evening.

However, I managed to inveigle some of them and, after about half a dozen dances, was passed on to a very shy young woman with widely spaced brown eyes, dark hair and a rather dark skin, and we danced together awkwardly. After a bit we sat out, watched the others and talked uneasily, chiefly about Russia. I was strongly attracted to her. She was with a large party of brothers and sisters, who were linked up with Stracheys and Ricardos and with my friend Dominic Spring Rice. He was, indeed, their cousin, though I did not know it. It was ten years before I met this young woman again and married her. She was Ray Marshall.

There was always a pleasure in going to see the Hobsons; always a pleasure if Harold's father were present. J. A. Hobson

208

was a taste which grew with the years, as one learnt to understand his character.

He was tall and very thin, with a moustache sprouting at odd angles, dark eyes behind glasses and nervous twitches, shakings and mannerisms. He was an economist with a brilliantly original mind, who had, in the opinion of the orthodox, "done for himself" by propounding what they referred to as "Hobson's fallacy", but which turned out later on to be a point of departure for Keynesian economics.

Of all this I knew and understood nothing. For me the pleasure of J. A. Hobson's company was in his sense of humour, which was unique and expressed not only in his remarks, but in his facial play, semi-stammers, and a curious chortle in his throat which sounded like the noise when one pulls the plug and the cistern is empty.

He was brilliant in his comment and humour on every subject, but an unfailing stand-by was his wife. When Mrs Hobson came out strong, as she often did, with some platitude, a glint would appear in J. A. Hobson's eye, his face would begin to twitch like a horse's skin when it unseats flies, and a premonitory gurgle would sound, followed very often by silence, sometimes by a devastatingly innocent remark.

Hobson was a man with intensely strong feelings of political honour; he cared more for honesty and decency in public life than for anything, and he had naturally become cynical. He was a Liberal of the *Manchester Guardian* school; the Boer War outraged him; he took it almost personally; and the steady corruption of the Liberal Party in power, and the ascendancy of Lloyd George, completed his disillusion.

One day I went with Noel and some of her sisters to a tea-party given by Mrs Hobson at Elmstead—a house which looked out upon a corner of the golf-course on Limpsfield Common from under the branches of spreading elms. There was a croquet lawn in front and a tennis lawn behind. These two lawns were for me the choice between Scylla and Charybdis. On the one hand I couldn't play tennis and Harold and Ted Scott—a son of the editor of the *Manchester Guardian*,

who married Harold's sister Mabel—were both good and relentless players. On the other hand, Mrs Hobson was a croquet-addict and, like all players of the game I've ever met, was liable to lose her temper if she happened to make two or three bad strokes, or whenever anyone else made two or three good ones.

She was a firmly-corseted, powdered American lady, affecting the Pompadour style, or the Marquise disguised as a Dresden Shepherdess, with very clear brown eyes and very regular features. She must have been a most beautiful girl.

It was bad luck to be her partner in a game of croquet, because she did not like it if one played badly and liked it still less if one played better than she did. Luckily there was little risk of that with me.

We would play carefully and all would go well for a bit and then either Harold or his father would get in form and start knocking her balls about, and this would go on and on, with Mrs Hobson becoming stiffer and stiffer all the time. Neither of them would take the slightest notice of the danger signals; or if they did notice them, they rejoiced at the opportunity of getting a bit of their own back.

Suddenly Mrs Hobson's eyes would blaze and she would literally and figuratively *fly off the handle*, flinging her mallet away and marching off to her boudoir and the game would be broken up in a manner embarrassing for the visiting hobbledehoy.

On this occasion, after tea was over, croquet followed and Daphne Olivier committed the unforgivable sin of playing well. An explosion shortly afterwards took place and Mrs Hobson marched off the field. Embarrassed, yet thankful for small mercies, we visitors trooped round to the other lawn and interrupted Teddy's and Harold's set of singles and made them play doubles. Noel and I were busy retrieving the balls for our betters out of the vegetable garden and the herbaceous borders, when suddenly two strange figures marched round the corner of the house and interrupted the game. One of them was Adrian Stephen, the other a dark young man, who gave

the impression of being slightly made, though he was really five foot ten and well-proportioned. He had very clear grey-blue eyes and a beautiful expressive mouth and held himself with unconscious pride.

> Here come the Grants o' Rothiemurchus
> Ilka ane as proud as a Turk is

Sir Walter Scott's lines are doggerel, but they are true.

The proud young man's name was Duncan Grant. It turned out that Adrian and he had come down to see Noel, had called at The Champions and that Lady Olivier had sent them on.

Mrs Hobson, who was probably still fuming over the game of croquet, was inquisitive at the invasion and marched out to intercept them. Duncan saw her coming and turned aside to greet her—with hesitation and shyness I have no doubt—but in three sentences his perfect manners had her tamed.

The Oliviers, however, were already taking leave, and I went with them and their remarkable visitors. As we walked back toward The Champions, I should have liked to have mono-polised Adrian, but Duncan took me off his hands, knowing that he wanted to talk to Noel. But with the proud figure I was shy and I found little to talk about.

Adrian Stephen and Duncan Grant were among the heroes of the *Dreadnought* hoax and Virginia Stephen was its heroine. With Adrian's friends, Horace Cole and Anthony Buxton, they had descended upon the flagship of the Channel Fleet, with Virginia dressed as a Prince of Abyssinia and Duncan as an Ethiopian Court attendant and the unfortunate Admiral May had shown them all over the battleship. Adrian published a short account of the details of that amusing episode many years later and I only refer to it here because in my eyes it shed glory upon Adrian, when I got to know him first. But if Adrian liked me, as he obviously did, it was certainly not because I looked upon him as a heroic figure.

He liked me, I think, only partly because I was sincere and simple and because he was very tolerant of such half-baked

creatures. There was something else: an instant recognition of an affinity. We were warm friends at sight.

Love revealed itself suddenly, desperately, in the early spring of 1911 in an imagined passion for a distant object. I had corresponded with Ursula ever since her visit to The Champions with Lenotchka. But Ursula had gone to Moscow and a few words I heard dropped by Natasha coupling Ursula's name with that of Kirik Levin (the baby Alexandr Ivanitch had found in the snow) aroused a sudden passion of jealousy.

One night the devil of jealous love drove me out onto Hampstead Heath. It was bitterly cold, and I rushed up and down blindly to keep warm. Next morning I suddenly said to Constance: "I want to go to Moscow, to see Ursula."

"Certainly; you could go out at Easter," said Constance, as though it were the most natural thing in the world. She would be able to find the money somehow and the object of money was to enable you to do the things you really wanted to do.

Edward took the same line; from dreadful despair I was transformed into eager preparation. Edward would lend me his heavy ulster, which ought to be warm enough for Russia in the spring. I wrote to say I was coming; Ursula and her mother were sharing a large flat with the Ertels; there was a spare room and they would be able to put me up.

The last week or two rushed by in preparation. Then I set off, via Harwich and Flushing and found myself sitting early next morning in the express train rushing eastwards across Germany: first stop, Hanover: next stop, Berlin.

Looking out of the window I was drunk with excitement. Only one thought pulled me up short—the thought of meeting Ursula, for whom my passion of love, jealousy and misery had evaporated.

But I dismissed my fears with the reflection that when I saw her my intense and dreadful feelings would return. Of course they would. They must. Otherwise I should be spending Constance's hard-won savings on a joy-ride, obtained on false pretences. But my thoughts shied away from the pros-

pect of meeting Ursula, and I was glad the journey was a long one.

In Westphalia, I could see storks striding about the wet fields, but everything after Berlin was shrouded in darkness, and, when I awoke next morning, it was to find we were already on the frontiers of Russian Poland, at Thorn. We descended at the frontier, passed the customs and took our places in a broad-gauge Russian train.

A whole day went by, broken only by arrival at Warsaw and a drive across the town. Next morning we were in Smolensk and the sun shone brightly over the snow. The scene as we came into Moscow through patches of birch-forest, in brilliant sunshine, was like fairyland. The golden sunlight poured down onto the unspotted snow; the white-trunked trees threw blue shadows; through them I caught a sudden glimpse of golden cupolas and the ancient palaces of the Kremlin.

A few minutes later Ursula was rushing up to me, giving me a kiss, grabbing some of my luggage. With what red cheeks, what merry eyes, what shouts of laughter we left the station; and with what sharp practicality she shouted "Otstai!"—that is, "get out!"—at a beggar and bargained quickly with the row of waiting isvostchiks! Then we were rattling down the cobbled streets of Moscow. The snow had melted a week before and the snowstorm in the west had not touched Moscow.

Nothing could have been more delightful than my reception in Moscow. Ursula was delighted to see me, was as merry and as kind as always, and had determined to show me everything in Moscow. Plans for going to the Opera at the Big Theatre and to plays at the Artistic Theatre were discussed over dinner at Yar—the smartest restaurant—after which we sat and drank in the American bar, where there were extraordinary drinks on the list. I remember a Cobbler Count Tolstoy.

Nevertheless, I went to bed that night feeling awkward and uneasy. I had said nothing to Ursula about my passion, or the reason for my visit. I was embarrassed by the presence of

Ursula's mother, who undoubtedly knew all about it and I felt slightly ill at ease with the Ertels.

The next day was too delightful and exciting to worry about the matter and I spent the morning going all over the Kremlin, looking at the little rooms dating from the time of Ivan the Terrible, which are inlaid with different kinds of wood; then going through the saloons built by Alexander I after the Napoleonic wars; then looking at a fresco of Jonah and the Whale painted by a Russian who had never seen the sea or a ship, let alone a whale; then climbing up the belfry, Ivan Veliki, in which the Great Bell of Moscow was to have been hung—only it fell down and was broken.

When we got back I was introduced to a rather serious young Scottish soldier who had come to Moscow to learn Russian. Army Officers in India got extra pay if they knew Russian. His name was Archibald Wavell and I took an instant liking to him. He had acquired a considerable reputation among the Russians. What astonished them was his energy: he was as keen at learning Russian as he was on the ice-hill tobogganing. But it was not his energy alone that astonished them; it was that any young man with that amount of energy should be happy to be a professional soldier and conventional enough to accept the world as he found it. In Russia any young man with as much energy could only have been a Revolutionist. No other occupation would have offered an outlet for it.

On the evening of my third day in Moscow I was no further advanced with Ursula. Indeed, the reality of our friendship was fatally destroying my dream of being in love with her. She had accepted an invitation to a party that evening and I went with her as far as the door. Then, feeling suddenly that I must at all costs bring matters to a head, I went back some hours later, wrapped in Edward's ulster, to meet her on her way home. Winter had suddenly come back: it was snowing and bitter cold. I walked up and down the street, the snow freezing on my coat and hat. An hour went by and in that icy air, with the snow freezing everywhere it settled, a strange exaltation overcame me.

214

At last the door opened, a light showed: a figure came out: it was not Ursula. A moment or two later the door opened again, and this time I recognised the burly little figure hurrying towards me. I moved stiffly towards her, half-frozen; she looked at me astonished and recognised me.

Then, in my exalted mood, I spoke freely and easily: telling her, without shyness, how I had been thinking of her all the winter; how I had come to Moscow because I was in love with her. She did not interrupt or try in any way to stop me, nor did she seem either annoyed or embarrassed.

When we got back about midnight into the Ertels' flat I was so stiff with cold that I could not take my coat off without her help, and my coat was frozen. Ursula told me she was not in love with me, kissed me, gave me a hot drink and talked to me while I thawed. She was so tender to me, so full of kindness, that when I went into my room after a kiss, I was happy enough and went to sleep with a feeling that a load which had been weighing on me was discharged. At all events the subject could be postponed till a later date without dishonour. Meanwhile, I was free to enjoy Moscow for another ten days.

A rich woman friend of Ursula's had a plan of taking a house for the summer in the country, within easy reach of the city— a house in which she could entertain her young friends. She answered advertisements and made looking over houses an excuse for a series of all-day picnics in the country. So on Sunday morning when the pious were going to church, Ursula and I hurried off to the railway station, Ursula dressed in sweater and breeches and top boots. Her friend was a pleasant woman of about thirty—and half a dozen young people were her other guests. Among them I was at once struck by a tiny, slender girl wearing white breeches and white Valenki (felt top-boots). Her name was Lidia Arbatskaya, and she belonged to an old Moscow family. She was obviously sought out by two or three young men and I felt inclined to follow their example. She was so attractive a midget in her cream-coloured skiing-dress and white felt boots that she had all the glamour of the circus.

Directly we got out of the train we found ourselves in deep snow: a couple of sledges were waiting for us and, after putting the large hamper which our hostess had provided into one of them, we set off to drive a short distance to a large wooden house standing at the end of an avenue of lime-trees.

After we were let in, we began running from room to room. Most of them were empty; the windows were sealed up; the noise of laughing, frivolous young people filled the long deserted saloons and corridors, but our hostess was plunged in difficulties. Who would have which room? Where should she put her pianola? We were hungry and she broke off discussing her problems to tell the caretaker to light the samovar. Then, postponing all decisions, we went outside to explore the park and came back to picnic on the snow and eat our lunch in the warm sunlight.

Picnic indeed! There was grey caviare, red caviare, little pies, eggs and mayonnaise, roast fowl, roast turkey, fruit pies, sweetmeats, gruyère cheese, Crimean wine, kvass, port, and Russian tea. The experience of sitting on a field of hard, dry, frozen snow in really hot sunshine was astonishing. I managed to sit between Ursula and Lidia and have seldom enjoyed a picnic more.

By the time we had finished lunch and had rambled over the park and gone into the adjacent village, our hostess had come to the conclusion that the house would not suit her; she had an order to view another, which she suggested that we should inspect in a week's time. The verdict was warmly applauded; no one regretted the great empty mansion with its yellow corridors of varnished pine, and we climbed gaily into the sledges and drove back to the railway station. Before we parted, Lidia asked me to tea next day.

The Arbatskys' house was a large rambling structure built round a courtyard. I rang the bell and was inspected with disapproval by the butler; my request to see Lidia apparently astonished him. I was left waiting for some time, during which I was able to examine the solid old-fashioned furniture, which had obviously been made by a Russian carpenter, the inlaid

wood floor, the dark passages leading away from the hall and the birchwood staircase rising up. Finally I was taken to Lidia's sitting-room and found her looking very different, demurely dressed in a quakerish grey frock and rather shy.

One day Lidia came to visit me in my room at the Ertels'. She had a passion for all physical sports and gymnastics, and when I happened to tell her about Giblin's Japanese exponents of ju-juitsu, she insisted on my showing her the falls I knew.

Only one occupation could have been more agreeable, and we were lying on the floor, locked in a most complicated position, when the door was suddenly opened and Ursula's mother stood staring at us with an expression of horror.

I was angry with the wretched woman, who must, I think, have either been listening at the door or looking through the keyhole. She retired unconvinced by our explanation and of course Ursula regarded it as a huge joke, retailed it with embellishments to Archibald Wavell at the dinner-table, and no doubt repeated it to all Lidia's friends in Moscow.

Both Lidia and I felt rather ill-used. If only Mrs Cox had not burst in unannounced, we could have gone on wrestling and perhaps something else might have come of it.

A week slipped away quickly, with an expedition to the Sparrow Hills, where Napoleon caught the first sight of Moscow, an evening at the Artistic Theatre, and another at the opera in the gigantic Big Theatre. The Artistic Theatre was one of the first theatres to be decorated with plain wood and no gilding or paint. The seats were extremely comfortable and on the drop curtain there was a single symbolic seagull with spread wings. For not only had the Artistic Theatre under Stanislavsky made Tchehov's reputation as a dramatist—but the great success of Tchehov's *The Seagull* had made the reputation of the Artistic Theatre and of Stanislavsky. How I wish that when that curtain went up it had been upon *The Seagull*. But the play I saw that night was, alas, not Tchehov. It had indeed been specially chosen by Lenotchka and Ursula, as more likely to be appreciated by me than *Uncle Vanya*. It was Maeterlinck's *The Blue Bird* and, although I understood it

almost perfectly, for it was largely mimed, and though I might not have understood much of *Uncle Vanya*, it was a wretched piece of sentimentality. It was admirably produced, but later I realised that the consideration of those kind girls had cost me an experience to set beside my memory of Eleanora Duse.

There was one more week-end picnic party, but on this occasion the snow was melting and there were violent rushing streams pouring down every ditch. The sun was hot; the earth was everywhere like a piebald horse's hide; a fresh smell and the sound of rushing water filled the air. It would have been impossible to sit out of doors, and we ate our luncheon in a large empty conservatory, looking out over the sodden steaming garden. That day I learned the literal meaning of Turgenev's title to one of his best stories: *The Torrents of Spring*.

The food was as delicious as before and the company as delightful. But Ursula had maliciously spread the story of the ju-juitsu lesson and Lidia was a little shy of talking too much to me.

Although I had left England on Good Friday, it was Good Friday in Moscow a fortnight later—for Russia in those days persisted in the use of the unreformed calendar and the date was thirteen days earlier than it was in England. Thus the Russian Easter broke upon me just before I was due to return home, and on the night of Easter Sunday I accompanied Ursula and the Ertels to a service in the great white-and-gold Moscow Cathedral. Before we set out, the flame burning in front of the one icon in the Ertels' flat was extinguished, and each of us was supplied with an empty jam-pot and a taper. When one first entered the Cathedral it seemed to be almost in pitch darkness, for it was lighted only by the candles on the altar—a golden bank of little starry flames.

Once inside, Ursula led me to the top of a twisting stair where, from a balcony, we could look down upon the whole body of the nave. It was not easy to get there, as, in the obscurity, sandwiched between large numbers of human

bodies, movement was difficult and slow and it was sometimes impossible to tell where one was.

Ursula, however, found the way and pushing me before her or pulling me after, mounted the stairs and secured the position she wanted. From our eyrie, we could look down on the dim crowd in the obscurity of the nave and choir and, only when we looked at the altar, could we discern the individual figures of officiating priests.

The choir sang in two halves: a boy's shrill voice mounted higher and higher and then the grim response of the bass singers grumbled out in the unknown, hieratic tongue of Old Slavonic. Ursula told me that the service was partly concerned with a conversation between the penitent and the unpenitent thief.

After every response, the priest blew out several candles— at first batches were extinguished, then they were put out more slowly, one by one. I had thought the darkness absolute when I entered, but I soon learned to see by the light of the distant altar. Now this was being extinguished and there was no light by which one could see. Only one tiny taper glimmered feebly in the far distance, its flame rising and falling on the altar. And the groans of the service became terrifying.

For what seemed a long while, the service continued with confessions of sin. But, after one of these spasms, the priest unexpectedly lit a second candle—then a third. The whole tone of the service changed and, after a while, the altar glowed again and if one strained one's eyes, the outline of one's neighbour became perceptible. Then, suddenly, I noticed that a spark from the altar had strayed to one of the congregation kneeling on the altar steps.

Another flickered into existence and another and another. And then, like flickering fireflies, all the tapers with which the vast congregation had provided itself were kindled from one to another and the lights travelled slowly down the nave. Slowly we watched, in a light which grew as bright as daylight, the tapers kindling each other until at last the flame came winding up the stair to reach us. Then our tapers were lighted

in their turn. The vast Cathedral was ablaze. But the congregation was already departing and soon the nave was half-empty; the service was over and a *sauve qui peut* followed, for it was considered lucky for one member of each family to be able to return with his taper still alight in order to rekindle the light which, except on that one evening of atonement, burned all through the year in front of the icon.

When we were at last able to descend, carefully shielding our tapers under their jam-jars, there were hundreds of little lights dispersing through the great square. This piece of ritual seemed to me one of the prettiest symbols of human brotherhood. Nothing could have been lovelier than seeing near at hand the grave face of some young worshipper, lit by his taper; next to him, perhaps, an old woman shielding her little flame; and the lights flickering, failing, twinkling, as they were carried through every street and into every house, in the ancient city.

I was lucky: my taper burned steadily, and when I went to sleep it was with the satisfying knowledge that I had carried the flame which had relit the only icon there was in the flat, among whose inhabitants there were not very many orthodox believers.

And that is my last impression of Moscow, for I left early next morning. Ursula gave me a warm kiss and, in a whirlwind of mixed emotions, I waved back. Lidia had given me an immense casket of chocolate truffles and an inscribed photograph of herself. Gazing at the fresh young features I felt very miserable—and put another truffle into my mouth to help stop my heart-ache. But I knew I could not ask for another ticket to Moscow, however much my emotions crystallised about the image of Lidia.

Early in the summer, I paid a visit to Grantchester and then went on, with Rupert, for a week's sailing-trip on the Broads. Our party consisted of Dr Rogers as chaperone, the four Oliviers and one or two others. Dr Rogers was an old friend of my parents and the Olivier family. He was a very large man and extremely gullible, particularly on subjects such as hypno-

tism, but our holiday was not marred by any practical jokes at his expense.

On one occasion Godwin had been the ringleader of a band of undergraduates who all pretended to be hypnotised at once. Dr Rogers had been frightened by discovering that the hypnotic state was sometimes infectious. He told me also that he had found out that Godwin was an extremely unstable character as a result of hypnotising him. I thought this was comic, when he said it, but afterwards came to agree with Dr Rogers's diagnosis.

In those days the broads were practically deserted and no motor-boat nor power-driven cruiser disturbed their placid waters. One large sail provided the motive power of our wherry, but when we came to a reach, where the wind was contrary, the sail was lowered and a patient horse appeared with a boy sitting sideways on its back. The horse was hitched to a tow-rope, and we proceeded slowly on our way. When we got a fair wind the sail was hoisted, we forged ahead and the boy and horse were left behind. As our course was sinuous, they were often able to leave the tow-path and follow a road which went straight to the point where we should want them next.

Life on board was peaceful. We swam in the mornings and then lay on deck and talked while Rupert sat forward, propped against the mast, rewriting his thesis on *John Webster and the Elizabethan Drama* for which he was given a fellowship. Unfortunately, though I had read some Restoration drama, I had not at that time read any Elizabethan dramatist except Shakespeare, so when Rupert read some chapters aloud they did not mean very much to me.

We had a sailing dinghy in tow and, if the breeze tempted us, some of us would go off for a sail. In the evenings the wherry was moored to the bank and the couple of paid hands who navigated it departed to the nearest pub. The day ended with a swim in the darkness and then, with the girls' goodnights ringing in our ears, Rupert and I retired to the cabin which we shared. The sound of their gossiping and their laughter often went on and served as a stimulus for our dreams.

221

I was very happy and was aware that for some reason Rupert liked me. That holiday was the time of my closest friendship with him. His immense charm and intelligence had not yet been spoilt by success and by certain *idées fixes*, which later came to resemble hallucinations. With me, in our midnight cabin talks, he was simple, sincere and intimate, with a certain lazy warmth. It was only later that he was apt to utter warnings about the wickedness of other people.

In the cloudless hot days which followed during that summer, Harold and I got into the habit of sleeping out in the woods behind the Cearne, under a great Scot's pine tree which had two branches, like the arms of a candelabrum. Every evening we unrolled our sleeping-bags and crept into them, making sure of finding our hip-holes scraped deep into the pine-needles and humus. Often we talked late; sometimes we drank whisky with hot water and lemon. In the mornings we slept late until the sun was high. During the day we bicycled to Edenbridge to bathe in a pool where the weeds and water-lilies had been cut away.

Almost the first night that we slept out Harold told me that his father thought we might be at war with Germany next day. We imagined the war as a purely naval one, and it did not occur to us that it might affect either of us personally. It was the Agadir crisis. In two or three days the excitement was over and the likelihood of war forgotten.

Harold was my constant companion during that wonderful hot summer. He was studying engineering at King's College, Strand, living at home with his parents in Hampstead and afterwards in lodgings. He had grown tall, was thin and muscular and full of nervous energy, for which he could never find sufficient outlet. His mood was always impatient, often exasperated. When he gave himself time to reflect, his conclusions were raw and bitter. He was intolerant of hypocrisy and saw almost all human institutions, civilised behaviour and culture, as manifestations of triumphant hypocrisy. Had he read Voltaire's *L'Ingénu* he would have recognised himself in

the Huron hero. All the hypocrisies he detested were personified for him in his mother and there was a good deal of truth
in his unfilial judgments of her.

He seemed to believe that the whole social structure, with
its pretences and proprieties, was the work of parasitic women
intent on thwarting the natural instincts of men, whom they
exploited and enslaved. This crude philosophy is American;
its finest exposition is to be found in Van Wyck Brookes's
analysis of Mark Twain, who was, all his life, a rebel against
female apron-strings and for whom culture was personified
in a hateful school-marm. Like Mark Twain, Harold took a
childish pleasure in indecent stories, because they were asser-
tions of male freedom.

Harold was in too much of a hurry to be able to find out what
might underlie the hypocritical tributes to culture he heard expressed in his mother's drawing-room. Only when he discovered
some art for himself could he appreciate it. Thus he had a love
of the memorial brasses to be found in village churches, and in
previous years, I had bicycled long distances with him from
church to church, making rubbings of them with black cobbler's
wax on rolls of white wallpaper. One evening, when we were
sleeping out, he began reading Byron and was delighted with
the philosophy of Don Juan. Usually, he regarded poetry
with strong dislike. The intensity of his hatreds made him
curiously blind to his future. Women were already beginning
to look at him and speak of him as very handsome, but it did
not occur to him that this might lead to his modifying his
opinion of them. Nor did he expect worldly success. Once, he
told me that he never expected to make more than six hundred
a year. I replied that he was talking nonsense and prophesied
he would make two or three times that amount.

We were not always alone under our pine tree. Maitland
came down several times; Godwin one week-end, and, on the
latter occasion, Rupert Brooke and a silent Cambridge don
were brought along by the Oliviers. The girls were not sleeping out, but they sat and talked, and then Rupert told us the
story of the Machine Messiah.

Before Mrs Eddy founded the religion called Christian Science, there was much excitement about animal magnetism in the United States. It was believed to be the source of God's power, the force behind all miracles. If only enough animal magnetism could be generated in one place, man could either scale Heaven, or make Heaven upon earth.

Suddenly a woman (whose name I can't remember, but I will call her Alice), one of the Elect, had a vision in which an angel of the Lord came to her and announced that he had brought her instructions on how to build a machine. Just as the dynamo will generate electrical power, so this machine would generate spiritual power.

And after saying that when she had made arrangements with engineers to carry out the work, he would return and reveal to her the detailed instructions, the angel disappeared. Alice told the story of her vision and it created immense excitement.

Finally, an engineer in a town on a hill overlooking the Missouri River offered his help; some thousands of the faithful invaded the town, and every night Alice was visited by the angel and awoke with instructions about a new crankshaft, flywheel or connecting-rod.

Before her visions Alice had been totally ignorant of engineering and it was astonishing with what precision she specified nuts, bolts and rocker-cams. The machine was a large one and, although all the parts were listed by the angel, no instructions were vouchsafed on how to put them together. Soon the engineers abandoned the problem and then the faithful began to build it themselves and progress was more rapid.

The day came when Alice declared that the machine was complete. It was about as big as a threshing machine and unlike anything ever seen before. The news of its completion roused immense enthusiasm and thousands of believers assembled to see the machine work. But Alice now had a new revelation: the machine did not *produce* spiritual force; it merely harnessed and multiplied the force of prayer and, to set it in motion, intense prayer was needed.

So they prayed. Nothing happened. Then Alice, who was a

resourceful woman, said that animal magnetism was like gravity, strongest at the centre of the earth and the machine should not have been built on a hill. So, with great difficulty, it was taken out of the town where it had been built and down the hill to where a low bluff overhung the Missouri River.

And there, with thousands camping around it in the fields and trampling down the crops, the great test was made and, with Alice leading them, they prayed. And, in the blinding sunlight and the clouds of dust, amid the chanting of multitudes, the Machine Messiah was seen to tremble and for a moment the flywheels spun . . .

In their astonishment, some doubting spirits must have relaxed, for a second later, they saw it standing idle and motionless again. After that nothing would make it move and, after a month or two, the crowds diminished and the weaker vessels drifted away. Then, one night, the local baptists who had banded themselves together, outraged at the impiety of the proceedings and at the trampling down of their cornfields, suddenly rushed the camp and with crowbars and rollers lifted the strange God and hurled it over the bluff into the waters of the Missouri. Alice never got a second chance as a religious leader, for by the time she had recovered from the disaster, Mary Baker Eddy was in the field.

When Rupert had told us this story, we walked back to The Champions with the girls and then came back and lay down to sleep under the pines. There was not a breath of dew that night. In the morning we were woken up early by the sound of ecstatic cries and, peering out of our sleeping-bags, we beheld Rupert's friend, the Cambridge don, rushing naked about the woodland glades, flagellating his limbs with a bunch of bracken. I learned afterwards that he had gone off later that morning, had proposed marriage and had been accepted.

This was the only visitation of Pan among the Cambridge dons of those days which I actually witnessed, but it serves to show how true to life are the novels of E. M. Forster. The only doubt which has crossed my mind is the question: did Pan

visit the dons before they read Forster, or only after they had read him?

Later that summer, a friend called Mrs Anthonius came to stay at the Cearne. I had not seen her for several years and, in the interval, she had made an unhappy marriage. She had huge dark eyes which seemed to grow bigger as she responded to my father's teasing, or when my uncle Arthur made her the object of one of his crushing sarcasms, which were quite incapable of crushing her, for she was full of spirit. Her presence added, therefore, a good deal of liveliness to the party and she was a good foil to Arthur, who was on his usual footing of comradeship, free from any sentiment, which he achieved with almost all women. Women, I think, liked him all the better because they could not entangle him, or get their claws into him.

By nature, she was free and bold and never hung back in conversation. Unfortunately, she was conscious of being ill-used by her husband, from whom she had escaped, and of whom she was afraid, and by her family, who were not very sympathetic with her in her troubles. She was, therefore, glad to come to stay for some time at the Cearne.

One day, we ran out of milk and I was despatched to fetch some from a farm half-way down Crockham Hill. I hung the can on my handlebar and went flying off. At the bottom of the hill at Kent Hatch, the can caught between the frame of the bicycle and the handlebar, locking the steering, and I went smash on to the road, cracked an elbow and sprained a wrist.

A couple of days later my arm was giving me great pain and so Mrs Anthonius kindly offered to massage it. On the hot summer afternoons, we would retire to my little bedroom. I was scantily dressed in a pair of white cotton trousers and half a shirt. My bandages were loosened and Mrs Anthonius would lean over my body and, with great skill, give me vibratory massage. It was the right treatment, for the elbow was cracked —and very soon pain was pleasure—and pleasure pain, and very soon I was distracted by overwhelming feelings elsewhere.

Mrs Anthonius was cool and brown and was healing one inflammation only to kindle another. I could not speak and remember feeling great embarrassment as my condition became obvious and I could not hide it.

Later, we went to pick blackberries together and she suggested we should lie down. She lay near me, touching me, and my embarrassment returned. But this time she encouraged me to speak and told me that I could become her lover. She was obviously pleased, but she did not kiss me and made no effort to show a tenderness which she did not feel.

The liaison, thus begun, did not last more than a few months because, after a little while, I felt myself in a false position. I was not in love with Mrs Anthonius and she was too honest to pretend more than she felt for me. I broke off the relationship instead of allowing it to drag on unsatisfyingly. It taught me something about physical love, but the lesson that a liaison is not satisfactory for more than a few weeks, unless one is in love, was not in the least what I had expected, or what I wanted to know at nineteen.

XI

IN July 1911, I passed the end of the year's examinations with ease and, in the paper on Mathematics and Mechanics, I came out second in the first class. When the results were put up I looked through the list of those in the second class and thought I had failed, until a friend, standing beside me, pointed out my name above.

I think the hot weather may have had something to do with it; my brain functions better on hot days. During the examination week I only ate a sandwich or two for lunch and drank tumblers of Vermouth and soda, with the result that I was cool and confident, when other students were hot and flustered.

During the year following, when I began to specialise in Biology, I got to know a demonstrator in the Zoological Department called H. G. Newth. He remained my closest friend for the rest of the time that I was at the Royal College of Science.

Newth was a small, long-headed, dark man of the Mediterranean type, with reddish-hazel eyes and a white skin with a great many little brown moles on it. He had a considerable sense of humour and, by the time I knew him, his opinions were already completely formed and did not afterwards change. He had a passion for Schumann's music, which he knew extremely well. In literature, he had a devotion to Samuel Butler and took Butler's views on evolution seriously.

Newth was a powerful influence in my development as a science student: he was intelligent, unworldly, heretical. For several terms he and I used to have lunch together, with one or two research students from the Zoology Department, in the Huxley Museum, where we were surrounded by wax models of foetuses and hundreds of specimens preserved in jars of alcohol. In the season we often ate Cornish oysters, which we

bought wholesale at ten shillings a hundred. The rest of the meal was bread and cheese, apples and coffee.

My friendship with Newth was followed, a year later, by a friendship with H. Takeda, a Japanese research student, who was the demonstrator in the advanced course on the morphology of gymnosperms.

Takeda was very tall for a Japanese, being nearly six foot in height. He had a very clear mind, with a strong dislike of dogmatic theorising and great technical skill. In one way he was unlike other scientists I have known. Whereas Occidentals study science because in the last resort they have a passion for knowledge, it seemed to me that Takeda had become a botanist because he loved the living plants themselves.

Both he and Newth sometimes came down to the Cearne for week-ends. Newth and Edward took an immediate liking to each other and Newth greatly enjoyed Edward's ironical turn of mind.

Takeda and Constance made friends over her garden and he gave her many seeds of wildflowers, which he had collected in the mountains of Japan. One of these was a most delicate blue primrose, which he had discovered, and which was named after him, and this very rare little plant grew and flowered at the Cearne for two or three years after Takeda had gone back to Japan. There were also beautiful wild pinks, which flourished for many years.

These two friendships with older, more experienced biologists, were of great help to me in my work and gave me a more mature outlook than any of my fellow students.

That summer term of 1912, I worked hard and passed all my examinations with ease, fairly well up in the list. I was beginning to realise that success in biology depended not on memory and cramming, but on technical skill, which I was rapidly acquiring.

It was during this term that I first went to a few lectures given by Clifford Dobell, for whom I conceived an immense respect. He was under thirty: a handsome young man with long golden hair brushed straight back, bright blue eyes, an

aquiline nose, a corn-coloured moustache and a determined chin.

His lectures were brilliant and revealed a clear, firm iconoclastic mind. Implicit in them was his refusal to accept the popular version of the Darwinian theory of evolution. The opposition to Darwinism, on all sorts of quite unscientific grounds, had led Darwin's supporters to put forward a simplified popular version, which, by many, was presented with as much dogmatism as had been displayed by those who opposed it on the religious grounds that God had created all the birds, beasts and fishes and man on the fifth and sixth day.

As presented by Haeckel, the dogma took the form that all life had developed from simple unicellular blobs of protoplasm, exemplified by the amoeba, into complex multicellular forms, and the development of the vertebrates was traced from simple creatures like barnacles to complex animals like man.

All this tended to be accepted by the ordinary biologist, and Dobell was concerned to point out that much of the dogma was fallacious. Dobell had specialised in the study of the protozoa. He pointed out that they were by no means simple blobs of protoplasm. Many of the amoebae had complicated shells and were, perhaps, as highly evolved as larger creatures. Moreover, the comparison of a non-cellular animal such as the amoeba with a single cell in a cellular animal was fallacious. Dobell challenged also the popular concept of simple and complex with delightful clarity. Unconsciously man judged the importance of living creatures by their size, and this quite unscientific assumption underlies language itself.

In a paper called *Principles of Protistology* published in the *Archiv für Protistenkunde* he illustrated his argument with the words: Compare the opening words of the Magnificat: "My soul doth magnify the Lord."

This was giving the accepted ideas of older biologists a badly needed shaking up. William Bateson, who had founded the School of Geneticists at Cambridge, was giving the theories of inheritance just such a shaking up, and his work on Mendelism had altered the older ideas of how variations were trans-

mitted. I often went to see Bateson at week-ends at the Sir John Innes Institute, where he had retired after leaving Cambridge. He was a great man, large and good-humoured, with almost universal interests—in painting, poetry and literature, as well as in science.

Once, when he was showing me round, we passed a pen of poultry and saw a cock treading a hen. Bateson remarked in a reflective manner: "Every hen has a cock *underneath*," and he explained that femaleness was due to the presence of one extra chromozome, absent in the male and that, sometimes, the female would develop male characteristics and begin to crow. He was, perhaps, particularly kind to me, because of his friendship with my mother when he was an undergraduate at Cambridge. But he must have observed me fairly acutely because he once told Arthur Waley, "I don't think David Garnett will stick to Science. He has an artist's temperament." This was said four or five years before I wrote *Lady into Fox*.

While Bateson had been studying inheritance statistically, the mechanics of inheritance had been discovered by John Bretland Farmer, afterwards head of the Royal College of Science Botanical Department. His discovery of the meiotic division, which results in the egg and sperm carrying a halved number of chromosomes, led also to the explanation of the alternation of generations in plants such as the ferns and mosses. A similar alternation was to be traced in many other plants.

Both Dobell and Farmer lectured in the big room at the top of the old Science and Art building of the Royal College of Science in Exhibition Road. Art had been banished an untold number of years before, but had left behind her a number of casts: of the Discobolus, the Hermes of Praxitiles and other familiar plaster figures, which in their exposed portions had grown almost as black as the sooted pilasters of St Paul's.

Those figures had been at the back of that room behind a sheet as long as anyone living could remember and a question about them led to a remarkable anecdote being told me by the

old man who worked downstairs as an assistant in the Huxley Museum. His job was to take out the specimens, which the professor wanted for his lectures, put them back again, and sometimes bottle a new specimen or macerate an animal's skeleton to add to the collection. This ancient had started as a "lab" boy when Thomas Henry Huxley was Professor of Zoology at the Royal College of Science. One day, when he was setting out the exhibits that Huxley would require for his lecture on the theory of evolution, an eminent figure, bearded and beetle-browed, came into the lecture room before any of the students had arrived. It was Charles Darwin.

"Don't tell Professor Huxley or anyone else that I am here," he said, and edged in behind the statuary where he remained in hiding, listening to Huxley's exposition of the Darwinian theory. Not until the professor and the last student had disappeared, did Darwin come out of his hiding-place and steal downstairs into the street.

In my development as a botanist, I owed much to my having gone outside the botanical department and made friends with the zoologists. When the examination for the Associateship of the Royal College of Science came in 1913, I passed very easily. By that time my chief interest had become the investigation of the modes of reproduction and spore formation in the ascomycete fungi.

In October or November 1913, I went down to Silchester and after a long walk with Godwin's sister, Ruth Baynes, spent some time looking for ascomycetes on Silchester Common. I found several varieties, including one which I had never seen before. My efforts, later on, to identify it proved fruitless, so I took it round to the botanical department of the Natural History Museum and showed it to my friend Dr Ramsbottom. He at once identified it as a species which had been first described in print a few weeks before by the French systematist Boudier. It had been collected by an Aberdeenshire postman called Menzies, who was an amateur mycologist. It was rather a disappointment to find that I had been so near to discovering a new species. However, Ramsbottom was able to show that it

had been wrongly placed in the genus *Calycella* and that it was in fact a *Discinella*.

In the Christmas holidays of 1913, I went again to Silchester to collect more material of the fungus and, to my delight, found it growing in profusion on the common in places which had been burned a few years before and where the gorse had sprouted. Not only was the material abundant, but the little discs were of all sizes from the large ones, which were about a third of an inch in diameter, to tiny ones, the size of a pin's head. This was useful as I could study the development of the fungus in all stages. So persistently did Discinella associate with young gorse that I came to the conclusion that the reason it had not been found earlier was that mycologists disliked getting their fingers pricked.

On this visit I stayed at the Silchester pub, and not with the Baynes family. If not very comfortable, I was at least not embarrassed by not knowing how to behave at morning prayers.

When term began I hurriedly examined some of my new material and was astonished to find that the smallest specimens were not immature, but ripe fruit bodies, full of spores measuring about half the length of those of Discinella Menziesii.

I hurried round to see Ramsbottom and was naturally a good deal excited when he confirmed my hope; the small specimens were a new species, unknown to science, identical in all respects, but size with the one I had first found and Ramsbottom wrote a delightful description of it in botanical dog-latin, in which it was described as *isabellina*, that is the colour of Queen Isabel's shift, after the siege of Calais, and we called it *Discinella Minutissima* Ramsb. et Garn.

The discovery of this little species was a great piece of luck for me, as it pleased Professor Farmer and I had only to link my discovery with the research work I was planning, to be reasonably sure of getting the Diploma of the Imperial College for a piece of original work. In the event I did better and was also awarded the Marshall Prize, worth about sixty pounds. Professor Farmer recommended me for a Remanet scholarship,

which amounted to rather more. I was thus able to stay on for a fifth year at the Royal College of Science at no cost to Edward or Constance.

The botanical department had moved to a new building, where my individualism did not fit in. But I got Professor Farmer's permission to continue working in the old laboratory at the top of the Royal College of Science building if Dobell would agree, which he did. I thus did most of my advanced work alone, joining the Professor of Zoology, MacBride, and Dobell and Newth for tea in the library. Dobell and Newth had an immense contempt for MacBride, chiefly because his research work was always messy.

One day Dobell looked up at tea-time and said: "This Finnish paper is extremely interesting."

"What language is it in?" asked Newth.

"Finnish," replied Dobell.

"You don't mean to say you can read Finnish!" I exclaimed in astonishment.

"Well, I do find it a bit hard," replied Dobell, "but I know Swedish so well that I can usually guess the meaning."

I should have been silent. But I was not naturally tactful and I blurted out: "Swedish could not help you with Finnish, which is not even an Aryan language. It's nearer Hungarian and Turkish in affinities than it is to Swedish. Finns usually know Swedish and I've no doubt that's what your paper is written in."

MacBride had been listening and now guffawed hugely over the joke and Dobell turned very pale and went out of the room.

Later Newth said to me: "Dobell will never forgive your pointing out that bloomer in front of MacBride."

It was an unfortunate beginning to the research work I was starting on under Dobell's supervision, the sad story of which belongs to the next volume.

XII

OUR gentle neighbour, Richard Heath, died in February 1912, at the age of eighty. It was fortunate that he did not live to see the war with Germany. He was buried in Limpsfield churchyard and Ramsay MacDonald and J. A. Hobson, both old friends of his, spoke at the side of the open grave. What they said was true and for that reason preferable to the usual service, but I have always disliked speeches at funerals and I did not like these. I remember looking at MacDonald's noble head with admiration, but wishing he would be silent.

Richard Heath's death was to change our lives considerably, for Nellie decided to give up Gracie's Cottage and to move to London. Her move coincided with our giving up the workman's flat in Hampstead. For a year we lived in the upper half of a little house in Downshire Hill and then, in 1913, moved, on my persuasion, to South Kensington, so that I could be near the Imperial College of Science. We took a maisonette at 19 Pond Place, Fulham Road, and Edward lived there till the end of his life.

One evening, while we were still living in Downshire Hill, Edward came back from a concert with a very handsome, big, dark woman, a poetess called Anna Wickham, who lived a few houses away, across the street. Constance made coffee, and I sat in a corner of the room devouring our visitor with my eyes, for I was very much attracted by her. She was tall, had a dark nectarine colouring, was large and free in her movements and, though dressed in beautiful clothes, was careless of her appearance. She had a warm contralto voice, full of humour, to which I immediately responded.

She thanked Constance for the coffee and for welcoming her so late. Then she apologised for talking about her personal affairs, but told us that she had lost her temper with her

235

husband and had smashed a glass door with her fist. He had come to the conclusion she must be mad and had got a medical acquaintance to bring another doctor and they had certified her that afternoon. She had escaped to go to the concert, at which she had promised to sing and was on her way home, from which she fully expected to be taken to an asylum. She had been very glad to come back with my father and spend a little while with us first. She was calm and not frightened or worried as most people would have been in her place. "If I'm as sane as I think I am, I suppose they won't be able to keep me more than a month or two," she said, and added with a whimsical smile: "It's a lesson to me not to have such an uncontrollable temper."

When she said good-bye, I went down the stairs with her and across the street to her house. I was shocked by her story and suggested that, if she was taken to the asylum, we ought to do something immediately to get her released. She replied that she was quite sure that would be a mistake. It was for doctors to decide the matter of one's sanity and they would back each other up, if attacked. She had only got to be perfectly sane and they would soon recognise it.

We exchanged a long look and she went in. Next day my mother called on Anna, but was told she was out and it was not known when she would be back. Constance called a second time and was told she had gone away for a long visit to the country.

Two or three months later I met Anna in the street and rushed up to her. "It worked out as I expected," she said. "I put the whole thing out of my head when I got there, sent for a copy of Todhunter's arithmetic and spent most of the day doing sums. When the visiting doctors came round they let me out." I went back to her house with her and, either then, or soon afterwards, met her husband. He was a tall, thin handsome man—a balloonist and an accomplished amateur astronomer. In spite of their temperamental differences, Anna was extremely proud of him and excited at his having made a discovery about the nature of Saturn's rings. I had fallen in love with Anna,

when I first saw her and we became great friends and spent a good deal of time together, going for walks at night on Hampstead Heath, or to Bohemian parties. She knew a number of Slade students, painters and models, Augustus John and Jacob Epstein. With Anna I went sometimes to the Café Royal and with her joined a little night club in Greek Street, called the Crabtree, which Augustus John had had a hand in founding shortly before.

At this time Anna was writing a great deal of poetry. Many of her early poems are on subjects I gave her and she usually had one or two new poems for me to read when we met. Many of these were published in her first book, *A Man With a Hammer*.

Owing to my friendship with Anna, I met T. E. Hulme, a big, rather overbearing man who was a philosopher, but who looked like a farmer at a fair and, by his own account, was a man of astounding sexual prowess, who was always trying to pick up women in places like the British Museum and enjoy their favours in most unsuitable places. Hulme would suddenly pull out his watch while a group of his acquaintances sat talking with him at a table in the Café Royal. "I've a pressing engagement in five minutes' time," he would say and stride out of the building. Twenty minutes later he would return, wipe his brow, and complain that the steel staircase of the emergency exit at Piccadilly Circus Tube Station was the most uncomfortable place in which he had ever copulated. All this rather offended my youthful idealism. Perhaps, if I had been a philosopher, instead of a biologist, I should have liked Hulme better.

In the Crabtree one sat round in a big bare room and drank with one's friends at little tables, while some woman sang, or couples danced. Sometimes the tables were pushed back and dancing was general. The only remarkable thing about the Crabtree was that drink and cigarettes were cheap and it was not a den to extort money from the gilded rich for doctored whisky and bogus champagne.

I made friends with a number of people there, including a girl called Lillian Shelley, who often sang. She had a dead

white face, very black hair and a positive genius for picking up the most penniless, dirty and squalid down-and-outs among the artists of London. Epstein did a very fine head of her. I also made friends with Eric Sutton, who later became an accomplished translator. He used to concoct a drink which I thought delicious. It was oily and potent and I have preserved the recipe:

Five parts gin, three parts brandy, two parts orange Curaçoa, a dash of orange bitters.

It is a drink which should be made to last a long time.

At this time, I used also to go to the house of Mrs White in Frith Street, who was at home one evening a week. Hulme was always there: one evening I met W. H. Davies who greeted me as an old friend. A young man whose appearance fascinated me was Gaudier, the sculptor, often called Gaudier-Breszka owing to his association with a Polish woman. Their attachment is the subject of an interesting book by H. S. Ede with the rather absurd title of *Savage Messiah*. Gaudier was very civilised and had no message and no following.

Hulme and Ezra Pound were the first people in London to recognise Gaudier's genius and help to keep him from starvation. Hulme commissioned various things from him and bought his work. I was able to see some of Gaudier's drawings and sculpture at Frith Street and was very much excited by them. I made friends with him one evening, and talked to him for a little while about the work of Brancusi, which I had seen at an ill-starred exhibition of modern art in the Albert Hall. Unfortunately, the next time I met Gaudier, he was holding forth on the subject of his having an intuitive knowledge and understanding of mathematics owing to his being a sculptor, dealing with masses and their relationships in stone and metal.

I thought this was the sort of nonsense that ought to be stopped and rather rudely, I suppose, told him I thought it was a mistake to talk nonsense about the sciences, which were a matter for logic and reason, and not intuition. He was annoyed and next time I saw him, he did not speak to me. I have always

greatly regretted that I had not the sense to hold my tongue. There was in that company an atmosphere of swashbuckling, a tendency to talk for display in order to impress or score off others, an anxiety to be among the first to *épater le bourgeois* with fashionably outrageous ideas, which has never appealed to me. This hid an inner uncertainty, perhaps not in Hulme himself, but in his circle of friends. Had I been older, I should have been more tolerant and might have got something out of the opportunity of knowing Hulme.

In the early summer of 1912, Godwin Baynes went to Paris to study hypnotism at La Saltpetrière. Rosalind and I saw something of each other in his absence and when Ursula came back from Moscow for a visit to England, I persuaded both of them to come for a boating holiday with me on the Severn. With us came a Creole boy of my own age, a Jamaican of pure British ancestry, called Theodore Williams. He was an old friend of the Oliviers.

We went on Newth's advice to Worcester and hired a double-sculling gig. Our rolls of tents and blankets were piled in the bows, a packing-case full of provisions went behind the steersman's seat and, five minutes after our arrival, we pushed off into the stream. The rest of that week was unblemished happiness. We camped in lovely meadows, our tents a little way apart, we swam, rowed upstream, stopped to have meals, swam again, rowed further. The weather remained perfect; there were no quarrels, no unhappiness, no broken hearts or wounded feelings. We laughed a lot. Ursula's dark eyes almost vanished when she went into a roar of laughter and afterwards she would chuckle merrily for a long time.

Rosalind's laughter was thin and a little fastidious in comparison and sounded like a spoon ringing against a china cup. She was a lovely creature—a russeted apple in face, cool, delicate and critical in spirit. I was linked with her by my love of Godwin and felt a fraternal pride in her beauty. I remember, however, once, while we lay sunning ourselves upon a willow trunk hanging over the river after our bathe, wondering

239

whether she was not almost too perfect a creature for Godwin, whom I saw momentarily, in a flash of realism, as an old bumble-puppy.

When we reached the rapids, we spent the day in bathing dresses, hauling our boat up with a line and carefully noting the channels, so that we could shoot them safely on our return downstream. What had happened to the devils which inhabit each of our hearts, tormenting us with passions of egotism, lust, selfishness, and shame? Those passions which the young are always supposed to be feeling? Somehow, we four young creatures escaped their clutches for about ten days, while our camping holiday lasted.

The Ertel family visited England in the early summer of 1912 and stayed at the Cearne for a wet week. It was a pitiful return for their bountiful hospitality to us in Russia—small crowded rooms; the rain beating endlessly on the leaded window panes; the flowers in the garden beaten down and drenched and showers of water falling down one's neck, whenever one's head knocked against a twig on one of the paths. It was one of the few occasions I can remember when I was seriously embarrassed by my parents' poverty.

But for two people the weather did not greatly matter. Harold came over every day and was greatly attracted by Lola. When the time came for the Ertels to go back to Russia, Harold was invited to accompany them and went with them on the ship.

About the same time, I set off for Germany, having arranged to go to a few lectures on botany in Munich. Harold was to come back from Russia, by way of Munich, and we planned to spend a week or two together.

I was very pleased when my solitary existence in Munich was broken by the arrival of a letter from my father suggesting that I should meet the author of *The White Peacock*, which I had read, and which had made a great impression on me.

On the heels of my father's letter came one from D. H. Lawrence, asking me to come out and see him, and adding as a

postscript: "I look fearfully English and so I guess do you, so there is no need for either of us to carry the Union Jack for recognition." On the day appointed, I set out for Icking by the little light railway which winds along the valley, getting glimpses of the milky-green waters of the rushing Isar, of sloping fields of corn and white dusty roads, with wild Canterbury bells growing beside them.

At every station, the train stopped to set down summer visitors, day-trippers and holiday-makers in gay Bavarian peasant costumes: bevies of stout, laughing women with embroidered blouses, bare legs and sandals; or to take in real Bavarian peasant women in their best black stuff dresses, with occasionally a gayer male wearing a gnome's green cap, embroidered braces and be-ribboned leather shorts. Clusters of children, sometimes crowned or garlanded with flowers, crowded on the platform, waving handkerchiefs. I could hardly bear to wait in the train, for though we had all the windows open, the carriage was like an oven. I remember the clean beads of sweat on a healthy German woman's neck who was romping with her five children, while the rest of us sighed and wiped our faces.

When I got to the right station, I did not need to linger, while the embracing Germans cleared away, to recognise Lawrence. He did look fearfully English. The bare-headed, slight figure moved towards me; I noticed a scrubby little moustache, and I was looking into the most beautiful lively, blue eyes. We set off to the house where he was living.

Lawrence was slight in build, with a weak, narrow chest and shoulders, but he was a fair height and very light in his movements. This lightness gave him a sort of grace. His hair was of a colour, and grew in a particular way, which I have never seen except in English working men. It was bright mud-colour, with a streak of red in it, a thick mat, parted on one side. Somehow, it was incredibly plebeian, mongrel and underbred. His forehead was broad, but not high, his nose too short and lumpy, his face colourless, like a red-haired man's, his chin (he had not then grown a beard) altogether too large, and round

like a hairpin—rather a Philip IV sort of chin—and the lower lip, rather red and moist, under the scrubby toothbrush moustache. He looked like a mongrel terrier among a crowd of Pomeranians and Alsatians, English to the bone. He was the type of the plumber's mate who goes back to fetch the tools. He was the weedy runt you find in every gang of workmen: the one who keeps the other men laughing all the time; who makes trouble with the boss and is saucy to the foreman; who gets the sack; who is "victimised" the cause of a strike; the man for whom trades unions exist; who lives on the dole; who hangs round the pubs; who bets on football and is always cheeky, cocky, and in trouble. He was the type who provokes the most violent class-hatred in this country: the impotent hatred of the upper classes for the lower. Certainly Lawrence had no need to carry the Union Jack.

He was all this, but once you looked into his eyes you were completely charmed, they were so beautiful and alive, dancing with gaiety. His smile lit up all his face as he looked at you, asking you silently: "Come on . . . let's have some fun", and the invitation of this look was irresistible, at least to me. I could no more hold out against it than a well-behaved spaniel can resist the mongrel terrier's invitation to slip off poaching. The mongrel gives one glance out of the tail of his eye, spreads his front legs, crouches on his elbows, yaps once—then they trot down the garden path and are away like the wind, scampering madly. Whistle and shout as you like, you'll never get your spaniel back now—not till he comes in yellow with sand from the bury, at the end of the day.

No doubt Lawrence made me talk about myself as we walked from Icking to Irschenhausen, and then into the woods where he said there were roe deer. In the afternoon we walked further down the valley through a wood by the river's edge. *Osmunda regalis* was growing in the shadow of the trees and the river tore past the rocks and the white sandbanks. I bathed amid clouds of horseflies and we went on to Wolfratshausen, where Lawrence led me into an orchard behind the house and introduced me to Frieda.

At first sight, she might have been a handsome sister of the sweating German mother in the train: she had the same sturdy body, as strong as a horse, the same magnificent shoulders, but her head and the expression of her eyes were very different. Her head and the whole carriage of her body were noble. Her eyes were green, with a lot of tawny yellow in them, the nose straight. She looked one dead in the eyes, fearlessly judging one and, at that moment, she was extraordinarily like a lioness: eyes and colouring, and the swift power of her lazy leap up from the hammock where she had been lying.

I have always been particularly attracted by happy lovers and attached to them: Lawrence and Frieda were more than twice as attractive to me together than they would have been separately. I was completely charmed by each of them and at once worshipped them.

They on their part flattered me, buttered me up, laughed at me and became fond of me, accepting my worship and lecturing me for worshipping other people. After that first visit, they asked me again several times, introduced me to Frieda's sister and brother-in-law and, in a week or two, I was at home in a new family circle.

After they had packed up and gone to the Tyrol, planning to make their way by stages into Italy, letters and messages reached me, saying that I must join them at Mayrhofen in Zillerthal—the wild flowers in the mountains were wonderful, and I should make great additions to my herbarium.

Harold was not due to arrive from Moscow for three or four days. If I waited for him I might miss the Lawrences. So I left a letter telling him that he must follow me by train and set off to walk by the Achensee to Mayrhofen.

I was caught by a thunderstorm, benighted on the pass, which is just on the German side of the frontier, and reached the frontier post a little before midnight, tired out and soaked to the skin. I beat on the door and a furious officer consigned me to the devil and refused to allow me to spend the night there. I was dropping with fatigue, but I struggled on and, to my astonishment, a mile further on found a brilliantly lighted

Wirtschaft, where a gay party was still in progress. My appearance, sodden and dripping with water, was greeted with enthusiasm. I was taken upstairs to a room, given some dry clothes to change into and taken downstairs again to eat a meal, which had been immediately prepared—and my glass was filled and filled again with a delicious white wine.

My host was a man of about fifty and treated my arrival as a reason for prolonging a delightful party; his daughters, both very pretty girls, seated themselves beside me and questioned me in broken English; I talked to them and ate and drank like someone in a dream, and thanked them with all the grace I could muster when the party eventually broke up and they departed across the street.

I was dog-tired and next morning the good people at the Wirtschaft let me sleep late. When I woke, I found all my clothes were dry and my shirt had even been washed and ironed. As I breakfasted, I inquired about my host of the night before. He was, I learned, "ein sehr berühmter Dichter", an Austrian writer, who visited the village every summer: he and his family lived across the road.

When I had finished I asked for the bill—but the famous author had, I was told, settled the bill the night before. This was too much, and I hurried round to protest to my benefactor. But, alas, he and his whole family had gone out for the day into the mountains and were not expected to return till nightfall. His name meant nothing to me then and I have forgotten it, but I have often wondered who he was.

I wrote a letter, in the best German I could muster, expressing my gratitude and my sorrow at not being able to express it in person—then shouldered my rucksack and went on my way.

That afternoon I reached Mayrhofen, where I took a room in a house across the street from the Lawrences. I explained that Harold was due in a day or two, and Lawrence and Frieda agreed to wait until he turned up.

There was an oleander in flower before the door and strings of mules, with swinging red tassels, loaded with huge Gruyère

D. H. LAWRENCE IN 1913

cheeses, came down the village street out of the forest and the mountains. Lawrence pointed everything out: he knew everyone in the village by name and all their peculiarities and love-affairs. Frieda and he had been there nearly a week.

He was just finishing *Sons and Lovers*, he was writing some stories and a lot of poems, but his work did not affect our daily life. It never occurred to me, or I think to Frieda, not to interrupt him, and we spent all the day together in one room, while he scribbled away at odd moments in the corner, jumping up continually to look after the cooking.

Scratch, scratch, scratch, went pen or pencil on the squared foreign paper; then, scratch, scratch, with the penholder at the back of his low-class head of hair. Scratch on the paper again—and then Lawrence would jump up and begin to make fun of himself, or else Frieda was bubbling over with some new thing she had seen out of the window, or else the soup was burning.

Lawrence was a natural copy-cat; indeed, he was the only great mimic I have ever known; he had a genius for "taking people off" and could reproduce voice and manner exactly. He told you that he had once seen Yeats or Ezra Pound for half an hour in a drawing-room, and straightway Yeats or Pound appeared before you. The slightest affectation of manner or social pretence was seized on mercilessly. One realised the enormous aesthetic enjoyment which the poor are afforded by the spectacle of the imbecilities of the rich, of the endless "copy" which they provide—but the person whom Lawrence most constantly made fun of was himself.

He mimicked himself ruthlessly and continually and, as he told a story, acted ridiculous versions of a shy and gawky Lawrence being patronised by literary lions, of a winsome Lawrence charming his landlady, a sentimental Lawrence being put in his place by his landlady's daughter, of a bad-tempered whining Lawrence picking a quarrel with Frieda over nothing. There was more than a little of Charlie Chaplin in his acting: but bitterer, less sentimental. Frieda and I laughed at him until laughing was an agony.

245

In the evenings we all three of us acted complicated nonsense charades, without an audience. The last time we met, Frieda asked me: "Do you remember, David, the head of Holofernes?" and she collapsed helplessly with laughter and could only explain: "Oh, you looked such a fool!" Alas, I have forgotten the Holofernes we acted at Mayrhofen.

There was one bad moment of the day for both of them, when the post came from England, but Lawrence's courage, his high spirits, his perpetual nagging mockery, kept us all gay. For his courage and his mockery of the slightest hint of self-pity rose with danger and difficulty and at that time both their difficulties were very great.

Lawrence and Frieda set off for Italy with twenty-three pounds between them and with no certainty of any more until *Paul Morel* was published, and *Paul Morel* had to be entirely rewritten and transformed into *Sons and Lovers*. About money Lawrence was almost painfully scrupulous, never getting a farthing in debt, extremely economical, and always ready to give money away. At Mayrhofen, I borrowed money from him and didn't pay it back, though my father did. Lawrence offered to lend me the money to accompany them into Italy, whence I should return to England by boat from Genoa. Though much tempted, I refused, and have regretted it ever since.

After I had been a few days at Mayrhofen, Harold joined us. He had not met Lawrence or Frieda before and very soon made great friends with them. Neither of them had the faintest trace of that hypocrisy which Harold hated more than anything else. They cared nothing about pretences or proprieties and Lawrence and Harold swopped bawdy stories and Frieda and I laughed at them. Harold, therefore, felt completely reassured, and Lawrence liked Harold because of his uncompromising honesty and natural force and Frieda was not untouched by his good looks and masculine charm.

A few days after Harold's arrival, Lawrence and Frieda sent off all their worldly possessions in two suitcases by train to Italy, and we set out to walk over the mountains rising up through the wet forests, with their yellow foxgloves and *noli-*

me-tangere flowers, to the rocky pastures, where the trees stopped and the belt of *alpenrosen*, dwarf rhododendrons, began. Towards evening we found a Hay-hut Among the Mountains, which was not so bad as Lawrence makes out in his account in *Love Among the Haystacks*.

There had been no rain until we had to take refuge in the hay-hut, but it rained violently during the thunderstorm in the middle of the night. When we looked out in the morning, the snow had come low down on the nearer slopes. But the sun shone hot during the next day and Harold and I were often glad to stop and bathe in the mountain torrents of ice-water rushing from the glaciers. At one moment I was very nearly carried over a waterfall, but Harold pulled me out. Every few yards, Lawrence or I would find some new flower and tear it up by the roots to add to my herbarium, which was enriched in three days by nearly two hundred Alpine species. Lawrence was interested in botany and loved flowers, which at that time played a large part in his symbolism and personal mythology.

On the afternoon of our second day's walk we reached a rest-house called *The Dominikus Hütte*, which stood on a green alp at the foot of the bare mountains. Leaving Harold and Frieda to amuse each other as best they knew how, Lawrence and I climbed together up a wild tumbled scree of rocks, almost to the permanent snow-line, snatching at the new saxifrages we found. We were both absolutely exhausted when we returned, and as Frieda and Harold also seemed tired, we went to bed early.

The next day we climbed up to the pass—the Pfitzer Joch— and descended the mountain-side, which is cut into steps and steep as a flight of stairs. In an hour or two we had passed from drifted snow to houses where the grapes hung in black clusters over the lintels and a tobacco harvest stood in queer pagodas drying in a garden.

There we parted, and though I saw a good deal of Lawrence in the three or four years that followed, whenever he was in England, I never saw him so well or so happy, so consistently gay and light-hearted.

He came with us for part of the way when Harold and I walked in to catch the Verona night express at Sterzen. When we stopped and said good-bye, he said something about not needing me to repay the money I had borrowed for my fare home. It was dark, there was a smell of flowers, and Lawrence's light feet were noiseless in the dust of the road.

XIII

IN the autumn of 1912, the Balkan War was exciting the sympathies of all those English men and women who had committed their hearts to the Greeks, or to the Serbs, or to the Bulgars, or to the Albanians—or to the Turks, whether Young Turks or Old Turks. Thus there were not many people left who felt neutral. Nevertheless, passionately though we all felt, or were made to feel, about the war—and the second Balkan War, when the allies split up and attacked each other, was a very dishonourable affair—we did not think that it would touch our pockets or our stomachs, still less did we think that anyone we cared about would suffer a cut finger as a result.

One day I got a letter from Ursula, who had gone back to Moscow about the same time as the Ertels, to say that a friend of hers called Boris Sokolov was arriving in London and she asked me to put him in touch with English journalists who might be useful to him. She had told me, when we were camping out together early that summer, that he had been an active revolutionist when he was a boy of sixteen in the abortive rising of 1905. I wrote to him and he came to see me at the Students' Union when the day's work was over.

He was a tall, grey, lanky young man of twenty-three, with fair hair, cold grey eyes, a grey skin and lantern jaws. Years later I found out that his real name was not Sokolov, which means Falcon, but Volkov, which means Wolf. His real name suited him far better. He was like a wolf. We sipped Indian tea and ate buttered scones and suddenly my visitor, who had not had anyone to talk to for several days and was starving for a listener, began to tell me how delighted he was by the Balkan War.

Thinking of Turgenev's hero Insarov, I asked him whether he attached great importance to the defeat of the Turks, but

Sokolov only snorted scornfully at the idea. He didn't care a hoot about Turks or Serbs or Bulgars. No, the important thing was that the Balkan War, if it ended with a triumphant Serbia, as seemed likely, would infallibly bring in the Austro-Hungarian Empire—and that would bring in Russia, Germany, France and England in a general European war. Russia was incapable of fighting a major war, so that whichever side won, she would inevitably be defeated, and defeat would be the last nail in the coffin of the Russian autocracy. The revolution would follow.

I listened with incredulity to this exposition of European politics—and finally, asked him whether a war involving all the Great Powers and millions of dead was not rather a high price to pay for the Russian revolution.

Sokolov looked at me with pity and replied that he was not concerned with the ethics of history, but with what was inevitably going to occur in the next few years.

I asked him when the European war would begin and he replied that he did not think it could be delayed much after the summer of 1913. He wanted to meet some left-wing English journalist who might help him to get an article printed and I gave him an introduction to Brailsford or Nevinson, or both.

Sokolov's ruthlessness reminded me of Savarkar. But there were two main differences. There were no four-armed Goddesses in the background to be appeased by a holocaust of lives and, even more important, Sokolov, whatever his faults, was not an amateur. I was a good deal impressed by him and we liked each other. I saw him once or twice again before he returned to Russia.

My chief interest in the Balkan war was because Godwin Baynes went out in charge of a unit of the Red Crescent to reorganise a Turkish hospital behind the Tchatalja lines, where thousands of wounded Turks were lying out in melting snow and deep mud, and his marriage to Rosalind was delayed until he came back and bought a practice in England.

Adrian Stephen and his sister Virginia had recently moved to a lovely house in the middle of the north side of Brunswick

Square and Adrian invited me to come round there to tea. As in most of the Brunswick Square houses, the big ground-floor dining-room had a round end and this room Adrian later on let to Maynard Keynes. Duncan Grant and his friend Frederick Etchells had painted its walls with a continuous London street scene, in which the centre of dramatic interest was a fallen cabhorse with the driver of the hansom still perched precariously aloft, though the cab was tilted forward with the shafts touching the pavement.

Adrian's friends met in the big drawing-room which stretched across the whole front of the house on the first floor. On its west wall, opposite the fireplace, was a huge painting executed by Duncan and Adrian working together, representing, in post-impressionist style, a mixed tennis doubles. One of the players, a female in the left foreground, was almost a triangle of yellow skirt, standing on one foot with the other one raised stiffly. In spite of the distortion and the violent colours, I liked it very much.

Besides these mural paintings there were several by Duncan standing around or even hanging on the walls, for he appeared to be almost an inmate of the house. On my first visit, Adrian and I sat in this room and ate a great many buttered muffins and crumpets and when I went away he invited me to come one evening and play poker.

When the time came I dressed up in a white waistcoat and tails. I had heard someone say that a young man was always acceptable in evening dress and I implicitly believed it. If the others weren't dressed, I argued that they would assume I had been out to a smart dinner party, or was intending to go on somewhere else later on. The real reason for my dressing was that my evening dress was the only well-cut, decent suit I possessed and I knew that I looked my best in it.

Afterwards, I went to a great many of Adrian's poker parties, and my memory of the first has fused with a score of others. I never lost or won outrageously inconvenient amounts of money. I was a rather good player and won slightly more often than I lost.

The other members of the party were usually Gerald Shove, a dark man with high cheekbones, who was a master of vehement biting phrases. Many of Gerald's contemporaries at Cambridge regarded him as the man of their generation most likely to distinguish himself and leave a mark upon the world. It was indeed easy to imagine him as a young member of Parliament achieving a reputation like that of F. E. Smith. But everyone has hidden qualities and Gerald had a capacity for tender devotion and unselfish love which none of us suspected. After his marriage to Fredegond Maitland, a cousin of Adrian Stephen's, he sank back into being a retiring don at King's College, Cambridge, teaching Economics and devoting all his free time to his invalid wife and to the cats which they kept.

Then there was Saxon Sydney-Turner, an almost silent figure in a neat pepper-and-salt suit, with whom I soon felt a strong current of sympathy and understanding. At Cambridge he had been a contemporary of Clive Bell, and Thoby, Adrian's elder brother, who had died in 1906; and he was an intimate friend of all present except myself. Maynard Keynes was frequently one of the party. Noel Olivier came sometimes and so did two sisters, Karen and Ray Costello.

During my visits, I felt a strange mixture of emotions: the excitement of meeting people who were more charming and more intelligent than the people I met elsewhere—and a feeling of peacefulness, of being at home—almost a premonition of *belonging*, as though I were a stray kitten which had firmly made up its mind that it was going to be adopted. Thus I sat while the pack was shuffled and cut, gloating with happiness. But as the evening went on, other people would come in after dinner parties or the opera: Adrian's sister, Vanessa, and her husband Clive Bell, Virginia with a female friend in tow, Leonard Woolf and Duncan Grant.

With these arrivals, interest in the game would unfortunately slacken and I soon found myself alone and out of place. Sometimes Duncan would come in early and as all the company except myself were fond of him and he disliked cards, he would

effectively break up the game by talking to the others. On such occasions, there seemed nothing for me to do but to get up and go and I felt miserably unhappy and jealous. For in some way I felt that Adrian's house in Brunswick Square was my spiritual home and his friends—except for Duncan Grant —were the people I should most like to know.

I liked the way they sat about, the way they talked, the entirely casual way in which one of them (usually Gerald) would fill up his tumbler with Adrian's whisky, without being asked, and others just shook their heads if offered it, without bothering to say thank you.

But I was, I knew, outside this paradise and, if Adrian stopped inviting me, I should never be able to enter it again. I learnt later that, at that time, Adrian was the only person in the group who did like me and that the others could see no point in me at all, partly because of my habit of appearing week after week in full evening dress. Nobody else ever wore even a dinner-jacket, except Clive, unless some late-comer came on from a seat in the stalls at the Russian Ballet or the Opera. Duncan, in particular, disliked me, mistaking my shy silence for an affectation of superiority and worldliness. But, in spite of protests, Adrian continued to invite me.

He was always unexpected. One night we stayed playing late and did not break up till about two o'clock in the morning. The Piccadilly tube would be shut; I should have to walk home to South Kensington, for though I had been winning, I should never at that time have taken a cab for myself alone, even if I had had ten pounds in my pocket.

"Let's go to the races," said Adrian as we got up from the table. Gerald Shove and Clive greeted the suggestion with enthusiasm. Maynard was more cautious.

"What races?" he asked.

"There are sure to be races somewhere," said Adrian, and as we went out into that clear odd light there is in London in the very early hours of a June morning, Adrian called out to a passing cab:

"Will you drive us to the races, cabby?"

The taxi-man drew up and looked at us curiously. We were not bookies or ordinary race-goers and he was puzzled and for a moment or two seemed lost in thought.

"We could make it all right, but it's a long way."

"Where are they?" asked Maynard.

"Pontefract," replied the cabby, "in the West Riding."

Even Adrian's casual enthusiasm was put off by the notion of a two-hundred-mile taxi-drive and amidst general laughter the project was postponed for another occasion.

In June 1913, just before my examination for the Associateship of the Royal College of Science, Lawrence and Frieda returned from Italy and came to stay at the Cearne. There was trouble between them, which kept flaring out in Lawrence's behaviour. Frieda loved her children and had sacrificed her happiness in them to live with him. Any kind-hearted man would have felt an added tenderness and sympathy for her. But there was a streak of cruelty in Lawrence; he was jealous of the children and angry with Frieda, because she could not forget them. Now that she had come back to England, she was longing to see them, and the spiteful, ill-conditioned, ungenerous side of Lawrence's character was constantly breaking out in different ways. He lacked what are called "the instincts of a gentleman"—and he most certainly wasn't one. Of course, he rationalised his jealousy and his spite, attributed the whole trouble to faults in Frieda's character and never admitted the existence of imperfections in his own. This did not make him any more attractive. But he was ill. Once I caught sight of one of Frieda's handkerchiefs, marked with a coronet in the corner, crumpled in Lawrence's hand, after a fit of coughing and spotted with bright arterial blood—and I felt a new tenderness for him and readiness to forgive his bad moods. But my sympathy was really all for Frieda and as she could get no support from Lawrence, I spent several afternoons in London with her, hanging round St Paul's School in the hope that she could intercept her son and see him for a moment or two.

Frieda's character was so full of love and she had such a genius for expressing it, that when she was suffering she was as painful to watch as an animal in a trap. Indeed, she was—and probably still is—more like a noble animal than most women. A wholly admirable animal, let me add, such as all sensible men would have been lucky, in Whitman's words, to be able to turn and live with.

She could no more forget and abandon her children than a lioness or a puma can forget the cubs which the hunter has taken away, and her unhappiness in being separated from them was something simple and elemental, and like everything else in Frieda's nature, noble. At the time Lawrence's evil moods were not lasting; the gay lively charmer whom I had met a year before on the Isar was always popping out and amusing us.

In the summer of 1913, Noel and I planned a camp on the Severn, starting at Bridgnorth, where Ursula, Rosalind and I had left off, and going up the river as far as possible in Canadian canoes, which would be far better for shooting the rapids coming down.

The party consisted of Brynhild and her husband, Hugh Popham, Daphne, Noel, Harold Hobson, myself and Pauley Montagu whom I had not previously met. There were thus four men and three girls and we travelled in three canoes. The weather was lovely, one day we found ourselves close to the Wrekin and we all set out and climbed it. On the way down we stopped at a farm and bought some of the most delicious fresh Cheshire cheese I have ever tasted, as well as quantities of eggs and milk.

Paul Montagu was a zoologist, who had just left Cambridge and was going on an anthropological expedition to New Guinea or the Solomon Islands. He was musical and from his schooldays had carried on research into early English songs and music. He was also an extremely skilful joiner and had made himself a full-sized lute and a gittern; thus a most delightful feature of the Severn camp was his singing round the camp fire.

The three Olivier girls joined in and Pauley's stock of ballads seemed inexhaustible. He had frequently found an earlier or better version of a well-known song. Thus the words of his version of *The Golden Vanitie* were better and far more vivid than any I have heard since. Favourite songs of his were *John Dory*, the *Friar and the Well* and the tragic ballad of *Little Musgrave*.

Pauley seemed to belong to the time of the old ballads himself. He had the head one often sees in Holbeins and Elizabethan paintings—a forehead with no hollow at the temples and long eyes. His limbs had the smooth roundness of a savage's, with no knots of muscle or knobbly knees. His mind was simple, direct and uninhibited, and he appeared to know where he wanted to go and what he wanted to do, but he was in no hurry to tell one about it.

In the late autumn, I set off with Margery, Daphne and Noel to walk to Fernhurst, where James Strachey was staying alone in a cottage belonging to one of his family.

We were a gay and brave looking party; Daphne carried slung upon her back a Spanish guitar, which I had given her, and the long red and yellow ribbands with which it was adorned seemed appropriate to the autumn colouring of leaves and berries.

There was a heavy mist when we started in the morning, but the day cleared. Only in the late afternoon did we discover that we had set out with hardly any money. By that time we had covered nearly twenty miles and were more than half-way to Fernhurst, so there could be no question of turning back. We were tiring and the prospect of going on walking through the night did not appeal to us. We managed to find a barn after dark and spent the night in it without being detected. We were comfortable and able to sleep, but when we woke up we were all extremely hungry, as we had eaten the last of our provisions the night before.

When we went out, at first light, into a field of mangolds,

256

we were surprised to find there was a hard frost and their leaves were stiff. Nevertheless, we pulled up one apiece and peeling them with our knives, tried to eat them. I had never tried a mangold before and hastily spat out the first piece. Only Daphne, I think, persisted as far as a second mouthful, bravely saying that it was better than nothing. Rose hips were better, but did not provide enough to be worth the trouble of preparing them. So we walked on with empty stomachs, and with eyes keenly alert for anything edible.

At last we came to a village and with our few pennies, bought a loaf of bread and some cups of milk. Nothing was ever more delicious and no loaf ever disappeared more rapidly. Our money was exhausted before our appetites were nearly satisfied. However, we were filled with renewed strength and covered the rest of the way to Fernhurst and our next meal, walking much faster than was usual on such expeditions.

James Strachey had been ill and, in those days, was not at all an athlete. He greeted our story with a pretence of horror, gibbering at us like a marmoset and, immediately, glasses of ovaltine were prepared for us and biscuits and then cake, and then, luckily, luncheon was ready.

James was the first of his family I got to know and I was immediately struck in him by what I later discovered was a very marked characteristic of the whole family: an astonishing inelasticity of values, a rigid adherence to certain limitations which they have imposed upon themselves. The last thing a Strachey would ever propound is Ford Hueffer's statement that truth is relative. For the Stracheys truth is absolute. Thus were a Strachey to accept William James's pragmatic theory of truth, he would believe the theory was absolutely true. To know Stracheys well, one has to be ready to accept the atmosphere in which they live.

James was one against four, but he immediately transformed our party and, by tea-time, my careless companions were scarcely recognisable: the body was forgotten, the mind supreme. We did, it was true, retain enough independence of mind to tease him a little, but our teasing was mixed with

respect, and on the part of my companions with a concern for his health and comfort, which I had never observed in them before.

Between every meal a glass of ovaltine was prepared and administered to James as though it were a sacrificial rite, while I looked on amazed. What unutterable contempt would have been shown by all of them had Harold or I declared that we required a glass of ovaltine between every meal and had we expected one of them to prepare it! This domination of the ruthless Valkyries of my childhood by James Strachey proved there was some strange virtue, some source of power, in him which made him unlike the rest of us.

I gathered, however, that he would have been astonished at the possibility of such a view, but that he regarded his elder brother Lytton rather as we regarded him. The subject of Lytton cropped up because there was a little volume of miniature photographs of him at Fernhurst so arranged that, if one flipped through it, one saw a moving photograph of him registering the emotions of surprise, horror, despair and then accepting a cup of tea. The moving record certainly bore out James's claims that Lytton was a unique and formidable figure. I was greatly impressed, as only the young can be, by what I heard of him.

Brynhild had married Hugh Popham, a cousin of the Radfords. I felt a brotherly pride in her beauty, and I always found it hard to understand it on the rare occasions when the young men I knew did not fall in love with her. Very many of them did, and among those who had been attracted and who attracted her, was Maynard Keynes, whom she had met with a riding party on Salisbury Plain.

I went to Paddington to see Hugh and Brynhild depart on their honeymoon, and certainly could not have felt more had she been my sister. She was glowing with beauty; wearing a rust-coloured tweed dress. As the train drew away my eyes fell on one of the bridegroom's friends, whom I had never met before, and his aloof and sensitive face made an indelible

impression on me. It was Arthur Waley—or Schloss, as he was called in those days.

Hugh Popham and Brynhild took a flat in Regent's Square, off Hunter Street. I went one evening to a party there and, towards the end of the evening, was sitting in a corner of the room, carrying on a slightly flirtatious conversation with Daphne, when two late arrivals came into the room. They were Cambridge friends of Hugh Popham's and they were strangers to me. Both were rather short. Suddenly the smaller of them, a tousled gnome-like creature in spectacles, said in a very loud voice to Brynhild: "Who is that handsome fat man over there?" and waved a stubby-fingered paw in my direction.

Brynhild brought him up and introduced us. He was Francis Birrell, the son of Augustine Birrell, then Irish Secretary and a member of Mr Asquith's Cabinet.

Frankie was sweating profusely, rather dirty and, judging by his conversation, more than a little drunk. He almost immediately told Daphne and me that his companion, called Luce, with whom he had been to the ballet, was the greatest poet since Shakespeare and then began to talk at random about Shakespeare's sonnets and Mr W. H.

I was feeling annoyed by his calling me handsome and fat. Either epithet would have been objectionable, together they were intolerable. I was very much thinner than his gifted friend. However, I behaved civilly and shortly afterwards escaped from him by asking Daphne to dance with me in the next room.

The dance was scarcely over when this tiresome individual came up to us again and, lurching heavily, trod with all his weight on my toes. I was wearing evening dress and rather tight patent-leather shoes and it hurt. His apologies, however, were more annoying than the pain and, as he seemed intent on following me about, I said good-bye a little earlier than I should otherwise have done and left the party, hoping that I should never meet him again.

A day or two later Brynhild invited me to tea and Daphne was there also; both of them were distressed and amused when

I told them exactly what I thought of Birrell. Apparently, they had told him that he had driven me away from the party and he was much distressed. He had told Brynhild that he had never met anyone more charming and had begged her to arrange a meeting at which he could efface the unfortunate impression he had made on me.

All this made me cross and I replied that I did not in the least want to meet him and the matter was left at that, after Brynhild had told me I was being ridiculous.

However, soon afterwards, when Daphne and I were at a performance of *Le Sacre du Printemps*, Hugh Popham came up with Frankie Birrell and Arthur Waley during the interval and invited us to join them, after the performance, at the Café Royal. We accepted and, an hour or so later, I was listening to Frankie Birrell and Arthur talking extremely well. We were all in a state of great enthusiasm, for it was Nijinsky's only season as an independent producer and *Le Sacre du Printemps* and *Le Coq d'Or* were entirely new departures in choreography and the most interesting ballets I have ever seen. By the end of the evening I had revised my first impression. Frankie was living with his father in Elm Park Gardens, only a short distance from our flat off the Fulham Road. He had just come down from Cambridge and soon afterwards got a job in the Textile Department of the Victoria and Albert Museum. The head of the department soon expressed the opinion that it would be valuable for Frankie to acquire a practical knowledge of carpet-making. There was at that time a small carpet shop, in which carpets were repaired, in the arcade which forms part of South Kensington Underground Station. For several weeks Frankie spent some hours a day there and passers-by were offered the extraordinary spectacle of him sitting cross-legged in the window attempting to darn a carpet. I use the word extraordinary as he was so clumsy with his fingers that he could scarcely do up his buttons correctly and a well-trained bear could have made a better job of threading a needle. While it lasted, Frankie in the window of the carpet shop was one of the sights of London.

Very soon I was seeing a good deal of him and enormously enjoying his random talk, his bubbling wit, and immense repertory of anecdotes.

Godwin and Rosalind were married, and set up house in Bethnal Green, where Godwin had bought a practice. I was a continual and welcome visitor in the little house and there I got to know many of Godwin's friends, in particular Bertie Farjeon, who had fallen in love with Rosalind's sister Joan Thorneycroft. I had also brought in friends of my own to Godwin's circle, perhaps the most important being Edward Thomas, who through Godwin, got to know Clifford and Arnold Bax and a new world of leisured people. I believe, indeed, that the friendships he formed at this time did more to liberate him as a poet than anything he had experienced before.

At Bethnal Green, Godwin was hard-worked, yet there was a feeling of gaiety and an absence of strain remarkable in a busy doctor's household. This charm and light-heartedness were reinforced by two tame jerboas which became playful as the evening wore on. One night Godwin, in pouring out some Chartreuse, spilled a few drops upon the floor. One of the jerboas tasted the precious liquid, found it agreeable and tasted again. Suddenly it leaped up on the divan bed on which Bertie Farjeon and I were idly watching it. It jumped four feet in the air and fell back beside us with a flop. Presently it began wandering about. But when it reached the edge of the mattress it stepped blithely into space and tumbled to the ground. Godwin picked it up, reported it under the influence of drink, with blurred responses, and tucked it up in bed in its cage to sleep off the effects.

In the middle of April 1914, T.T., a girl of seventeen, still at school, whom I had known since she was a small child, came to stay with us. She was a wild creature; at moments fierce, at others confiding. She had a small face with a sharp chin, little

261

pointed eye-teeth, a beautifully shaped big mouth, a pale face and pale grey eyes and long straight gold-brown hair.

There must have been some crisis in her home—a brother with measles, perhaps—which had led to her visit.

For several days we were together, going for walks in the spring woods and looking for early birds' nests. The weather was warm. One morning, I stood behind her, both of us waist-deep in a thicket of dead bracken, almost touching her and knowing that if I put my hand on the ropes of lovely hair hanging loose on her shoulders, I should say *I love you*. But I believed myself in love with another girl, moreover T.T. was a mere child. So I pushed forward past her into the wood and, as we talked, I avoided looking at her.

"You're an ass!" she cried.

That evening we were alone together and before she went up to bed she put her hands on my shoulders.

"You're not an ass," she said, and gave me a swift kiss on the mouth and then went upstairs, leaving me full of flattered surprise. The goodnight kiss was repeated the next evening, given with greater freedom and received with greater eagerness.

The Oliviers were at The Champions and during the day we often joined them, sometimes amusing ourselves on a line of beeches by climbing from the top boughs of one tree into those of the next and so on. In one or two places this could only be done by a wild leap across an intervening chasm of two or three yards. Margery Olivier was particularly reckless and successful in such leaps and there was a wild and yet soft happiness in her face when at last she touched earth and put on her skirt again with a sort of absent-minded reluctance. In that moment one had seen the real Margery, a creature akin to the gentle and yet untamed satyrs and fauns, which people the woods in seventeenth-century pastorals. Or she might have been one of the young women who are found near streams in the pages of *Don Quixote*. One day Ursula joined our party, and, climbing with eager incompetence, fell smack out of the tree. Luckily she was not high up : some of our difficult traverses took place at a height of twenty-five feet.

In the evening there was music—with Daphne and T.T. playing their fiddles. But in the sunny spring mornings, T.T. and I would each take a book and go up into the wood to find a lonely sunny patch under a pine tree. There we would rest and then embrace and laugh and I would stroke her hair, content not to be an ass after all.

Circumstances soon brought our little exchanges to an end. Constance had to go away; Hermine Bréal, a schoolfellow of T.T.'s, came to keep her company, and Godwin's sister, Ruth, arrived to stay one night, after which I planned to walk with her part of the way to her home in Berkshire. T.T. had played the fiddle to Constance and me every evening. On the arrival of Hermine and of Ruth, music and kisses were discontinued.

T.T. and Hermine retired early. Ruth and I were alone and I heard the notes of an early nightingale. I threw open the window and we leaned out to listen and then I said something about the bird's song. Unknown to me, T.T. was leaning out of the window just over our heads and suddenly a fierce young voice said angrily: "I think it's only a silly chicken," and the window upstairs was closed.

Next morning, we got up very early and all four of us set off across the fields. The daisies were all shut when we set out, but the spring sun rose and shone brilliantly and soon was reflected in the thousands of lesser celandines, which studded every bank and bordered every ditch with gaping lacquered gold.

We covered about ten miles in company and then separated. By then the freshness and glory of the morning had departed; there was a heavy shower of rain and Ruth and I finished our journey in a crowded third-class carriage on a branch railway. She went on home. I got out at the station nearest to Silchester.

Next morning, my troubled feelings about the girls were forgotten. *Discinella* was growing in the utmost profusion under the low gorse and I was able to gather and pickle fruit bodies in all stages of development. There would be no lack of

material for the research work I was going to carry out that summer.

In July, Lawrence and Frieda came back to England and stayed with us at The Cearne. Lawrence had finished *The Rainbow*, for which Methuen's offered him £300 advance. In spite of all Edward could do, Duckworth would not give so much, but agreed to publish a volume of short stories, which came out several months later under the title of *The Prussian Officer*.

The Lawrences were lent a little house off the Fulham Road by an agreeable Irishman called Campbell who, though an Ulsterman and a Protestant, had joined the Irish Volunteers as a gesture against Carson. They were getting married, and I thought it would be pleasant to organise a dinner at which they could meet some of my friends.

It took place in the back room at Gustave's, which at that time provided the best food in Soho. There were about eighteen people there: Frankie Birrell, Karen Costello, David Garnett, D. H. Lawrence, Frieda Lawrence, Katharine Mansfield, Middleton Murry, Daphne Olivier, Noel Olivier, Ethel Pye and Adrian Stephen. Gilbert Cannan and his wife, James Strachey and Arthur Waley, may also have been there. Both Lawrence and Frieda were extremely sociable and agreeable.

One evening Frankie and I went to the Café Royal and saw in the evening papers that the Archduke Franz-Ferdinand, heir to the throne of Austria-Hungary, had been assassinated. We fell in with a friend of Frankie's, the private secretary of a minister, who told us that he thought the Archduke's death would greatly weaken the war party in Austria and that our relations with Germany might be much better in consequence.

The Oliviers were planning a camping party on the Helston River in Cornwall and Frankie and I were invited to join them. It fitted in well with my other plans; for I was going to stay with my uncle Arthur on a houseboat anchored at Feock in Falmouth Harbour.

When I arrived there I found the other members of the party consisted of Arthur's friend Charles Dear, his wife Lil, their baby and a New Forest gipsy girl of seventeen, called Ann Witcher, who acted as the baby's nurse and did a lot of the work.

Dear was small and dark. At Cambridge he had been a great beagler; then, while he was still at the university, he had come into money and taken the Mastership of a pack of hounds and spent his inheritance in about five years. After that he entirely renounced blood sports and became a landscape painter. He and his wife lived on a tiny income in a caravan in the New Forest. Ann was the daughter of one of their gipsy neighbours.

I had brought a little light-weight tent with me and slept out in it. Ann liked the look of it and we at once made friends. She was fair-haired, but had real gipsy features. After a few days, the Dears left, inviting me to visit them at Becka Falls on Dartmoor, where they were to camp for the rest of the summer. A few days were spent in swimming and sailing and diving off the roof of the house-boat. Then I packed up and set off to walk to Dartmoor along the Cornish coast. It was about a hundred miles to Becka Falls and I covered it in four days, camping out each night and cooking my breakfasts and my evening meals. I got in late, but was warmly welcomed.

"Ann's been talking about you ever since we left Cornwall," said Dear.

"I am sick and tired of hearing about your little tent," said Lil. "I think she wants to live in it with you."

"You devils, man and woman," exclaimed Ann and ran out into the darkness.

Becka Falls was only a mile or two from Manaton, where Jack and Ada Galsworthy were living. I talked to Ann and realised that she had never been into any house where servants were kept and that she was consumed with curiosity to see inside one. So I wrote a note to Jack, saying I was camping in the neighbourhood and might I come to see them and bring a gipsy girl with me. He replied, asking us to tea. Ann spent half the morning, washing herself in the stream, did her hair in

gipsy plaits, with lots of pins, and put on a terrible bright blue serge coat-and-skirt, which I had never seen before.

Jack and Ada were most kind, but obviously puzzled by my companion. Jack soon took me to show me his horses and garden and Ann was left to Ada.

Later we were given tea and Ann behaved perfectly, as though she had been going out to tea all her life. Her manners were quiet and modest and she appeared unaware of the close scrutiny she was undergoing. Ann's gipsy way of speech and accent was too much for our hosts. They meant to be kind and believed they were being so, but it was clear that they thought I was having an undesirable relationship with her. Actually, I had never even tried to give her a kiss. We did not stay long, but though the Galsworthys must have felt our visit rather an imposition, it was nevertheless worth it. Ann had been thrilled. The carpets, flowers, pictures, shining polished furniture and, above all, the maid bringing in the tea, had provided her with a wonderful experience to be dreamed about and treasured up for the rest of her life. I did not ask her what she thought of the Galsworthys and the only remark she made on the way back to Becka Falls which might have been interpreted as a criticism of them was: "My mother's names are Faith and Hope and my auntie's name is Charity."

Coming back one day from a long walk over the moor in the rain, I found Ann standing in the porch of the bell tent. I pushed past her and sat down. For a long while there was no sound but the rattle of the rain on the canvas and an occasional flap in the wind. When a hard gust came, the tent-pole creaked.

At last Ann said: "I've been watching the rain in the trees. It's beautiful."

I was surprised at the word. Usually she said: "I likes it." We stood for some time watching the rain like smoke veiling the oak trees, when Charles Dear threw open the door of the van, put his head out and shouted: "Look at the Dartmoor mist" and slammed the door shut again. He, an artist, did not look at it for five seconds together. Ann often stood happily

and watched the rain, or the waterfall, for most of the afternoon, content to gaze and to say nothing. She made me realise how very few of my educated friends ever really looked at the things they so much admired.

Leaving the Dears, I walked across Dartmoor to Ivybridge where I met Bertie Farjeon, his wife Joan and Ursula. We walked to Yerme Head, where we found a little dingle of short green grass in the midst of the moors. For some reason I stayed on alone at Yerme Head and though it rained so as to keep me in my tent for two days, I enjoyed being alone.

When I emerged, I met a postman and discovered that the world was being shaken by two pieces of news: the Gordon-Bennett balloon race had been started just before the storm and some of the balloons had been driven immense distances into Central Europe. The assassination of the Archduke had had the opposite effect from that which Frankie's friend had predicted. War was imminent, but the fate of one or two balloons, which had not yet reported, seemed almost as exciting in the newspaper as the prospect of war. All the powers were mobilising, and the postman, who was a reservist, was being called up. He was overjoyed at the prospect. The declaration of war had actually been made by the time I joined Frankie at Exeter. The train was full of naval reservists.

The camp at Helston had been organised by Noel. The tents were pitched on a rounded field perhaps a quarter, or half a mile, from the estuary of the Helston River. There were several tents; one with Hugh and Brynhild and their baby Anthony, a bell tent with the other three Oliviers, a tent with Bertie Farjeon and Joan, a tent of stores and, on the evening of our arrival, Geoffrey Keynes was departing. I pitched the little lightweight cambric tent which Ann Witcher had coveted and which Frankie and I shared. He had never camped out before and I don't think he was very comfortable.

The atmosphere of the camp was naturally disturbed. For the greater part of the time we forgot the war: bathed, cooked, and played stump cricket at which Frankie, to the annoyance of the Oliviers, showed brilliance. For though he could scarcely

tie his own shoes, and was helpless at folding a blanket or washing up, Frankie had an eye for ball games. He could play squash well, was fair at golf and tennis, brilliant at ping-pong. At stump cricket he was in a class far above any of us.

In one game Frankie, Bertie and I took on the four Oliviers, Joan and Hugh Popham and beat them by an enormous number of runs. I remember Daphne and Brynhild getting quite angry as Frankie, armed with a cricket stump, swiped ball after ball into the outfield.

Soon a flood of letters began to arrive from Constance, sometimes two by the same post. They were very largely practical. She was immensely aware of England being an island dependent on imported food, of all commodities vanishing: paraffin and flour were unobtainable in the village shops; universal famine was to be expected. However, the crop of potatoes was good in the Cearne garden and with luck, she thought, we might be able to live there on our own fruit and vegetables for several months, while the rest of England starved; she exhorted me to return home while it was possible and the trains still ran. I am afraid I did not pay much attention to these letters, and left them lying about.

Maynard Keynes arrived the day after I left. He found Constance's letters lying about, picked them up, read them, decided they were of historic interest and preserved them. He was greatly struck by the contrast between her grasp of the economic situation and the grotesque lack of sense of reality, which made her believe that the results likely to occur after two years of rigorous blockade would happen in a fortnight.

One evening, sitting round the fire, we suddenly became serious. Hugh Popham said that he was glad the war had come, and particularly glad we had come into it. I do not know what the others said, but everyone there was in agreement with him.

I remember my reply clearly. I said that it was criminal to welcome war; that millions of men would die, millions who had no quarrel with each other and could know nothing of the quarrel in which they lost their lives and all the belligerent countries would suffer ruin, whether they won or lost.

I poured out my views on the futility of war, thinking of Tolstoy and of *War and Peace*. I said that we were fighting to preserve the Tsar's Government in Russia, in an attempt to postpone an inevitable revolution. Suddenly I had said all that was in me and I heard Hugh Popham make some comment in a tone of nausea. But I believed that whatever the impression I produced, in the long run what I had said was true, that I was right and that Hugh and the others were wrong.

Daphne, Noel and Frankie were not altogether out of sympathy with me. But I was, nevertheless, in a minority of one. A day or two later as Constance was clamouring for my return while it was still possible to travel, I went home, and as Augustine Birrell had asked Frankie to go back for other reasons, he travelled with me as far as London.

Once home at The Cearne and listening to Constance's excited anticipations of our surviving the war on a diet of slugs and snails like a marketwoman during the siege of Paris, I relapsed into childishness. At one moment I said to myself that supposing I were to take part in a cavalry charge, I might be awarded the V.C. A momentary flicker of my intelligence informed me that such idiocy was nauseous at my age. But what were the limits of the idiotic? It was obvious that the war was to be the greatest experience of all to my generation: it clearly offered death to many and high honours to a few. Could I not gain honour and renown by the part I played?

That surely was a shameful approach. How could I be most useful? In what respects was I qualified to help? Obviously, with my training, I could easily become a dispenser, a bacteriologist, an assistant with useful qualifications in the Royal Army Medical Corps. I was better qualified as a bacteriologist, for example, than the ordinary army doctor.

At that moment the news reached me that Geoffrey Keynes had joined the R.A.M.C. and was leaving for France in a few days. I at once went up to London and found Geoffrey occupying Maynard's room in Adrian Stephen's house in Brunswick Square. He was engaged in collecting his equipment, had already got into uniform. When I told him that I wanted to join

him, to go out as a dispenser or bacteriologist, or even as his batman, Geoffrey was at first intensely pleased. The whole concept of military organisation was entirely unknown to me and had it been explained it would have shocked me profoundly to learn that, at the beginning of a war, enthusiasm would not open all doors in the British Army. I never imagined that my idea of joining a field hospital at the last moment, without training, was fantastic. Nor, I think, had Geoffrey. But he had sufficient worldly wisdom to realise that there might be all kinds of difficulties. However, he was vague enough to promise, before we parted, to speak to his Colonel about me, and we arranged that I should come back two days later, prepared to go off with him to France, as his batman, or as a hospital orderly, if no opportunity for a bacteriologist was available. When I returned, my knock was answered by his brother, Maynard. Standing in the doorway he looked at me without surprise; quiet, receptive, friendly, but entirely undemonstrative. His absence of anything like briskness made him as unlike Geoffrey as anyone could well be.

I told him why I had come. "Geoffrey went off to France last night. Come in and have some tea." Geoffrey was always in a hurry; Maynard very seldom hurried. However full his day, it was planned to be taken comfortably. As I sat down in a large comfortable chair, it was clear that there was no hurry.

Maynard told me that he had succeeded in raising enough money for Ferenc Bekassy to leave England the night before. The banks were all shut owing to a moratorium and Bekassy was anxious to return to Hungary to fight against Russia. War had not been declared between Britain and Austria-Hungary until the morning after Bekassy left.

I said that I thought Maynard should have refused to find the money on the double grounds that he was sending a friend to his death and strengthening the enemy forces.

Maynard disagreed violently. He said he had used every argument to persuade Bekassy not to go—but having failed to persuade him, it was not the part of a friend to impose his views by force, or by refusing help. He respected Bekassy's

freedom to choose though he regretted his choice. My second argument was ridiculous: what was one man in a score of millions? I agreed that friendship was far more important than patriotism, but asked him if he would restrain the friend who contemplated suicide, or would he lend him the money to buy poison? Maynard replied that in certain circumstances he would lend him the money—if it was a free choice, made by a sane man after due reflection, for compelling causes. I remained unconvinced and have never been able to settle the question in my own mind. It seems to me that in theory Maynard's view is right—but that in practice there is more to be said for mine. Bekassy was killed in the Carpathians. If he had been interned until 1918, he would probably be alive today. Maynard's high ideal of friendship in fact cost his friend his life. I knew Bekassy as a friend of Noel's, and as a most charming and attractive figure. But I had not then read any of his poems, which were published later by Leonard and Virginia. Maynard knew him as an undergraduate at King's College.

From this discussion of ethics, Maynard went on to talk about the war. Much to my surprise, I discovered he was extremely optimistic about the larger issues. He told me that he was quite certain that the war could not last much more than a year and that the belligerent countries could not be ruined by it. The world, he explained, was enormously rich, but its wealth was, fortunately, of a kind which could not be rapidly realised for war purposes: it was in the form of capital equipment for making things which were useless for waging war. When all the available wealth had been used up—which, he thought would take about a year—the Powers would have to make peace. We could not use the cotton factories in Lancashire to help our navy blockade Germany; Germany could not use its toymakers' factories to equip her armies.

These views were stated with extraordinary clarity and absolute conviction and I unhesitatingly believed them. What is more, in spite of all evidence to the contrary, I went on believing what he had said until well into the late spring of 1915, when I was surprised to find that no perceptible slackening in

the preparations for war had been forced on us by economic reasons.

It was clear, if Maynard Keynes was right, that it was scarcely worth while interrupting my research work and sacrificing my two scholarships in order to enlist in a war in which I was unlikely to take part, since it would probably be over by the time my training was completed. I returned in an undecided frame of mind to Pond Place and was greeted by Edward, who begged me not to enlist without much greater thought. He embraced me with emotion when I said that I should not enlist since the war would be over before I could take part in it. It was a great relief for us all to have Maynard's assurance on this point.

END OF VOLUME ONE

D0999818